SO-BOO-829

A PROSE AND VERSE ANTHOLOGY OF
MODERN IRISH WRITING

A PROSE AND VERSE ANTHOLOGY OF

MODERN IRISH WRITING

edited by GRATTAN FREYER

With a Preface by Conor Cruise O'Brien

Irish Humanities Centre
23 Westland Row, Dublin 2, and
Keohane's, Ltd., Ballina and Sligo

1978

First published in 1979 by
The Irish Humanities Centre Limited,
23 Westland Row, Dublin 2, and Keohane's, Ltd.,
Ballina and Sligo

Cloth edition ISBN 0–906462–00–2–H
Paperback edition ISBN 0–906462–01–0

Acknowledgements are due for permission to reprint from the authors represented: to the Goldsmith Press and to S. E. O Cearbhail, Sean O'Riordain and Juanita Casey for the poems which first appeared in *Choice* and *Rogha an Fhile*; to Maire Cruise O'Brien; to Liam O'Flaherty; to Peadar O'Donnell; to A. D. Peters Ltd. for permission to reprint Frank O'Connor's *Guests of the Nation*; to Sean O'Faolain and Constable and Co. Ltd.; to the Dolmen Press and the executors of Donagh MacDonagh and of Austin Clarke; to Mrs Katherine Kavanagh; to Mrs Beatrice Behan; to Mrs Evelyn O'Nolan; to Benedict Kiely and Victor Gollancz Ltd.; to Edna O'Brien and Jonathan Cape Ltd.; to Faber and Faber Ltd. for permission to reprint from *Nightlines* by John McGahern, from *Sailing to an Island* and *High Island* by Richard Murphy, and from *Wintering Out* and *Door into the Dark* by Seamus Heaney; to John Hewitt; to John Montague; to Thomas Kinsella; to Padraic Fiacc; to Tom Murphy; to Michael Molloy; to John Morrow and the Blackstaff Press; to Eavan Boland; to Richard Murphy; and to Francis Stuart. Grateful acknowledgment is also made of a grant from the Arts Council of the Republic of Ireland against the royalties due under these permissions.

Distributed in Great Britain by
Colin Smythe, Gerrards Cross, Buckinghamshire

Printed in Great Britain by
Billing & Sons Limited,
Guildford, London and Worcester

Contents

Contents

Editor's Foreword

The form of this anthology was first suggested by the publishers of a Polish literary review. They had had special numbers on Yeats, Joyce, O'Casey, Beckett. Would I compile an anthology from modern Irish writers who, if not necessarily 'minor' writers, were as yet less widely known outside their own country?

It seemed a sensible idea. Anyone interested in modern literature will have read, and will probably possess, the more important works of the writers just mentioned. There may be many, however, both in Ireland and beyond, for whom a selection from writers outside the main canon may serve a useful purpose. Thus, this anthology contains excerpts from some authors who may already be on the road to classic status – Patrick Kavanagh, Flann O'Brien, Thomas Kinsella – along with work from a score or so writers, some of whom, I believe, have not been anthologized before.

Inevitably the selection is based on personal choice. I have included nothing I myself cannot read with either pleasure or excitement. But in choosing one author, or one piece of writing, in preference to another, I have been guided by a wish to illustrate within the confines of a moderate-sized volume different tendencies in modern Irish writing. Literature and history, history and politics, are more closely intertwined in Ireland than in any other country. In the inter-connected commentary introducing the various sections, I have aimed to place the authors concerned against the background of the evolving Ireland of the last half-century.

Conor Cruise O'Brien has been kind enough to spare time from his many activities to contribute a Preface.

G. F.

Preface

The Irish Literary 'Renaissance' or 'Revival' of the 'nineties was a cultural movement removed, although in part derived, from the actual culture of the majority of the Irish people: Catholics. The movement's leaders, Yeats and Lady Gregory, and its most vaunted discovery, Synge, were Protestants, associated in various ways and degrees with the Protestant landlord Ascendancy, then entering upon its euthanasia. In a sense, it was a brave bid, on the part of members of a declining social group, to reassert their leadership on new terms: spiritual and cultural terms, in place of the old social and political ones. A brave bid, one might think, but a hopeless one. The old primacy of Protestant over Catholic was, after all, something imposed by material force from outside, never something voluntarily accepted by the Catholic majority. The new 'spiritual' leadership would have to be voluntarily accepted or it could not exist.

Could that voluntary acceptance be attained? Yeats certainly thought it could. He had before him, to the point of obsession, the masterful image of Charles Stewart Parnell, a Protestant landlord who became the *chosen* leader of the Catholic people. Powerful though that image was, it was also ambiguous. This Protestant had become leader of the Catholics, but on their terms. His mission was to destroy the political, economic and social power of the Protestant landlord class to which he himself belonged. That was the indispensable and sacrificial condition for Parnell's rise to power, and for his hold upon the Catholic people.

Could there be an equivalent condition, for an acceptable kind of *cultural* leadership by Protestants in Catholic Ireland? This was not an academic question, for Yeats's generation and social group. At the period when the 'Revival' began, in the 1890s, democratic self-government for Ireland was already probable. It was also, for any Protestant, tinged with menace. Just as the rise of Parnell had shown that a Protestant could become a leader of Catholic people, so the fall of Parnell, after the divorce crisis, had brutally determined the limits of such acceptability. In doing so it had exposed, in lurid flashes of the lightning of democratic conflict, the bleak and craggy landscape of clerical power:

> *The Bishops and the Party*
> *That tragic story made . . . .*

To the authority of the Church in Catholic Ireland there has only been one serious challenger: Cathleen ni Houlihan, romantic manic nationalism. Cathleen came in on cue in 1902, in the spectacular shape of Maud Gonne, intoning the lines of Yeats's play. That proved to have been just the dress-rehearsal for the real thing, fourteen years later. The fevered mind of Constance Markievicz, under sentence of death in Aylesbury Jail, for having played Cathleen with live ammunition in the Rising of 1916, went back to the glories promised at the dress-rehearsal . . . 'They shall be remembered for ever, . . . and even poor me shall not be forgotten'.

Yeats had been told by the Fenian John O'Leary that 'in Ireland a man must have the Church or the Fenians on his side and you will never have the Church'. In the 'cultural nationalism' of the earlier phases of the Literary Revival, both the Protestant writers and their Fenian allies temporarily established a zone precariously free from the otherwise all-permeating influence of the Catholic Church. Yeats, like Parnell, had to pay a price for the leadership he exerted within his special zone. He later came to identify that price and to regret it:

> *We had fed the heart*
> > *on fantasies*
> *The heart's grown*
> > *brutal from the fare.*

Of all Yeats's many and various gnomic sayings about Ireland, that is the one that has most often come to mind during the last ten years. The Fenians—of whom the Provisional I.R.A. are only the latest wave—have shown themselves a far more noxious, intimidating and regressive force than even the most hostile of reasonable minds could think of the Catholic clergy in Ireland then or now as being.

ii

The Ireland reflected in Grattan Freyer's sensitively-chosen
anthology is Catholic Ireland—the 97.5% Catholic Republic of
Ireland, plus the Catholic third of the population of Northern
Ireland. In this anthology, the one Ulster Protestant included, John
Hewitt, is only a partial exception.* He is of Protestant stock, but
unlike the vast majority of Ulster Protestants, he also accepts the
basic political thesis of Irish nationalism, which in Ulster is generally
regarded, for practical purposes, as being the political synonym for
Irish Catholicism. He states his lonely and torn position in the poem
in this collection called 'The Dilemma, 1969'

> *So, while my logic steered me well outside*
> *that ailing church which claims dominion*
> *over the questing spirit, I denied*
> *all credence to the state by rebels won*
> *from a torn nation, rigged to guard their gain,*
> *though they assert their love of liberty,*
> *which craft has narrowed to a fear of Rome.*

Anyone who reads this collection—the selections from Sean
O'Faolain, Austin Clarke, Patrick Kavanagh, Benedict Kiely,
Edna Obrian among others—will wonder how anyone who regards
Catholicism as an 'ailing church which claims dominion over the
questing spirit' could feel himself to belong to the same country
as writers who must be to him so culturally alien, belonging in a
collectivity so saturated in Catholicism as the Republic of Ireland.

Most Ulster Protestants agree with Mr. Hewitt in feeling 'well
outside' Catholicism, but also feel 'well outside' a State based on and
reflecting a Catholic community: the Republic. Culturally, they
believe they are closer to Britain, though most British people
do not agree. In practice, they do share a strange and tragic kind of
culture, not with the Republic, but with the Catholics of Northern
Ireland. They share, that is, the common culture of the ancient
antagonism they have inherited, as the Douglas and the Percy
shared the culture of the Scottish Borders—or as blacks and whites
did in a way share in the old culture of Dixie. They have in common
the knowledge of the rules, the significance of the counters, the
calendar of commemoration, the interpretation of names, addresses,

---

* John Morrow is also of Northern Protestant stock, working-class. G.F.

accents, facial expressions, movements of feet, a commonly pro-
grammed computer for the assessment of the stranger, and of the
manner and degree to which the novelty of his presence modifies the
immediate social environment—and in whose favour it has been
modified.

Northern Ireland does possess a common culture in that particular
sense, real but so rarefied as to be hard to breathe. It would even be
possible to construct an anthology representative of that common
culture. Such an anthology would, however, have to be confined to
Northern Ireland because it is only there that the common culture of
antagonism now exists.

This anthology is drawn almost exclusively from Catholic Ireland
—with Mr. Hewitt there as a sort of doubtful marker to show where
Catholic Ireland begins to end. But the anthology is permeated, not
just by the atmosphere of Catholic Ireland, but by the specific
atmosphere of the Catholic Republic where Catholics are not at all
on the defensive, where they constitute the Government, the opposi-
tion, the working-class, the middle-class, the country and the city.
The Northern Catholic writers, Seamus Heaney, Benedict Kiely and
John Montague, have chosen to live in the Republic, apparently
preferring its homogeneously Catholic culture to the rather specialized
austere and monotonous forms of satisfaction to be derived from the
common culture which, in Northern Ireland, they shared with
Mr. Hewitt's co-religionists.

Not only has the Catholic Republic attracted Northern Catholics;
it has attracted, assimilated, absorbed, Southern Protestants. As a
proportion of the population, Protestants have been falling, in every
inter-censal period since the foundation of the Irish state. Those who
found the Catholic atmosphere uncongenial left early. For others,
who remained, acceptance of the State was often a prelude to the
acceptance of the Church—not by themselves, but by their children.
The children married Catholics, the children's children are Catholics.
This was a minority that nobody persecuted; it has simply been
quietly absorbed (with a few exceptions, most of whom have already
been politically absorbed, as a preliminary, into Irish nationalism).

As Donagh MacDonagh wrote in 'A Warning to Conquerors'
about the Normans:

...... *This soft land quietly*
Engulfed them like the Saxon and the Dane

But kept the jutted jaw the slitted eye:
Only the faces and the names remain

There are many people in Ulster for whom those lines, if they came
across them, would feel like a sequence in a horror film.

For some Catholics, too, Irish Catholicism has had its nightmare
aspects, but these aspects have tended to recede. For Austin Clarke,
the nightmare was strong and permanent. He hated Catholicism as
Europeans of the Enlightenment hated it. (There was some ambi-
valence also among these). There is a typical reference in 'A Straying
Student' in this collection, to

> . . . . . *this land where every woman's son*
> *Must carry his own coffin and believe*
> *In dread, all that the*
> > *clergy teach the*
> > *young*

In Kavanagh's *The Great Hunger* there is the nightmare of Catholic
poverty, the punitive apparatus of sexual deprivation, but already
the rejection is narrowed: some Irish Catholic practices are being
criticized, but there is not, as with Clarke, a combined intellectual
and emotional rejection of Catholicism itself. Sean O'Faolain has
come back to Irish Catholicism by way of Rome: the mood is one of
astringent, ironic acquiescence. Benedict Kiely is neo-Chestertonian:
the 'neo' part being that it is now acceptable for Catholicism to be
bawdy as well as beery. This development would, of course, have
removed the principal intellectual difficulty of many earlier writers
of Catholic stock and predicament. Edna O'Brien's still-much-
banned case shows that *for a woman* to be bawdy is not yet acceptable. However, I think she is finding her way back into the Irish
Catholic consensus by the same route through which many Protestants
enter it: the route of *political* identification with the Catholic
community. 'Seek ye first the *political* kingdom', as Kwame Nkrumah
used to say, 'and all the rest will be added unto you'.

iii

Of politics there is little trace in this volume: one poem from the
North recounting in horrible detail one particular atrocity carried

out by members of the other tribe: Brendan Behan's *The Big House* rejoicing in the downfall of the old Ascendancy. These are the most 'nationalist' pieces in the collection, and they are not the best. Catholicism on the other hand, struggled against or accepted, or both, is everywhere. Catholicism in its Irish form, with the weight of Irish history behind it, is the culture of which this anthology is representative: it is that which alone now makes a separate anthology of Irish writing, in English, a meaningful enterprise.

To grow up in English-speaking Catholic Ireland is to live on two levels, in two worlds. This, of course, is true, though in different ways, for Southern Protestants as well as for Catholics. Yeats's Sligo, Lady Gregory's Kiltartan, Synge's Wicklow and Aran are Catholic places, although in them the Protestant writers reached out, rather wistfully, towards the element of the pagan behind the Catholic. The idea of the pagan wiped out history and its barriers; it removed from Catholic Ireland, by an effort of imagination, that which was injured, implacable and—MacDonagh's word—engulfing.

That particular need for the pagan has gone, yet the idea of the pagan, behind the Catholic, retains some of its appeal, as we shall see.

In this collection, the most representative piece is Sean O'Faolain's *Lovers of the Lake* about the power exerted by a medieval pilgrimage over a modern middle-class couple. There is nothing fanciful about that story. It is true to the realities of modern Irish life, to the humdrum magic of the Catholic island in the Anglo-American secular sea. The waves beat louder now, with television, but the island remains intact.

To live on such an island, in such a sea, can benefit a writer strong and subtle enough to endure and appreciate the conditions. I shall leave the last word with Seamus Heaney, certainly the finest poet on the island, and perhaps the finest also in the sea:

I think I am a Christian because the Sermon on the Mount satisfies so much in me that pines consciously and unconsciously for appeasement. But I have no doubt that I am also a pagan, and that every poet is: the poet will have to be standing with Oisin against Patrick, he will have to roost in the tree of his instincts with Mad Sweeney while St. Moling stands ideologically in the cloister. The poet in this way is deeply conservative, hoarding the wisdoms and consolations that the old religions discovered and rendered into the ever-stable currency of myth and literature. Yet perhaps the Catholic poet is

> lucky, because Catholicism managed to preserve part of the old feminine religion in its structure. The Virgin Mary, intercessor, mother of mercy, star of the sea, occupies in the common psychology the place occupied by the Muse in the poetic psychology . . . .

Conor Cruise O'Brien

1. THREE POEMS TRANSLATED FROM THE MODERN IRISH

At the beginning of the present century, the small country of Ireland with a population less than one-tenth that of its powerful neighbour, Britain, experienced a period of intense cultural activity and excitement which historians refer to as the Irish Literary Renaissance. There are such periods in every nation's history, though it is not easy to say how they come about. Sometimes they coincide with a period of political activity and imperial expansion, such as that of Tudor England. More often, they seem to precede and prepare the way for significant political events, as Rousseau and Voltaire heralded the Great Revolution in France or the nineteenth-century Russian novelists prepared the way for the Bolshevik Revolution of 1917. In Ireland's case, the cultural phase fell between two periods of dynamic political activity—the Land War and Home Rule movement of the 1880's and the military events from 1916 onwards which led to the birth of the independent Irish state.

The revolutionary struggle of the Irish peasantry at the end of the nineteenth century had been completely successful in forcing the British government to divide up the estates of the large landlord proprietors. The national movement, which aimed at obtaining an Irish parliament in Dublin, was less successful. It had been led by Charles Stewart Parnell, whose name passed into symbolic legend for later Irish writers. It broke up in a manner which might seem strange to outsiders, but which was tragic for Irishmen, when Parnell was involved in a divorce case in 1890. Foreign readers can obtain some impression of the partisan passions engendered by this event by reading the Christmas dinner scene in James Joyce's *Portrait of the Artist as a Young Man*.

Men turned from practical politics in bitter disillusionment. Significantly, the poet W. B. Yeats had foreseen, even at the height of Parnell's power, that the first lull in the day-to-day political struggle would provide an opportunity for a new movement of the national imagination. So it was. Yeats was the centre of this movement and the greater part of his work was produced in association with it. He was followed by writers such as John

1

Millington Synge and Sean O'Casey whose plays rapidly obtained an international audience. Though Joyce stood apart from the movement, it is impossible to believe that his genius was not nourished by the atmosphere of mental exhilaration which was filling the Dublin of his formative years. There have been ups and downs since, but Dublin and Ireland remain today in the forefront of the literary map of Europe. In many universities, both in America and on the continent of Europe, special centres of Irish or Anglo-Irish studies now exist.

*   *   *

The country which shook itself loose from the bonds of British imperialism and came under the control of the new government in Dublin in 1922 was a predominantly rural one. An industrial-commercial economy is now making deep inroads, but even in modern Ireland few Irish writers fail to be influenced by this rural background, even though in many cases they find themselves entangled in a love-hate relationship with it. Particularly the West with its romantic landscape of the crumbling 'Big House' and tiny farms and rocky islands, where men struggle to wrest a livelihood in intimate relationship with animals and nature, exerts its pull.

Here too is the last stronghold of the Gaelic language, which has died out in the more prosperous areas. It has been the policy of successive Irish governments to try to revitalize this and adapt it to modern life. This has been far from wholly successful and in recent years the policy behind the language revival has come under heavy criticism. But it has produced a small generation of young intellectuals and writers who are equally at home in Irish or English. Some of these have produced original work in Irish, as well as translations from the older Gaelic literature of the bardic poets and sagas. Their work accordingly links one of the oldest literary traditions of Europe with a very contemporary present.

It seems fitting therefore to open this anthology with three recent poems which were originally written in Irish and later translated, not always by the authors themselves, into English.

THAT MOMENT by S. E. O Cearbhail

Someplace
In from the road
On the edge of a hill
I stood still
Watching a star;
A bright single star
That stood above
Over the inkblack hedge
On a frosty night;
I stood
And the star stood
One moment,
As stands a deer
Or any creature of the wilds
In tingling hesitation;
In fear of me
A human being.
My heart stood
My body
My mind
My intellect
My life stood still (all that was me)
One moment—
Time eroding my persona
On me—an individual—
Stood a moment still.
Nothing in me aged
Nothing in me grew
That moment;
It was a moment when I sensed
A miss in the beat of time
And my whole being yearned

3

That there be built three tabernacles
On the spot:
One for he who was
One for he who would be,
And one for you
Christ—
Beginning and end
And final destiny of me,
Here standing at some unnamed crossroads
On the road of my being here
On my way to eternity;
When the whole world stood still
Just one moment
On a frosty night
And a bashful star
Stood above a hill
Frozen in the sky
Like a deer, alert, trembling
Staring
In the awe of a moment—
When a person, I, just sensed
For once and for the first time
The ecstasy
Of one in love
With God.

FROZEN by Sean O Riordain

On a frosty morning I went out
And a handkerchief faced me on a bush.
I reached to put it in my pocket
But it slid from me for it was frozen.
No living thing jumped from my grasp
But a thing that died last night on a bush
And I went searching in my mind
Till I found the occasion's equivalent—
The day I kissed a woman of my kindred
And she in the coffin, frozen, stretched.

NO COMPROMISE by Maire Mac An tSaoi

"I do not understand the fear of death ..."
And when she spoke I heard the bugles blow,
I saw the raging mob, blood in the streets,
And there were flames from torches and the wind
Filling the flags in that Frenchwoman's speech.

And I took fright, that she should be so strange,
Knowing how hard it is to lose the sun;
"Alas," I said, "long in the churchyard rests
The body and it's lonely in the clay."
But she turned towards me her wide open eyes,
And, proud, uncomprehending, did not yield.

2. STORY: "THE BLACK MARE"

LIAM O'FLAHERTY

Liam O'Flaherty (b. 1897) did not need to learn Irish in the new national schools, since he was born on the Aran islands where Irish is still the language of everyday speech. O'Flaherty's early writing even betrays by an occasional turn of phrase, as in Conrad, that English is not the writer's mother-tongue.

O'Flaherty was a flamboyant character who served with the British army in the 1914 war, then, after being invalided out, joined the Irish revolutionary movement. He was determined to be a writer and in the mid 1920's went to London where he showed manuscripts dealing with *amours* in high society to an English publisher. A fellow-writer, Sean O'Faolain, has recorded what happened. "Why do you not write of things closer to your own experience?" asked the publisher, recognizing the talents but dubious of the efforts before him. "But I only know of things like cows and seagulls", answered O'Flaherty miserably. "Then write about them."

O'Flaherty did, and produced wonderful stories of the simple things in country life, of which the story, "The Black Mare" here, is a good example. No other modern writer has O'Flaherty's capacity for feeling his way inside the animal creation, so that when he writes of a little seagull learning to fly we feel the terror it experiences when it first overbalances and falls from a rocky ledge, then the exhilaration as the wind whistles through its feathers and it is airborne, just as we feel the anguish of the mother cow who throws herself over a cliff after her injured young in another story "The Cow's Death".

O'Flaherty has also written novels and stories depicting in vivid language the mixture of introspection and violence involved in many of the characters thrown up in Ireland's revolutionary struggles. Some of these, such as *The Informer*, have been filmed.

Liam O'Flaherty

THE BLACK MARE

I bought the mare at G—, from a red-whiskered tinker and, if the truth were only known, I believe he stole her somewhere in the south, for he parted with her for thirty shillings. Or else it was because she was so wild that there was not another man at the whole fair had the courage to cross her back with his legs and trot her down the fair green but myself, for it was not for nothing that they called me Dan of the Fury in those days. However, when I landed from the hooker at the pier at Kilmurrage and, mounting her, trotted up to the village, they all laughed at me. For she was a poor-looking animal that day, with long shaggy hair under her belly, and the flesh on her ribs was as scarce as hospitality in a priest's house. She didn't stand an inch over fourteen hands, and my legs almost touched the ground astride of her. So they laughed at me, but I paid no heed to them. I saw the fire in her eyes, and that was all I needed. You see this drop of whiskey in this glass, stranger? It is a pale, weak colour, and it would not cover an inch with wetness, but it has more fire in it than a whole teeming lake of soft water. So the mare.

I set her to pasture in a little field I had between two hills in the valley below the fort. I cared for her as a mother might care for an only child, and all that winter I never put a halter in her mouth or threw my legs across her back, but I used to watch her for hours galloping around the fields snorting, with her great black eyes spitting fire and her nostrils opened so wide that you could hide an egg in each of them. And, Virgin of the Valiant Deeds, when she shed her winter coat in spring and I combed her glossy sides, what a horse she was! As black as the sloes they pick on the slope of Coillnamhan Fort, with never a hair of red or white or yellow. Her tail swept to the ground, and when the sun shone on her sides you could see them shimmering like the jewels on a priest's vestments; may the good God forgive me, a sinner, for the comparison. But

8

what is nearer to God than a beautiful horse? Tell me that, stranger, who have been in many lands across the sea.

And then the day came when all the unbroken mares of Inverara were to be shod. For it was the custom then, stranger, to shoe all the young mares on the same day, and to break them before they were shod on the wide sandy beach beneath the village of Coillnamhan.

There were seven mares that day gathered together from the four villages of Inverara, and there were good horses among them, but none as good as mine. She was now a little over fifteen hands high, and you could bury a child's hand between her haunches. She was perfect in every limb, like a horse from the stable of the God Crom. I can see her yet, stranger, standing on the strand stamping with her hind leg and cocking her ears at every sound. But it's an old saying, talk of beauty today, talk of death tomorrow.

I kept her to the last, and gave her to a lad to hold while I mounted a bay mare that my cousin had brought from Kilmillick, and I broke her in three rounds of the strand, although she had thrown three strong and hardy men before I seized her halter. And then my mare was brought down, and then and there I offered three quarts of the best whiskey that could be bought for money to the man that could stay on her back for one length of the strand. One after the other they mounted her, but no sooner did they touch her back than she sent them headlong to the ground. She would gather her four legs together and jump her own height from the ground, and with each jump they flew from her back, and she would run shivering around again until they caught her. I smiled, sitting there on a rock.

Then Shemus, the son of Crooked Michael, spat on his hands, tightened his crios around his waist, and said that if the devil were hiding in her bowels and Lucifer's own step-brother riding on her mane, he would break her. He was a man I never liked, the same son of Crooked Michael, a braggart without any good in him, a man who must have come crooked from his mother's womb, and his father before him was the same dishonest son of a horse-stealing tinker. 'Be careful', I said to him; 'that mare is used to have men about her that didn't drink their mother's milk from a teapot.' And when I saw the ugly look he gave me I knew that there was trouble coming, and so there was.

He got up on her all right, for, to give the devil his due, he was agile on his limbs and, although no horseman, there were few men in the island of Inverara that he couldn't throw with a twist of the

9

wrist he had. But as soon as his legs rubbed her flanks she neighed and gathered herself together to spring, and just as she was that way doubled up he kicked her in the mouth with his foot. She rose to her hind legs and before she could plant her fore feet on the ground again to jump, I had rushed from the rock and with one swing of my right arm I had pulled him to the ground. I was so mad that before he could rush at me I seized him by the thigh and the back of the neck, and I would have broken every limb in his putrid body if they didn't rush in and separate us. Then the craven son of a reptile that he was, as soon as he saw himself held, he began to bellow like a young bull wanting to get at me. But I took no heed of him. My father's son was never a man to crow over a fallen enemy'.

They brought the mare over to me and I looked at her. She looked at me, and a shiver passed down her flank and she whinnied, pawing the sand with her hind hoof.

'Take off that halter', said I to the men.

They did. I still kept looking at the mare and she at me. She never moved. Then coming over to her as she stood there without saddle or bridle, stepping lightly on my toes, I laid my right hand on her shoulder. 'Pruach, pruach, my beautiful girl', I called to her, rubbing her shoulders with my left hand. Then I rose from the strand, leaning on the strength of my right hand and landed on her back as lightly as a bird landing on a rose bush. She darted forward like a flash of lightning from a darkened sky. You see that strand, stretching east from the rock to where it ends in a line of boulders at the eastern end. It is four hundred paces and it rises to the south of the boulders into a high sand bank underneath the road. Well, I turned her at the sand bank with a sudden flash of my hand across her eyes, leaning out over her mane. And then back again we came, with a column of sand rising after us and the ground rising up in front of us with the speed of our progress. 'Now', said I to myself, 'I will show this son of Crooked Michael what Dan of the Fury can do on horseback.'

Raising myself gently with my hands on her shoulders, I put my two feet square on her haunches and stood straight, leaning against the wind, balancing myself with every motion of her body, and as she ran, stretched flat with her belly to earth, I took my blue woollen shirt off my back and was down again on her shoulders as light as a feather before we reached the western end, where the men stood gaping as if they had seen a priest performing a miracle. 'God be with a man', they cried. And the women sitting on the hillock that overlooks the beach screamed with fear and enjoyment, and of all the beautiful women that were gathered there that day there was not one that would not have been glad to mate with me with or without marriage.

Back over the strand again we went, the black mare and I, like lightning flying from the thunder, and the wave that rose when we passed the rock in the west had not broken on the strand when we turned again at the sand bank. Then coming back again like the driven wind in winter I rose once more, standing on her haunches, and may the devil swallow me alive if I hadn't put my shirt on my back again and landed back on her shoulders before we reached the rock. There I turned her head to the sea and drove her out into it until the waves lapped her heaving belly. I brought her back to the rock as gentle as a lamb and dismounted.

Ha! My soul from the devil, but that was a day that will never be forgotten as long as there is a man left to breathe the name of Dan of the Fury. But all things have their end, and sure it's a queer day that doesn't bring the night, and the laugh is the herald of the sigh. It was two years after that I got this fractured thigh. Well I remember that four days before the races where I got this broken limb, I met red-haired Mary of Kilmillick. As I was looking after her, for she had shapely hips and an enticing swing in them, my horse stumbled, and although I crossed myself three times and promised to make a journey to the Holy Well at Kilmillick, I'll swear by Crom that the spell of the Evil One was put on the mare. But that is old woman's talk. Mary promised me the morning of the races that if the black mare won, I could put a ring on her finger, and as I cantered up to the starting point I swore I would win both the race and the girl if the devil himself were holding on to the black mare's tail.

Seventeen horses lined up at the starting point. I took up my position beside a bay stallion that the parish priest Fr. John Costigan, had entered. He was a blood stallion and had won many races on the mainland, but the parish priest was allowed to enter him, for who could go against a priest. Then, as now, there was nobody in Inverara who was willing to risk being turned into a goat by making a priest obey the rules of a race. Six times they started us and six times we were forced to come back to the starting point, for that same braggart, the son of Crooked Michael, persisted in trying to get away before the appointed time. At last the parish priest knocked him off his horse with a welt of his blackthorn stick and the race started.

We were off like sixteen claps of thunder. We had to circle the

11

field three times, that big field above the beach at Coillnamhan,
and before we had circled it the second time, the bay stallion and
the mare were in front with the rest nowhere. Neck to neck we ran,
and no matter how I urged the mare she would not leave the
stallion. Then in the third round of the field I caught a sight of
Mary looking at me with a sneer on her face, as if she thought I
was afraid to beat the priest's horse. That look drove me mad. I
forgot myself. We were stretching towards the winning post. The
stallion was reaching in front of me. Mad with rage I struck the
mare a heavy blow between the ears. I had never struck her in my
life and as soon as I had done it I started with fright and shame. I
had struck my horse. I spoke to her gently but she just shivered
from the tip of her ears to her tail and darted forward with one
mighty rush that left the stallion behind.

I heard a shout from the people. I forgot the blow. I forgot the
mare. I leaned forward on her mane and yelled myself. We passed
the winning post, with the stallion one hundred yards or more
behind us. I tried to draw rein. Her head was like a firm rock. I
cursed her and drew rein again. I might have been a flea biting her
back. At one bound she leapt the fence and swept down the beach.
She was headed straight for the boulders. I saw them in front of me
and grew terrified. Between us and the boulders was the sand bank,
fifteen feet high. She snorted, raised her head and tried to stop
when she saw the fall. I heard a shout from the people. Then I
became limp. We rose in the air. We fell. The mare struck the rocks
and I remembered no more.

They told me afterward that she was shattered to a pulp when
they found us, and sure it's the good God that only gave me a
broken leg.

3. EXTRACTS FROM NOVEL: "THE KNIFE"

PEADAR O'DONNELL

Peadar O'Donnell is another rural writer, but a more politically conscious one than Liam O'Flaherty. O'Donnell was born in 1893 in rural Donegal, the most north-westerly county of Ireland. He began life as a country schoolmaster. But he was caught up in the nation's struggle for independence and became one of the leaders of the intransigents who opposed any compromise with Britain in 1921 and formed the forerunners of the IRA responsible for the fighting in Northern Ireland in the 1970's. Since events in Irish history provide the canvas for so much of modern Irish writing, it may be useful to summarize them here.

For seven centuries, punctuated by sporadic rebellions, Britain ruled Ireland. In 1916 a fresh Rising against the British took place at which an all-Ireland republic was proclaimed in Dublin. This rebellion, like its predecessors, was soon crushed, but was followed by widespread guerilla warfare. In 1921 the British offered a compromise: Dublin should rule the three-quarters of the island where there was a predominantly Catholic and nationalist population; Britain would retain the north-east, where there was a Protestant majority favouring union with Britain. After bitter debates, a narrow majority of the Irish nationalists accepted the compromise; but the minority who wished to fight on for the independence of the whole island took up arms against their fellow-countrymen, whom they regarded as traitors; and two years of civil war followed. In 1923 this terminated, after bitterness and bloodshed, leaving the island partitioned as it is today.

We find politics and literature intermingled in all O'Donnell's writings and nowhere more so than in his novel *The Knife* (1930) from which extracts are given below. In the foreground this is a tale of action, with some romantic interplay, and illustrates O'Donnell's shrewd grasp of life in a small rural community. Politics erupt and we see this peasant society polarized first in the struggle against the British, then in the civil war, where the stake-in-the-country men want to stop at the compromise, the men-of-no-property want to carry on to the social revolution. A scene in the

13

later part of the novel where the revolutionary, The Knife, invades the altar to prevent the priest talking politics in church and his sister, Nuala, shouts "Shut your mouth, and go on with the prayers," is in no way exaggerated and accurately reflects the temper of the times. The Church, with the exception of a few of the younger clergy, was bitterly opposed to the threat of social revolution.

But even more illuminating, in the light of later events, is the novel's setting. This is a village on the Northern border, where the two Irelands, Gaelic, Catholic native, and Protestant, pro-British colonist, confront each other in an uneasy mingling. O'Donnell was a nationalist, but unlike so many of his fellows, he knew intimately and never underestimated the other side. His portrait of the dour Orangeman (Protestant) Sam Rowan is far from an unsympathetic one.

The novel opens when a Catholic family, the Godfrey Dhus, has done an unprecedented thing—secretly bought a farm in what has previously been a solidly Protestant enclave.

From
THE KNIFE

CHAPTER ONE

Sam Rowan's farm was in the centre of a compact planter district.
Every rood of land was owned by a solid Orange stock. It was said
of the Rowans that a native never slept under their roof nor broke
bread at their table. Their servant men were housed and fed in a
loft over the stable.

William Rowan was old, wasted, asthmatic. He sat in his chair in
the corner, leaning forward so that he could spit easily into the fire.
He was alone. Rebecca had gone down to Richard Gregg to see
whether he could ease her mind of this rumour. William leaned
forward and coughed and waited. He took up the tongs and drew
aimless strokes in the ashes, his bushy eyebrows poked forward, his
cheeks puffing out and in as he breathed. His skin was puckered,
kippered, tawny. His eyes were sunken and wide and bright, his
hair bristling, short cropped, speckled.

He waited in patience. Rebecca would be back soon. He rested
the tongs against the wall and turned to keep his eye on the open
door. A hen thrust her head in and turned one questioning eye on
William, took a step forward, halted with one foot in the air, her
head twisted round to catch a sound outside, and then with a jerk of
her wings swung round and disappeared.

A big, black, long-haired dog, with dull eye and heavy step, came
softly in. He looked around listlessly, wagged his tail lazily, and
ambled over to a dish of hens' meat, nosed it, pulled his lips apart,
and nibbled listlessly at a piece of the feed, dropped it, and walked
lazily out. In the doorway he halted, one ear slightly raised, his tail
again wagging slowly. William sat up straight and leaned towards
the door, his hand cupped behind his ear to catch the message in
any sound outside. Sitting for years in a corner had made William
keen on sounds. When Rebecca's hard-heeled tramp caught his ear
he breathed in sharply.

Rebecca came quickly in; she came up and sat down on the chair

15

opposite him, and jerked her head backward on her lean, wrinkled neck.

'It's true,' she said, breathlessly, her stiffened arms reaching down between her knees, her fingers locked, her breathing laboured.

William looked quickly away; he stared into the fire. His fingers sought the tongs; he prodded the turf; he let the tongs fall; he uncrossed his legs, swung a limp leg back over a withered knee; jerked his slippered foot up and down; cleared his throat; glanced back at Rebecca; and then suddenly slouching forward in his chair, he picked up the tongs and drew strokes in the ashes.

'Am no' understandin' it,' he said quietly, almost to himself.

'It's devil's work,' Rebecca said angrily.

William looked up sharply. Anger surprised him, for William had only been troubled.

'Who would ye be blamin'?' he asked her.

'I dunno,' she said, getting to her feet. 'I dunno, but there's somebody.' She sat down again.

'We'll just ha' to wait till Sammy comes.' His cough returned. Rebecca sat motionless, her body stiff, her eyes staring unseeingly at the wall.

The dog made faint throatal greetings, and William's cough snapped quickly. Rebecca and he sat straight up and stared at the door. Sam Rowan came in. He was a big-framed man, now in the middle twenties. His eyes went straight to his aunt and father at the fireside; brown eyes with a cold tone in them. He hung his cap on a peg on the wall, took off his coat, and sat down to unloose his shoes.

'It's true then, Sammy,' Rebecca said, rising, her hands crushed against her breast.

Sam nodded. With his boots loose he moved towards the room door, struggling to undo his collar stud as he walked.

Rebecca sat down again; her hands were now limp in her lap. The stiffness left old William's body too; he leaned forward in his chair and coughed.

Men returning from the fair yelled in the roadway. Sam came down from the room in his socked feet, and he was now in his working clothes. He sought under the kitchen table for his heavy boots. Rebecca got wearily to her feet to set his dinner on the table.

Sam ate in silence. Rebecca went out into the yard. The old man drew strokes in the ashes with the tongs.

16

CHAPTER TWO

The news had burst on the fair without any warning for when the Godfrey Dhus had begun to work around Montgomerys, clearing up the walk, mending the roof, fixing gates and doing work inside, nobody was very much interested. The Godfrey Dhus were servant men who often took contracts. Last year they had put the Major's lodge in order, for The Knife was as good as any carpenter, folk said, although he had never been taught anything beyond what he picked up attending tradesmen here and there. Old Godfrey Dhu himself was a good worker in stone, and his two boys, The Knife and Hugh, took after him in that, so that it was natural they should have taken on the job of tightening things up around Montgomerys. It was years since the absentee owner had put in an appearance, and whether he intended to appear again or not, it was to his interest to keep the place from going to ruin.

Billy White had seen them there, of course, and he champed his jaws and passed on to look after his cattle, growling softly to himself. Sam Rowan had seen them there, and stopped to ask The Knife to come and try the pace of a new horse he had bought. He had waved his hand to Nuala, who had appeared in the doorway to call the men to a meal; sensible idea to have her come over and cook for the men on the job, he thought, as he drove away; good for the house, too, to have a fire in it. A bright sapling of a woman, he found himself thinking, as he turned to close the gate, and he looked up again sharply, but she was gone.

Godfrey Dhu himself was stamping up the walk; powerful trunk of a man, Godfrey Dhu. Sam recalled suddenly that he had heard that Godfrey Dhu had drawn a plough, and he could well believe it. He paused with the reins in his hands to look back, with the ploughing incident in his mind, but Godfrey had gone, and he thought again of Nuala. He stepped into the cart and drove off.

Sam Rowan had come close to Nuala Godfrey Dhu one other evening when she strolled among the trees around Montgomerys. She was singing as he drew near, and he walked softly for fear she might end the song. He stood in the shelter of an old tree while she came slowly towards him. Sam had heard little singing beyond hymns on a Sunday, and certainly he had never heard a voice like this. He peeped under the branches; she was standing on the path looking out, through a clearing in the trees, on to the fields of the Lagan. And his mind gave heed to the words, and as he listened the music ceased to give him pleasure. It was a Fenian song she was

17

singing. 'The dark-minded wee bitch,' he muttered, and stamped along on his way. He did not notice that the song broke off suddenly, for his mind was still resenting the words of that song; they were all alike, these servant men and women; just filled up to the neck with badness; can't sing anything but Fenian songs, he fumed. He cut out on the road, and strode past Doctor Henry, who was fishing a hole in the river.

'Whither goeth Goliath?' the Doctor challenged. 'You looked like you were going out to battle as you came along.'

'Well, maybe,' Sam agreed, coming towards the Doctor.

'And what was bothering you?'

'Oh, just a bit of a song.'

'Nuala beyond? Fine voice that girl.'

'Aye, 'twas Nuala.'

The Doctor made a cast; a trout flicked the water with his tail.

'He's a beauty, that boy, but saucy; we've been waving to each other for an hour.' Further up along the river somebody began to whistle. The Doctor paused in his cast, and smiled. 'Young Tommy Smith that's whistling,' he said.

'Aye, young Tommy,' Sam said.

'What's this you call that tune?' the Doctor asked.

'Your wee while in England must ha' cut chunks out of ye if ye no min' *Derry Walls.*'

'Aye, just so, *Derry Walls,*' he said with a grin.

'Well, it's a likely enough thing to whistle,' Sam said.

'Aye, Sammy. Jumping snakes! A beauty! I have him; jump, ye devil. Oh, Dolly's brae, oh, Dolly's brae. ... Listen to him, Sam; music; cold water and a string of gut! Atta boy; jump; easy boy, easy; only holding by a hair; easy boy, easy; brain that dog, Sam; oh, you beauty!'

'Shut up, Doctor Henry,' Nuala called, arriving at a run. 'Land your fish; I never knew a man to talk – Oh, my poor fellow! Make a dash, jump, jump!'

'Shut up, you hussy, or I'll brain you.'

'Jump! Make a hoop and snap!'

'Sam, pitch her in the river,' Doctor Henry urged.

'Hurrah! Oh, my poor, big fellow!'

After one last plunge the fish stood steady. The Doctor reeled in slowly, the fish was deep down. Nuala on a flag was gazing down into the river. Sam Rowan was tapping his legging with the gaff. The Doctor continued to reel in carefully. Suddenly the fish shot straight for the surface and rose high into the air. The Doctor, in tilting backwards, stumbled against Sam; the rod jerked violently, and the fish spun round in the air, and flopped back into the water, free. Nuala clapped her hands and cheered. The Doctor sat down on the bank.

'Don't cry, Doctor Henry, I'll give you a glass marble and a bit of string.'

'I could break your back, Nuala.'

'Let it be a warning to you not to sing party tunes when you're fishing Irish salmon; they don't like it.'

'Who was singing party tunes?'

'Well, not singing, but you were roaring *Dolly's Brae.*'

'I wasn't, Nuala!'

''Deed were you.'

'Well, I'm damned.'

Nuala glanced at Sam where he stood silently by the river. 'I'm glad he escaped,' she said. 'Still, he was a beauty.'

'Run, or I'll fling something at you,' the Doctor threatened.

Nuala laughed, made a face at him, and passed on.

'Going over to the shop,' the Doctor said, explaining her presence to himself.

'She's a forward bit of a strumpet,' Sam Rowan said.

'Don't be an ass, Sam Rowan. Did you ever see such a damn fine head of rusty hair,' he added.

'There's venom under it; you should hear the meanin' she was puttin' into that song.'

'Oh, my righteous Covenanter! Listen to the row young Tommy Smith is making with the *Boyne Water.* An' she says I was roaring *Dolly's Brae*; me!'

'Aye, and why not you?'

'I will even cast my fly again,' the Doctor said, getting to his feet. 'And run along, Sam, like a good boy, and take off your boots and catch minnows with your toes. By the way, Sam,' the Doctor called after his cousin, before he had disappeared round the bend, 'aren't the Godfrey Dhus a long time about Montgomerys?'

'The Godfrey Dhus are all right,' Sam said back over his shoulder; he was feeling grumpy with the Doctor. 'I suppose they're all the same,' he grumbled as he walked off.

'Sam!'

'Well?'

'Hasn't she a damn fine voice?'

'Never heard anything like it,' Sam enthused. 'The voice is all

19

right,' he grumbled, after a pause. The Doctor flicked his cast across the river, and Sam strode off through the fields.

CHAPTER THREE

Even in the morning there had been no ripple of news. Sam Rowan had not been early in the market but Billy White had been there. Billy grew tired of the market; prices were poor and it was a mean, drizzly day that made the world feel its old age, and made the lives of things in it the off-shoots of old age. Other farmers might have to sell, for grass was short, but there was no reason why Billy should remain nibbling at buyers; he had grass for the stock. So he whisked them out of the market, and sent them off in the care of a servant man from his neighbourhood. Billy would take a walk round and see the market, and call at Dan Sweeney's too, and have a drink; whiskey was made for such a day as this.

He pushed his way through the fair, wedging cattle aside here and there with a jerk of his thigh. A sale was taking place down near the Bank, and a big, interested crowd hung around; like crows round a stook of oats, Billy thought, spat out, and went on his way. He pushed open the door and entered Sweeney's bar. Inside, the air was thick with smoke and fumes and talk; the talk buzzed in a fog. Billy's stubble jaws felt their way among faces to the counter, and again he used his thighs to wedge obstacles aside, and a man cursed. Sweeney nodded to Billy, and filled out a double Scotch. Without a word Billy swallowed it down, and rapped the glass on the counter before Sweeney, who refilled it.

Billy rested his elbow on the counter and looked round. Talk, talk, a milling of words; here and there a song wriggled its way amid the confusion. Angry words stabbed the babel, clung on the whirl of heedlessness and hilarity, and then melted down into maudlin murmurs. Billy gazed round him; his small eyes that showed little white, blank, uninterested, just seeing, his head jerking round and round on his neck as his gaze swung.

The bar door came in with a bang, and the noise nipped off

suddenly. Two men continued to drone a song until their singing stood naked amid the silence, and then they sat down suddenly, spilling their beer over each other, laughing foolishly.

'Godfrey Dhu is buying the whole damn fair,' a man roared from the doorway.

Billy White struck his glass with his elbow and it spilled across the counter, emptying over into one of his boots. His head jerked forward towards the speaker, and then crouched, as though ducking a blow, between humped shoulders. He shot out his thigh, and a man stumbled; he dug into the crowd.

'Then by God it's true!' a voice gasped close to Billy's ear.

'What's true?' Billy barked.

'The Godfrey Dhus have bought Montgomerys.'

Billy White made a noise like an animal in pain, and stood stiff against the counter. 'The Godfrey Dhus, the Godfrey Dhus.' Recollection of The Knife and Nuala and the old man himself busy among the trees was rising in gusts of alarm in Billy White, until amid the roar he accepted in a riot of rage the truth of this news. He drove his fist into the roar around him, and found a man's face, and he was in the midst of the first group that was retched out of the bar in the great heave that tore the splintered door from its hinges.

The fair was leaping into rising billows of conflict and excitement. The servant men of the Lagan were building on the gathering down near the Bank, and the Orangemen, recognising each other across spaces in the emptying market-place, moved into knots among the cattle, and then churning together drew near the roaring natives. The Godfrey Dhus were in front, silent beside a cart, with the servant men of the Lagan piled in behind them.

Billy White raced towards the Godfrey Dhus. He ran forward with an awkward jog, one clawed hand raised above his bare head, sweat beaded on his face, and blood from a cut lip dripping off his short whisker. He came on steadily, his jog settling into a purposeful stride with its queer swing. His eyes were on the old man, and when The Knife stepped forward Billy halted. Behind him the farmers of the Lagan pressed steadily, silent, this news groping into the forefront of each mind, flashing, whirling, until the fair became unreal, bizarre.

'Godfrey Dhu,' Billy White bellowed, but the servant men of the Lagan roared him down.

Breslin pushed out in front and stood a pace before Godfrey Dhu, glowering at Billy White; two enemies of a score of years. The

21

Knife put a hand on Breslin's shoulder, and Sam Rowan walked to the front among the Orangemen. When The Knife raised his hand the market was silent.

'Is it true, Knife?'

'It's true, Sam.' And now a roar that was all challenge, the flinging of hats and of old threadbare caps: among the Orangemen a growl, here and there the sudden raising of a stick.

That scene burned deep into the minds of the Lagan. On one side the planter farmers, a solid crush of swarthy, big-bodied, well-coated men; opposing them the servant men of the Lagan, blue and grey eyes against shades of brown; fair skin against tawny, restless swaying bodies poised to spring, against a wall of stolid trunks. In front of the farmers, his small eyes blood-shot, his teeth bare, his jaws champing, his short legs wide apart, one hand clenched and held low, one raised and clawed, stood Billy White the Orangeman.

Blazing into Billy's eyes, his face thrust forward, his lips parted in a sneer, his fists pushed down along his sides by arms as stiff as ramrods, his knees bent to spring, stood Paddy Breslin, the Hibernian. Should these crowds clash, Billy and Paddy would meet first, Paddy with milling fist and butting head crashing into Billy's swinging boot and clawing hand.

Godfrey Dhu, nursing his secret of money from a dead brother's estate in Australia, had come into possession of a farm in the Lagan. Land in a compact planter district had always been disposed of by private treaty to British stock; it was part of the Orangemen's religion that the possession of soil must remain solid. This farm had passed to an absentee, and by some obscure process the absentee had let it slip into the hands of a Fenian, a papist; every native was both. Here in the market the crust of the centuries was burst; the past was boiling over, gushing out its lava of madness. Dazed, mystified, and angrier because of the mystery, the planters staggered under an eruption of boiling race hatred. One long, wild roar was ringing through the square from the servant men. Low growls from the sweating, compact, motionless Orangemen. Breslin and White, cheering and champing, straining forward. Should they meet this village will become a pit in a jungle of blind passion and men will rip one another to pieces.

Suddenly from among the natives a hand shot up commanding silence, and The Knife turned to the crowd behind him. Sam Rowan stepped to the front amid the Orangemen. His eye and The Knife's met, clear, hard looks, preoccupied; the concern of each was

22

back on his own crowd. The Orangemen tramped past, slowly, without a word, with heavy, stamping feet. The natives were alone.

And Sam Rowan went home with the tidings which had preceded him to the fireside of the Black Rowans.

CHAPTER ELEVEN

The Godfrey Dhus noticed that their nods were not returned by the neighbour farmers, and soon meetings went without greeting from either side. So that when The Knife went into the market to buy young beasts to put on the grass, he was more or less prepared for his reception. He first met Billy White, who had two bullocks for sale.

'What'll ye take for them, Billy?' The Knife asked. Billy was sitting on the side of a cart.

'I want nothing from you,' Billy said without looking at him.

The Knife strode leisurely up to Billy. 'So ye want nothing from me, Billy?' he said.

'They're sold,' Billy said, dropping to his feet.

After a short pause, The Knife walked away. He rapped many beasts but made no purchase. In the throng he came face to face with Sam Rowan.

'Have ye sold your beasts, Sam?' he asked. 'I like that wee polly.'

Sam hesitated. Then he looked at The Knife squarely. 'To tell you the truth, Knife, am no' sellin' anything to ye.'

'I'm in the market this couple of hours, Sam,' The Knife said, 'and to tell you the truth, I wouldn't take a present of most of the beasts I priced. I was in earnest with you. An' yer the only Orangeman in the fair I didn't make a liar of.'

'A liar?'

The Knife nodded. 'There's Bob Weldon. He asked me fourteen pounds for that wee bullock. Isn't that a plain lie to say that's his price?'

Weldon heard him, as it was intended he should. 'I wouldn't take

23

fourteen pounds of yer bloody money; there's no knowing how ye got it,' he retorted.

'Where's your Dick?' The Knife asked sharply.

'He's around the market. What ye want wi' Dick?' he added, annoyed with himself.

'I was wonderin' could he be got to say what you said.'

'I wouldn't ask ye for yer beast now, Sam Rowan,' The Knife continued, 'for if it was that ye sold to me every one of them would be nippin' at ye, the dark-minded lot of damn fools.'

'I wouldn't let me tongue get speeded up like that, Knife,' Sam said curtly.

The Knife and Sam straightened at the same instant and faced each other. The crowds had been gradually closing in behind them, for their meeting was of significance to the whole fair. Breslin was beside The Knife. Billy White pushed forward near Sam.

'Up, Montgomery,' Breslin taunted, his eye on Billy.

The Rowans had Montgomery blood in them, and Sam struck; The Knife dodged, and crouching, struck back.

The fair was in an uproar in an instant. The Knife and Sam hurled forward into conflict and the fair rocked under their impact. A silence swept across the market, clipping the words from ready lips, halting the bargaining hands in the air. From mind to mind, from body to body, excitement leaped in sudden heady flashes, and a hurried, restless local grouping took place all across the market, and then with a flick the groups rose tiptoe, and tipped towards the whirlpool in the centre. A roar leaped from so many throats that tired cattle pranced in affright, and then the groups linked, chained, and swung themselves round the fighters, pressing back to make space, bellowing a rage that seemed to break in adequate expression in the swirling, thumping, berserker bodies in front. Sam Rowan, suddenly lightfooted, quick-minded, headlong; The Knife, his lithe form nimble as cane, ribs like steel casing, knuckles like the teeth of a harrow, was lifted forward in a burst of madness such as never had burst in his soul. A wild, long roar; milling feet; repressed enmity suddenly ablaze. The damning years reel again under the impetus, and when they break two tidal waves will crash, and the very sun will be washed out of the blue heavens. Faster the pace between Sam and The Knife; gasps have a place in the medley; blood flows down fair and tawny skins; this is a fight that will end in one or both of these bodies sinking into the mud, as dead, as exhausted of purpose or meaning, as this missionless muck.

Police whistles have been sounding, and now a new shout, sharp, shrill, closer to action than that wild storm of sound. The police, with drawn batons, charge into the natives. The Orangemen, barricaded, leap forward. Men fall and are trampled, ribs crack under the vicious stamp of steel heel plates, sticks break across bleeding heads. Men drop under the rain of batons, the nervous whisperings of defeat melting the natives' passion. Suddenly police and Orangemen in a mighty heave fling the natives before them like a sapless crust of lost passion and the flight becomes a chase. Native Ireland was swept from the fair, and only women and children, wild-eyed, furtive, raced through the village to collect bellowing cattle and hurry them out to the little homesteads in the hills.

Sam Rowan had seen The Knife go down under the smash of a baton: then he lost vision of things. He was held erect by two stocky farmers while he gasped for breath and spat blood, and blinked sweat and blood from his eyelashes. The sharp tang of whiskey on his cut lips, the murmur of encouraging voices, the wild throatfuls of sudden cheer, these things he heard as they linked him from the field.

The Knife was taken to the police barracks.

4. STORY: "GUESTS OF THE NATION"

FRANK O'CONNOR

The impact of "the Troubled Times", as those who lived through them usually called the events from 1916 to 1923 was traumatic for the entire population of Ireland, but especially so for the imaginative writer. It is arguable that Yeats might never have emerged as the greatest English-speaking poet of his time had history not presented him with so fertile a theme in his middle age, at a time when signs were that his inspiration was running dry. Mature writers could grapple with the experience, though with difficulty. Young writers were in some danger of being overwhelmed by it.

Michael O'Donovan, who took the pen name of Frank O'Connor, was born of poor parents in Cork city in 1903. He played a minor role in the national struggle, taking the Republican side in the civil war. He had no post-primary education. His literary apprenticeship owed most to Daniel Corkery, the Gaelic language enthusiast and teacher; but though he published many translations from the Irish, O'Connor's own work was always in English.

"Guests of the Nation" is the title-story of his first collection, which appeared in 1931. The title of course is ironic: the unwanted guests are British soldiers who are being held hostage against the Irish claim for their men to be treated as prisoners-of-war. When the British shoot their prisoners, the Irish shoot theirs. The story's theme remains a contemporary one. Perhaps the most telling line in O'Connor's tale is the last: "And anything that happened to me afterwards, I never felt the same about again." One wonders whether the new generation of revolutionaries in Ireland or Europe share the sensitivities of the old.

O'Connor was an enormously prolific writer. Stories, translations, literary essays, journalistic articles flowed from his pen. He was also a relentless reviser of his own work, even after it had appeared in print. Sometimes this seems not for the best. One early story, "First Confession", definitely loses the freshness of the child's vision, when it is re-told in middle age. The version of "Guests of the Nation" given here is the 1963 revision the author made a few years before his death. In this case, the elimination of certain colloquialisms, and the tightening of the style, seem an improvement on the version of 1931.

GUESTS OF THE THE NATION

One

At dusk the big Englishman, Belcher, would shift his long legs out of the ashes and say 'Well, chums, what about it?' and Noble or myself would say 'All right, chum' (for we had picked up some of their curious expressions), and the little Englishman, Hawkins, would light the lamp and bring out the cards. Sometimes Jeremiah Donovan would come up and supervise the game, and get excited over Hawkins' cards, which he always played badly, and shout at him as if he was one of our own, 'Ah, you divil, why didn't you play the tray?'

But ordinarily Jeremiah was a sober and contented poor devil like the big Englishman, Belcher, and was looked up to only because he was a fair hand at documents, though he was slow even with them. He wore a small cloth hat and big gaiters over his long pants, and you seldom saw him with his hands out of his pockets. He reddened when you talked to him, tilting from toe to heel and back, and looking down all the time at his big farmer's feet. Noble and myself used to make fun of his broad accent, because we were both from the town.

I could not at the time see the point of myself and Noble guarding Belcher and Hawkins at all, for it was my belief that you could have planted that pair down anywhere from this to Claregalway and they'd have taken root there like a native weed. I never in my short experience saw two men take to the country as they did.

They were passed on to us by the Second Battalion when the search for them became too hot, and Noble and myself, being young, took them over with a natural feeling of responsibility, but Hawkins made us look like fools when he showed that he knew the country better than we did.

'You're the bloke they call Bonaparte,' he says to me. 'Mary Brigid O'Connell told me to ask what you'd done with the pair of her brother's socks you borrowed.'

For it seemed, as they explained it, that the Second had little

29

evenings, and some of the girls of the neighbourhood turned up, and, seeing they were such decent chaps, our fellows could not leave the two Englishmen out. Hawkins learned to dance *The Walls of Limerick, The Siege of Ennis* and *The Waves of Tory* as well as any of them, though he could not return the compliment, because our lads at that time did not dance foreign dances on principle.

So whatever privileges Belcher and Hawkins had with the Second they just took naturally with us, and after the first couple of days we gave up all pretence of keeping an eye on them. Not that they could have got far, because they had accents you could cut with a knife, and wore khaki tunics and overcoats with civilian pants and boots, but I believe myself they never had any idea of escaping and were quite content to be where they were.

It was a treat to see how Belcher got off with the old woman in the house where we were staying. She was a great warrant to scold, and cranky even with us, but before ever she had a chance of giving our guests, as I may call them, a lick of her tongue, Belcher had made her his friend for life. She was breaking sticks, and Belcher, who had not been more than ten minutes in the house, jumped up and went over to her.

'Allow me, madam,' he said, smiling his queer little smile. 'Please allow me,' and he took the hatchet from her. She was too surprised to speak, and after that, Belcher would be at her heels, carrying a bucket, a basket or a load of turf. As Noble said, he got into looking before she leapt, and hot water, or any little thing she wanted, Belcher would have ready for her. For such a huge man (and though I am five foot ten myself I had to look up at him) he had an uncommon lack of speech. It took us a little while to get used to him, walking in and out like a ghost, without speaking. Especially because Hawkins talked enough for a platoon it was strange to hear Belcher with his toes in the ashes come out with a solitary 'Excuse me, chum,' or 'That's right, chum.' His one and only passion was cards, and he was a remarkably good card player. He could have skinned myself and Noble, but whatever we lost to him, Hawkins lost to us, and Hawkins only played with the money Belcher gave him.

Hawkins lost to us because he had too much old gab, and we probably lost to Belcher for the same reason. Hawkins and Noble argued about religion into the early hours of the morning, and Hawkins worried the life out of Noble, who had a brother a priest, with a string of questions that would puzzle a cardinal. Even in treating of holy subjects, Hawkins had a deplorable tongue. I never met a man who could mix such a variety of cursing and bad language into any argument. He was a terrible man, and a fright to argue. He never did a stroke of work, and when he had no one else to argue with, he got stuck in the old woman.

He met his match in her, for when he tried to get her to complain profanely of the drought she gave him a great come-down by blaming it entirely on Jupiter Pluvius (a deity neither Hawkins nor I had ever heard of, though Noble said that among the pagans it was believed that he had something to do with the rain). Another day he was swearing at the capitalists for starting the German war when the old lady laid down her iron, puckered up her little crab's mouth and said: 'Mr Hawkins, you can say what you like about the war, and think you'll deceive me because I'm only a simple poor countrywoman, but I know what started the war. It was the Italian Count that stole the heathen divinity out of the temple in Japan. Believe me, Mr Hawkins, nothing but sorrow and want can follow people who disturb the hidden powers.'

A queer old girl, all right.

Two

One evening we had our tea and Hawkins lit the lamp and we all sat into cards. Jeremiah Donovan came in too, and sat and watched us for a while, and it suddenly struck me that he had no great love for the two Englishmen. It came as a surprise to me because I had noticed nothing of it before.

Late in the evening a really terrible argument blew up between Hawkins and Noble about capitalists and priests and love of country.

'The capitalists pay the priests to tell you about the next world so that you won't notice what the bastards are up to in this,' said Hawkins.

'Nonsense, man!' said Noble, losing his temper. 'Before ever a capitalist was thought of people believed in the next world.'

Hawkins stood up as though he was preaching.

'Oh, they did, did they?' he said with a sneer. 'They believed all the things you believe – isn't that what you mean? And you believe God created Adam, and Adam created Shem, and Shem created Jehoshophat. You believe all that silly old fairytale about Eve and

31

Eden and the apple. Well listen to me, chum! If you're entitled to a silly belief like that, I'm entitled to my own silly belief – which is that the first thing your God created was a bleeding capitalist, with morality and Rolls-Royce complete. Am I right, chum?' he says to Belcher.

'You're right, chum,' says Belcher with a smile, and he got up from the table to stretch his long legs into the fire and stroke his moustache. So, seeing that Jeremiah Donovan was going, and that there was no knowing when the argument about religion would be over, I went out with him. We strolled down to the village together, and then he stopped, blushing and mumbling, and said I should be behind, keeping guard. I didn't like the tone he took with me, and anyway I was bored with life in the cottage, so I replied by asking what the hell we wanted to guard them for at all.

He looked at me in surprise and said: 'I thought you knew we were keeping them as hostages.'

'Hostages?' I said.

'The enemy have prisoners belonging to us, and now they're talking of shooting them,' he said. 'If they shoot our prisoners, we'll shoot theirs.'

'Shoot Belcher and Hawkins?' I said.

'What else did you think we were keeping them for?' he said.

'Wasn't it very unforeseen of you not to warn Noble and myself of that in the beginning?' I said.

'How was it?' he said. 'You might have known that much.'

'We could not know it, Jeremiah Donovan,' I said. 'How could we when they were on our hands so long?'

'The enemy have our prisoners as long and longer,' he said.

'That's not the same thing at all,' said I.

'What difference is there?' said he.

I couldn't tell him, because I knew he wouldn't understand. If it was only an old dog that you had to take to the vet's, you'd try and not get too fond of him, but Jeremiah Donovan was not a man who would ever be in danger of that.

'And when is this to be decided?' I said.

'We might hear tonight,' he said. 'Or tomorrow or the next day at latest. So if it's only hanging round that's a trouble to you, you'll be free soon enough.'

It was not the hanging round that was a trouble to me at all by this time. I had worse things to worry about. When I got back to the cottage the argument was still on. Hawkins was holding forth in his best style, maintaining that there was no next world, and Noble saying that there was; but I could see that Hawkins had had the best of it.

'Do you know what, chum?' he was saying with a saucy smile. 'I think you're just as big a bleeding unbeliever as I am. You say you believe in the next world, and you know just as much about the next world as I do, which is sweet damn-all. What's heaven? You don't know. Where's heaven? You don't know. You know sweet damn-all! I ask you again, do they wear wings?'

'Very well, then,' said Noble. 'They do. Is that enough for you? They do wear wings.'

'Where do they get them then? Who makes them? Have they a factory for wings? Have they a sort of store where you hand in your chit and take your bleeding wings?'

'You're an impossible man to argue with,' said Noble. 'Now, listen to me—' And they were off again.

It was long after midnight when we locked up and went to bed. As I blew out the candle I told Noble. He took it very quietly. When we'd been in bed about an hour he asked if I thought we should tell the Englishmen. I didn't, because I doubted if the English would shoot our men. Even if they did, the Brigade officers, who were always up and down to the Second Battalion and knew the Englishmen well, would hardly want to see them plugged. 'I think so too,' said Noble. 'It would be great cruelty to put the wind up them now.'

'It was very unforeseen of Jeremiah Donovan, anyhow,' said I.

It was next morning that we found it so hard to face Belcher and Hawkins. We went about the house all day, scarcely saying a word. Belcher didn't seem to notice; he was stretched into the ashes as usual, with his usual look of waiting in quietness for something unforeseen to happen, but Hawkins noticed it and put it down to Noble's being beaten in the argument of the night before.

'Why can't you take the discussion in the proper spirit?' he said severely. 'You and your Adam and Eve! I'm a Communist, that's what I am. Communist or Anarchist, it all comes to much the same thing.' And he went round the house, muttering when the fit took him: 'Adam and Eve! Adam and Eve! Nothing better to do with their time than pick bleeding apples!'

33

Three

I don't know how we got through that day, but I was very glad when it was over, the tea things were cleared away, and Belcher said in his peaceable way: 'Well, chums, what about it?' We sat round the table and Hawkins took out the cards, and just then I heard Jeremiah Donovan's footsteps on the path and a dark presentiment crossed my mind. I rose from the table and caught him before he reached the door.

'What do you want?' I asked.

'I want those two soldier friends of yours,' he said, getting red.

'Is that the way, Jeremiah Donovan?' I asked.

'That's the way. There were four of our lads shot this morning, one of them a boy of sixteen.'

'That's bad,' I said.

At that moment Noble followed me out, and the three of us walked down the path together, talking in whispers. Feeney, the local intelligence officer, was standing by the gate.

'What are you going to do about it?' I asked Jeremiah Donovan.

'I want you and Noble to get them out; tell them they're being shifted again; that'll be the quietest way.'

'Leave me out of that,' said Noble under his breath.

Jeremiah Donovan looked at him hard.

'All right,' he says. 'You and Feeney get a few tools from the shed and dig a hole by the far end of the bog. Bonaparte and myself will be after you. Don't let anyone see you with the tools. I wouldn't like it to go beyond ourselves.'

We saw Feeney and Noble go round to the shed and went in ourselves. I left Jeremiah Donovan to do the explanations. He told them that he had orders to send them back to the Second Battalion. Hawkins let out a mouthful of curses, and you could see that though Belcher didn't say anything, he was a bit upset too. The old woman was for having them stay in spite of us, and she didn't stop advising them until Jeremiah Donovan lost his temper and turned on her. He had a nasty temper, I noticed. It was pitch-dark in the cottage by this time, but no one thought of lighting the lamp, and in the darkness the two Englishmen fetched their topcoats and said goodbye to the old woman.

'Just as a man makes a home of a bleeding place, some bastard at headquarters thinks you're too cushy and shunts you off,' said Hawkins, shaking her hand.

34

'A thousand thanks, madam,' said Belcher. 'A thousand thanks for everything' – as though he'd made it up.

We went round to the back of the house and down towards the bog. It was only then that Jeremiah Donovan told them. He was shaking with excitement.

'There were four of our fellows shot in Cork this morning and now you're to be shot as a reprisal.'

'What are you talking about?' snaps Hawkins. 'It's bad enough being mucked about as we are without having to put up with your funny jokes.'

'It isn't a joke,' says Donovan. 'I'm sorry, Hawkins, but it's true,' and begins on the usual rigmarole about duty and how unpleasant it is. I never noticed that people who talk a lot about duty find it much of a trouble to them.

'Oh, cut it out!' said Hawkins.

'Ask Bonaparte,' said Donovan, seeing that Hawkins wasn't taking him seriously. 'Isn't it true, Bonaparte?'

'It is,' I said, and Hawkins stopped.

'Ah, for Christ's sake, chum!'

'I mean it, chum,' I said.

'You don't sound as if you meant it.'

'If he doesn't mean it, I do,' said Donovan, working himself up.

'What have you against me, Jeremiah Donovan?'

'I never said I had anything against you. But why did your people take out four of your prisoners and shoot them in cold blood?'

He took Hawkins by the arm and dragged him on, but it was impossible to make him understand that we were in earnest. I had the Smith and Wesson in my pocket and I kept fingering it and wondering what I'd do if they put up a fight for it or ran, and wishing to God they'd do one or the other. I knew if they did run for it, that I'd never fire on them. Hawkins wanted to know was Noble in it, and when we said yes he asked us why Noble wanted to plug him. Why did any of us want to plug him? What had he done to us? Weren't we all chums? Didn't we understand him and didn't he understand us? Did we imagine for an instant that he'd shoot us for all the so-and-so officers in the so-and-so British Army?

By this time we'd reached the bog, and I was so sick I couldn't even answer him. We walked along the edge of it in the darkness, and every now and then Hawkins would call a halt and begin all over again, as if he was wound up, about our being chums, and I knew that nothing but the sight of the grave would convince him

35

that we had to do it. And all the time I was hoping that something would happen; that they'd run for it or that Noble would take over the responsibility from me. I had the feeling that it was worse on Noble than on me.

Four

At last we saw the lantern in the distance and made towards it. Noble was carrying it, and Feeney was standing somewhere in the darkness behind him, and the picture of them so still and silent in the bogland brought it home to me that we were in earnest, and banished the last bit of hope I had.

Belcher, on recognizing Noble, said: 'Hallo, chum,' in his quiet way, but Hawkins flew at him at once, and the argument began all over again, only this time Noble had nothing to say for himself and stood with his head down, holding the lantern between his legs.

It was Jeremiah Donovan who did the answering. For the twentieth time, as though it was haunting his mind, Hawkins asked if anybody thought he'd shoot Noble.

'Yes, you would,' said Jeremiah Donovan.

'No, I wouldn't, damn you!'

'You would, because you'd know you'd be shot for not doing it.'

'I wouldn't, not if I was to be shot twenty times over. I wouldn't shoot a pal. And Belcher wouldn't – isn't that right, Belcher?'

'That's right, chum,' Belcher said, but more by way of answering the question than of joining in the argument. Belcher sounded as though whatever unforeseen thing he'd always been waiting for had come at last.

'Anyway, who says Noble would be shot if I wasn't? What do you think I'd do if I was in his place, out in the middle of a blasted bog?'

'What would you do?' asked Donovan.

'I'd go with him wherever he was going, of course. Share my last bob with him and stick by him through thick and thin. No one can ever say of me that I let down a pal.'

'We've had enough of this,' said Jeremiah Donovan, cocking his revolver. 'Is there any message you want to send?'

'No, there isn't.'

'Do you want to say your prayers?'

36

Hawkins came out with a cold-blooded remark that even shocked me and turned on Noble again.

'Listen to me, Noble,' he said. 'You and me are chums. You can't come over to my side, so I'll come over to your side. That show you I mean what I say? Give me a rifle and I'll go along with you and the other lads.'

Nobody answered him. We knew that was no way out.

'Hear what I'm saying?' he said. 'I'm through with it. I'm a deserter or anything else you like. I don't believe in your stuff, but it's no worse than mine. That satisfy you?'

Noble raised his head, but Donovan began to speak and he lowered it again without replying.

'For the last time, have you any messages to send?' said Donovan in a cold, excited sort of voice.

'Shut up, Donovan! You don't understand me, but these lads do. They're not the sort to make a pal and kill a pal. They're not the tools of any capitalist.'

I alone of the crowd saw Donovan raise his Webley to the back of Hawkins' neck, and as he did so I shut my eyes and tried to pray. Hawkins had begun to say something else when Donovan fired, and as I opened my eyes at the bang, I saw Hawkins stagger at the knees and lie out flat at Noble's feet, slowly and as quiet as a kid falling asleep, with the lantern-light on his lean legs and bright farmer's boots. We all stood very still, watching him settle out in the last agony.

Then Belcher took out a handkerchief and began to tie it about his own eyes (in our excitement we'd forgotten to do the same for Hawkins), and, seeing it wasn't big enough, turned and asked for the loan of mine. I gave it to him and he knotted the two together and pointed with his foot at Hawkins.

'He's not quite dead,' he said. 'Better give him another.'

Sure enough, Hawkins' left knee was beginning to rise. I bent down and put my gun to his head; then, recollecting myself, I got up again. Belcher understood what was in my mind.

'Give him his first,' he said. 'I don't mind. Poor bastard, we don't know what's happening to him now.'

I knelt and fired. By this time I didn't seem to know what I was doing. Belcher, who was fumbling a bit awkwardly with the handkerchiefs, came out with a laugh as he heard the shot. It was the first time I had heard him laugh and it sent a shudder down my back; it sounded so unnatural.

'Poor bugger!' he said quietly. 'And last night he was so curious about it all. It's very queer, chums, I always think. Now he knows as much about it as they'll ever let him know, and last night he was all in the dark.'

Donovan helped him to tie the handkerchiefs about his eyes. 'Thanks, chum,' he said. Donovan asked if there were any messages he wanted sent.

'No, chum,' he said. 'Not for me. If any of you would like to write to Hawkins' mother, you'll find a letter from her in his pocket. He and his mother were great chums. But my missus left me eight years ago. Went away with another fellow and took the kid with her. I like the feeling of a home, as you may have noticed, but I couldn't start another again after that.'

It was an extraordinary thing, but in those few minutes Belcher said more than in all the weeks before. It was just as if the sound of the shot had started a flood of talk in him and he could go on the whole night like that, quite happily, talking about himself. We stood around like fools now that he couldn't see us any longer. Donovan looked at Noble, and Noble shook his head. Then Donovan raised his Webley, and at that moment Belcher gave his queer laugh again. He may have thought we were talking about him, or perhaps he noticed the same thing I'd noticed and couldn't understand it.

'Excuse me, chums,' he said. 'I feel I'm talking the hell of a lot, and so silly, about my being so handy about a house and things like that. But this thing came on me suddenly. You'll forgive me, I'm sure.'

'You don't want to say a prayer?' asked Donovan.

'No, chum,' he said. 'I don't think it would help. I'm ready, and you boys want to get it over.'

'You understand that we're only doing our duty?' said Donovan.

Belcher's head was raised like a blind man's, so that you could only see his chin and the top of his nose in the lantern-light.

'I never could make out what duty was myself,' he said. 'I think you're all good lads, if that's what you mean. I'm not complaining.'

Noble, just as if he couldn't bear any more of it, raised his fist at Donovan, and in a flash Donovan raised his gun and fired. The big man went over like a sack of meal, and this time there was no need of a second shot.

I don't remember much about the burying, but that it was worse than all the rest because we had to carry them to the grave. It was all made lonely with nothing but a patch of lantern-light between ourselves and the dark, and birds hooting and screeching all round,

38

disturbed by the guns. Noble went through Hawkins' belongings to find the letter from his mother, and then joined his hands together. He did the same with Belcher. Then, when we'd filled in the grave, we separated from Jeremiah Donovan and Feeney and took our tools back to the shed. All the way we didn't speak a word. The kitchen was dark and cold as we'd left it, and the old woman was sitting over the hearth, saying her beads. We walked past her into the room, and Noble struck a match to light the lamp. She rose quietly and came to the doorway with all her cantankerousness gone.

'What did ye do with them?' she asked in whisper, and Noble started so that the match went out in his hand.

'What's that?' he asked without turning round.

'I heard ye,' she said.

'What did you hear?' asked Noble.

'I heard ye. Do ye think I didn't hear ye, putting the spade back in the houseen?'

Noble struck another match and this time the lamp lit for him.

'Was that what ye did to them?' she asked.

Then, by God, in the very doorway, she fell on her knees and began praying, and after looking at her for a minute or two Noble did the same by the fireplace. I pushed my way out past her and left them at it. I stood at the door, watching the stars and listening to the shrieking of the birds dying out over the bogs. It is so strange what you feel at times like that that you can't describe it. Noble says he saw everything ten times the size as though there were nothing in the whole world but that little patch of bog with the two Englishmen stiffening into it, but with me it was as if the patch of bog where the Englishmen were was a million miles away, and even Noble and the old woman, mumbling behind me, and the birds and the bloody stars were all far away, and I was somehow very small and very lost and lonely like a child astray in the snow. And anything that happened to me afterwards, I never felt the same about again.

5. STORY: "LOVERS OF THE LAKE"

SEAN O'FAOLAIN

Three years older than O'Connor and a fellow-Corkman was the writer Sean O'Faolain. He too took part in the national struggle, though in his autobiography, *Vive Moi*, published in the 1960's, he insists he played a very minor role. That book has a revealing passage dealing with the days when Cork city was under British curfew. "It is difficult", he writes, "neither to exaggerate nor to minimize when remembering such things. The truth of it is that they were both wonderful times and nightmare times." O'Faolain's first book of stories, like O'Connor's, takes its title-story, "Midsummer Night Madness", from those days, and its contents might be regarded as a commentary on that phrase. But whereas O'Connor excels in character revealed through dialogue, O'Faolain's early tales are drenched in atmosphere—the brooding, nostalgic beauty of the southern Irish countryside where the long twilights and the dawn mists underline the uncertainties of a people gripped in violence and guerilla war.

Political events, however, are not O'Faolain's central preoccupation. Catholicism is the background from which almost all his stories, novels, and essays spring, and it is Catholicism of a peculiarly Irish, life-restricting kind. It is a fact of which every thoughtful Irishman is ashamed that one of the first acts of the newly independent legislature after 1922 was to pass a Censorship of Publications Act which made Ireland the laughing stock of intellectual Europe. Strangely, the banning was not concerned with politics, nor with doctrinal matters, but solely with books advocating contraception or works of fiction dealing frankly with sex. O'Faolain's fine novel *Bird Alone* was one of the first on the list. (One must add that the censorship act has now been modified and this book is freely available again.) It cannot have been pleasant for a writer sensitively concerned with youth's struggle towards maturity to find himself branded as a pornographer and it is small wonder we often find in O'Faolain a chip-on-the-shoulder defensiveness. One of his stories, "The Man Who Invented Sin", is a wonderfully ironic satire on killjoy clericalism.

Towards middle age O'Faolain visited Italy and the encounter with continental Catholicism brought a new breadth and freedom to his writing, even though he continued preoccupied with the Irish character and religious themes. The longish story here, "Lovers of the Lake", belongs to this later period. The protagonists are no longer guilt-troubled adolescents, but wealthy, even worldly, middle-class Catholics. The subtlety of their encounter with one of the great penitential pilgrimages surviving from mediaeval Europe provides a contrast to the agnosticism displayed in the greater part of modern European and American fiction.

LOVERS OF THE LAKE

'They might wear whites,' she had said, as she stood sipping her tea and looking down at the suburban tennis players in the square. And then, turning her head in that swift movement that always reminded him of a jackdaw: 'By the way, Bobby, will you drive me up to Lough Derg next week?'

He replied amiably from the lazy deeps of his armchair.

'Certainly! What part? Killaloe? But is there a good hotel there?'

'I mean the other Lough Derg. I want to do the pilgrimage.'

For a second he looked at her in surprise and then burst into laughter; then he looked at her peeringly.

'Jenny! Are you serious?'

'Of course.'

'Do you mean that place with the island where they go around on their bare feet on sharp stones, and starve for days, and sit up all night ologroaning and ologoaning?' He got out of the chair, went over to the cigarette box on the bookshelves, and, with his back to her, said coldly, 'Are you going religious on me?'

She walked over to him swiftly, turned him about, smiled her smile that was whiter than the whites of her eyes, and lowered her head appealingly on one side. When this produced no effect she said:

'Bobby! I'm always praising you to my friends as a man who takes things as they come. So few men do. Never looking beyond the day. Doing things on the spur of the moment. It's why I like you so much. Other men are always weighing up, and considering and arguing. I've built you up as a sort of magnificent, wild, brainless tomcat. Are you going to let me down now?'

After a while he had looked at his watch and said:

'All right, then. I'll try and fix up a few days free next week. I must drop into the hospital now. But I warn you, Jenny, I've

43

noticed this Holy Joe streak in you before. You'll do it once too
often.'

She patted his cheek, kissed him sedately, said, 'You are a good
boy,' and saw him out with a loving smile.

They enjoyed that swift morning drive to the Shannon's shore.
He suspected nothing when she refused to join him in a drink at
Carrick. Leaning on the counter they had joked with the barmaid
like any husband and wife off on a motoring holiday. As they rolled
smoothly around the northern shore of Lough Gill he had suddenly
felt so happy that he had stroked her purple glove and winked at
her. The lough was vacant under the midday sun, its vast expanse of
stillness broken only by a jumping fish or by its eyelash fringe of
reeds. He did not suspect anything when she sent him off to lunch
by himself in Sligo, saying that she had to visit an old nun she knew
in the convent. So far the journey had been to him no more than
one of her caprices; until a yellow sign-post marked TO BUNDORAN
made them aware that her destination and their parting was near,
for she said:

'What are you proposing to do until Wednesday?'

'I hadn't given it a thought.'

'Don't go off and forget all about me, darling. You know you're
to pick me up on Wednesday about midday?'

After a silence he grumbled:

'You're making me feel a hell of bastard, Jenny.'

'Why on earth?'

'All this penitential stuff is because of me, isn't it?'

'Don't be silly. It's just something I thought up all by myself out
of my own clever little head.'

He drove on for several miles without speaking. She looked
sideways, with amusement, at his ruddy, healthy, hockey-player
face glummering under the peak of his checked cap. The brushes at
his temples were getting white. Everything about him bespoke the
distinguished Dublin surgeon on holiday: his pale-green shirt, his
darker-green tie, his double-breasted waistcoat, his driving gloves
with the palms made of woven cord. She looked pensively towards
the sea. He growled:

'I may as well tell you this much, Jenny, if you were my wife I
wouldn't stand for any of this nonsense.'

So their minds had travelled to the same thought? But if she
were his wife the question would never have arisen. She knew by
the sudden rise of speed that he was in one of his tempers, so that

when he pulled into the grass verge, switched off, and turned towards her she was not taken by surprise. A seagull moaned high overhead. She lifted her gray eyes to his, and smiled, waiting for the attack.

'Jenny, would you mind telling me exactly what all this is about? I mean, why are you doing this fal-lal at this particular time?'

'I always wanted to do this pilgrimage. So it naturally follows that I would do it sometime, doesn't it?'

'Perhaps. But why, for instance, this month and not last month?'

'The island wasn't open to pilgrims last month.'

'Why didn't you go last year instead of this year?'

'You know we went to Austria last year.'

'Why not the year before last?'

'I don't know. And stop bullying me. It is just a thing that everybody wants to do sometime. It is a special sort of Irish thing, like Lourdes, or Fatima, or Lisieux. Everybody who knows about it feels drawn to it. If you were a practising Catholic you'd understand.'

'I understand quite well,' he snapped. 'I know perfectly well that people go on pilgrimages all over the world. Spain. France. Mexico. I shouldn't be suprised if they go on them in Russia. What I am asking you is what has cropped up to produce this extra-special performance just *now*?'

'And I tell you I don't know. The impulse came over me suddenly last Sunday looking at those boys and girls playing tennis. For no reason. It just came. I said to myself, "All right, go now!" I felt that if I didn't do it on the impulse I'd never do it at all. Are you asking me for a rational explanation? I haven't got one. I'm not clever and intelligent like you, darling.'

'You're as clever as a bag of cats.'

She laughed at him.

'I do love you, Bobby, when you are cross. Like a small boy.'

'Why didn't you ask George to drive you?'

She sat up straight.

'I don't want my husband to know anything whatever about this. Please don't mention a word of it to him.'

He grinned at his small victory, considered the scythe of her jawbone, looked at the shining darkness of her hair, and restarted the car.

'All the same,' he said after a mile, 'there must be some reason. Or call it a cause if you don't like the word reason. And I'd give a lot to know what it is.'

After another mile:

'Of course, I might as well be talking to that old dolmen over there as be asking a woman why she does anything. And if she knew she wouldn't tell you.'

After another mile:

'Mind you, I believe all this is just a symptom of something else. Never forget, my girl, that I'm a doctor. I'm trained to interpret symptoms. If a woman comes to me with a pain ...'

'Oh, yes, if a woman comes to Surgeon Robert James Flannery with a pain he says to her, "Never mind, that's only a pain." My God! If a woman has a pain she has a bloody pain!'

He said quietly:

'Have you a pain?'

'Oh, do shut up! The only pain I have is in my tummy. I'm ravenous.'

'I'm sorry. Didn't they give you a good lunch at the convent?'

'I took no lunch; you have to arrive at the island fasting. That's the rule.'

'Do you mean to say you've had nothing at all to eat since breakfast?'

'I had no breakfast.'

'What will you get to eat when you arrive on the island?'

'Nothing. Or next to nothing. Everybody has to fast on the island the whole time. Sometime before night I might get a cup of black tea, or hot water with pepper and salt in it. I believe it's one of their lighthearted jokes to call it soup.'

Their speed shot up at once to sixty-five. He drove through Bundoran's siesta hour like the chariot of the Apocalypse. Nearing Ballyshannon they slowed down to a pleasant, humming fifty.

'Jenny!'

'Yes?'

'Are you tired of me?'

'Is this more of you and your symptoms?'

He stopped the car again.

'Please answer my question.'

She laid her purple-gloved hand on his clenched fist.

'Look, darling! We've known one another for six years. You know that like any good little Catholic girl I go to my duties every Easter and every Christmas. Once or twice I've told you so. You've growled and grumbled a bit, but you never made any fuss about it. What are you suddenly worrying about now?'

'Because all that was just routine. Like the French or the

Italians. Good Lord, I'm not bigoted. There's no harm in going to church now and again. I do it myself on state occasions, or if I'm staying in some house where they'd be upset if I didn't. But this sort of lunacy isn't routine!'

She slewed her head swiftly away from his angry eyes. A child in a pink pinafore with shoulder frills was driving two black cows through a gap.

'It was never routine. It's the one thing I have to hang on to in an otherwise meaningless existence. No children. A husband I'm not in love with. And I can't marry you.'

She slewed back to him. He slewed away to look up at the long empty road before them. He slewed back; he made as if to speak; he slewed away impatiently again.

'No?' she interpreted. 'It isn't any use, is it? It's my problem, not yours. Or if it is yours you've solved it long ago by saying it's a lot of damned nonsense.'

'And how have you solved it?' he asked sardonically.

'Have you any cause to complain of how I've solved it? Oh, I'm not defending myself. I'm a fraud, I'm a crook, I admit it. You are more honest than I am. You don't believe in anything. But it's the truth that all I have is you and ...'

'And what?'

'It sounds so blasphemous I can't say it.'

'Say it!'

'All I have is you, and God.'

He took out his cigarette case and took one. She took one. When he lit hers their eyes met. He said, very softly, looking up the empty road:

'Poor Jenny! I wish you'd talked like this to me before. It is, after all, as you say, your own affair. But what I can't get over is that this thing you're doing is so utterly extravagant. To go off to an island, in the middle of a lake, in the mountains, with a lot of Crawthumpers of every age and sex, and no sex, and peel off your stockings and your shoes, and go limping about on your bare feet on a lot of sharp stones, and kneel in the mud, psalming and beating your breast like a criminal, and drink nothing for three days but salt water ... it's not like you. It's a side of you I've never known before. The only possible explanation for it must be that something is happening inside in you that I've never seen happen before!'

She spread her hands in despair. He chucked away his cigarette and restarted the car. They drove on in silence. A mist began to speckle the windscreen. They turned off the main road into sunless

47

hills, all brown as hay. The next time he glanced at her she was
making up her face; her mouth rolling the lipstick into her lips; her
eyes rolling around the mirror. He said:

'You're going to have a nice picnic if the weather breaks.'

She glanced out apprehensively.

'It won't be fun.'

A sudden flog of rain lashed into the windscreen. The sky had
turned its bucket upside down. He said:

'Even if it's raining do you still have to keep walking around on
those damn stones?'

'Yes.'

'You'll get double pneumonia.'

'Don't worry, darling. It's called Saint Patrick's Purgatory. He
will look after me.'

That remark started a squabble that lasted until they drew up
beside the lake. Other cars stood about like stranded boats. Other
pilgrims stood by the boat slip, waiting for the ferry, their backs
hunched to the wind, their clothes ruffled like the fur of cattle. She
looked out across the lough at the creeping worms of foam.

He looked about him sullenly at the waiting pilgrims, a green
bus, two taxiloads of people waiting for the rain to stop. They were
not his kind of people at all, and he said so.

'That,' she smiled, 'is what comes of being a surgeon. You don't
meet people, you meet organs. Didn't you once tell me that when
you are operating you never look at the patient's face?'

He grunted. Confused and hairy-looking clouds combed themselves on the ridges of the hills. The lake was crumpled and gray,
except for those yellow worms of foam blown across it in parallel
lines. To the south a cold patch of light made it all look far more
dreary. She stared out towards the island and said:

'It's not at all like what I expected.'

'And what the hell did you expect? Capri?'

'I thought of an old island, with old gray ruins, and old holly
trees and rhododendrons down to the water, a place where old
monks would live.'

They saw tall buildings like modern hotels rising by the island's
shore, an octagonal basilica big enough for a city, four or five bare,
slated houses, a long shed like a ballroom. There was one tree.
Another bus drew up beside them and people peered out through
the wiped glass.

'Oh God!' she groaned. 'I hope this isn't going to be like
Lourdes.'

'And what, pray, is wrong with Lourdes when it's at home?'

'Commercialized. I simply can't believe that this island was the most famous pilgrimage of the Middle Ages. On the rim of the known world. It must have been like going off to Jerusalem or coming home brown from the sun with a cockle in your hat from Galilee.'

He put on a vulgar Yukon voice:

'Thar's gold somewhere in them thar hills. It looks to me like a damn good financial proposition for somebody.'

She glared at him. The downpour had slackened. Soon it almost ceased. Gurgles of streams. A sound of pervasive drip. From the back seat she took a small red canvas bag marked T.W.A.

'You will collect me on Wednesday about noon, won't you?'

He looked at her grimly. She looked every one of her forty-one years. The skin of her neck was corrugated. In five years' time she would begin to have jowls.

'Have a good time,' he said, and slammed in the gears, and drove away.

The big, lumbering ferryboat was approaching, its prow slapping the corrugated waves. There were three men to each oar. It began to spit rain again. With about a hundred and fifty men and women, of every age and, so far as she could see, of every class, she clambered aboard. They pushed out and slowly they made the crossing, huddling together from the wind and rain. The boat nosed into its cleft and unloaded. She had a sensation of dark water, wet cement, houses, and a great number of people; and that she would have given gold for a cup of hot tea. Beyond the four or five whitewashed houses—she guessed that they had been the only buildings on the island before trains and buses made the pilgrimage popular—and beyond the cement paths, she came on the remains of the natural island: a knoll, some warm grass, the tree, and the roots of the old hermits' cells across whose teeth of stone barefooted pilgrims were already treading on one another's heels. Most of these barefooted people wore mackintoshes. They not only stumbled on one another's heels; they kneeled on one another's toes and tails; for the island was crowded—she thought there must be nearly two thousand people on it. They were packed between the two modern hostels and the big church. She saw a priest in sou'wester and gumboots. A nun waiting for the new arrivals at the door of the women's hostel took her name and address, and gave her the number of her cubicle. She went upstairs to it, laid her red bag on

49

the cot, sat beside it, unfastened her garters, took off her shoes, unpeeled her nylons, and without transition became yet another anonymous pilgrim. As she went out among the pilgrims already praying in the rain she felt only a sense of shame as if she were specially singled out under the microscope of the sky. The wet ground was cold.

A fat old woman in black, rich-breasted, gray-haired, took her kindly by the arm and said in a warm, Kerry voice: 'You're shivering, you poor creature! Hould hard now. Sure, when we have the first station done they'll be giving us the ould cup of black tay.'

And laughed at the folly of this longing for the tea. She winced when she stepped on the gritty concrete of the terrace surrounding the basilica, built out on piles over the lake. A young man smiled sympathetically, seeing that she was a delicate subject for the rigours before her: he was dressed like a clerk, with three pens in his breast pocket, and he wore a Total Abstinence badge.

'Saint's Island they call it,' he smiled. 'Some people think it should be called Divil's Island.'

She disliked his kindness—she had never in her life asked for pity from anybody, but she soon found that the island floated on kindness. Everything and everybody about her seemed to say, 'We are all sinners here, wretched creatures barely worthy of mercy.' She felt the abasement of the doomed. She was among people who had surrendered all personal identity, all pride. It was like being in a concentration camp.

The fat old Kerrywoman was explaining to her what the routine was, and as she listened she realized how long her stay would really be. In prospect it had seemed so short: come on Monday afternoon, leave on Wednesday at noon; it had seemed no more than one complete day and two bits of nights. She had not foreseen that immediately after arriving she must remain out of doors until the darkness fell, walking the rounds of the stones, praying, kneeling, for about five hours. And even then she would get no respite, for she must stay awake all night praying in the basilica. It was then that she would begin the second long day, as long and slow as the night; and on the third day she would still be walking those rounds until midday. She would be without food, even when she would have left the island, until the midnight of that third day.

'Yerrah, but sure,' the old woman cackled happily, 'they say that fasting is good for the stomach.'

She began to think of 'they.' They had thought all this up. They had seen how much could be done with simple prayers. For when

50

she began to tot up the number of paternosters and Aves that she must say she had to stop at the two thousandth. And these reiterated prayers must be said while walking on the stones, or kneeling in the mud, or standing upright with her two arms extended. This was the posture she disliked most. Every time she came to do it, her face to the lake, her arms spread, the queue listening to her renouncing her sins, she had to force herself to the posture and the words. The first time she did it, with the mist blowing into her eyes, her arms out like a crucifix, her lips said the words but her heart cursed herself for coming so unprepared, for coming at all. Before she had completed her first circuit—four times around each one of six cells—one ankle and one toe was bleeding. She was then permitted to ask for the cup of black tea. She received it sullenly, as a prisoner might receive his bread and water.

She wished after that first circuit to start again and complete a second—the six cells, and the seven other ordeals at other points of the island—and so be done for the day. But she found that 'they' had invented something else: she must merge with the whole anonymous mass of pilgrims for mass prayer in the church.

A slur of wet feet; patter of rain on leaded windows; smells of bog water and damp clothing; the thousand voices responding to the incantations. At her right a young girl of about seventeen was uttering heartfelt responses. On her left an old man in his sixties gave them out loudly. On all sides, before her, behind her, the same passionate exchange of energy, while all she felt was a crust hardening about her heart, and she thought, in despair, 'I have no more feeling than a stone!' And she thought, looking about her, that tonight this vigil would go on for hour after hour until the dark, leaded windows coloured again in the morning light. She leaned her face in her palms and whispered, 'O God, please let me out of myself!' The waves of voices beat and rumbled in her ears as in an empty shell.

She was carried out on the general sliding whispering of the bare feet into the last gleanings of the daylight to begin her second circuit. In the porch she cowered back from the rain. It was settling into a filthy night. She was thrust forward by the crowd, flowed with its force to the iron cross by the shingle's edge. She took her place in the queue and then with the night wind pasting her hair across her face she raised her arms and once again renounced the world, the flesh, and the Devil. She did four circles of the church on the gritty concrete. She circled the first cell's stones. She completed

51

the second circle. Her prayers were becoming numb by now. She stumbled, muttering them, up and down the third steeply sloped cell, or bed. She was a drowned cat and one knee was bleeding. At the fourth cell she saw him.

He was standing about six yards away looking at her. He wore a white raincoat buttoned tight about his throat. His feet were bare. His hair was streaked down his forehead as if he had been swimming. She stumbled towards him and dragged him by the arm down to the edge of the boat slip.

'What are you doing here?' she cried furiously. 'Why did you follow me?'

He looked down at her calmly:

'Why shouldn't I be here?'

'Because you don't believe in it! You've just followed me to sneer at me, to mock at me! Or from sheer vulgar curiosity!'

'No,' he said, without raising his voice. 'I've come to see just what it is that you believe in. I want to know all about you. I want to know why you came here. I don't want you to do anything or have anything that I can't do or can't know. And as for believing—we all believe in something.'

Dusk was closing in on the island and the lake. She had to peer into his face to catch his expression.

'But I've known you for years and you've never shown any sign of believing in anything but microscopes and microbes and symptoms. It's absurd, you couldn't be serious about anything like this. I'm beginning to hate you!'

'Are you?' he said, so softly that she had to lean near him to hear him over the slapping of the waves against the boat slip. A slow rift in the clouds let down a star; by its light she saw his smile.

'Yes!' she cried, so loudly that he swept out a hand and gripped her by the arm. Then he took her other arm and said gently:

'I don't think you should have come here, Jenny. You're only tearing yourself to bits. There are some places where some people should never go, things some people should never try to do—however good they may be for others. I know why you came here. You feel you ought to get rid of me, but you haven't the guts to do it, so you come up here into the mountains to get your druids to work it by magic. All right! I'm going to ask them to help you.'

He laughed and let her go, giving her a slight impulse away from him.

'Ask? You will *ask*? Do you mean to tell me that you have said as much as one single, solitary prayer on this island?'

'Yes,' he said casually, 'I have.'

She scorned him.

'Are you trying to tell me, Bobby, that you are doing this pilgrimage?'

'I haven't fasted. I didn't know about that. And, anyway, I probably won't. I've got my pockets stuffed with two pounds of the best chocolates I could buy in Bundoran. I don't suppose I'll even stay up all night like the rest of you. The place is so crowded that I don't suppose anybody will notice me if I curl up in some corner of the boathouse. I heard somebody saying that people had to sleep there last night. But you never know—I might—I just might stay awake. If I do, it will remind me of going to midnight Mass with my father when I was a kid. Or going to retreats, when we used all hold up a lighted candle and renounce the Devil.

'It was a queer sensation standing up there by the lake and saying those words all over again. Do you know, I thought I'd completely forgotten them!'

'The next thing you're going to say is that you believe in the Devil! You fraud!'

'Oh, there's no trouble about believing in that old gentleman. There isn't a doctor in the world who doesn't, though he will give him another name. And on a wet night, in a place like this, you could believe in a lot of things. No, my girl, what I find it hard to believe in is the flesh and the world. They are good things. Do you think I'm ever going to believe that your body and my body are evil? And you don't either! And you are certainly never going to renounce the world, because you are tied to it hand and foot!'

'That's not true!'

His voice cut her like a whip:

'Then why do you go on living with your husband?'

She stammered feebly. He cut at her again:

'You do it because he's rich, and you like comfort, and you like being a "somebody".'

With a switch of her head she brushed past him. She did not see him again that night.

The night world turned imperceptibly. In the church, for hour after hour, the voices obstinately beat back the responses. She sank under the hum of the prayer wheel, the lust for sleep, her own despairs. Was he among the crowd? Or asleep in a corner of the boatshed? She saw his flatly domed fingers, a surgeon's hand, so

53

strong, so sensitive. She gasped at the sensual image she had evoked.

The moon touched a black window with colour. After an age it had stolen to another. Heads drooped. Neighbours poked one another awake with a smile. Many of them had risen from the benches in order to keep themselves awake and were circling the aisles in a loose procession of slurring feet, responding as they moved. Exhaustion began to work on her mind. Objects began to disconnect, become isolated each within its own outline—now it was the pulpit, now a statue, now a crucifix. Each object took on the vividness of a hallucination. The crucifix detached itself from the wall and leaned towards her, and for a long while she saw nothing but the heavy pendent body, the staring eyes, so that when the old man at her side let his head sink over on her shoulder and then woke up with a start she felt him no more than if they were two fishes touching in the sea. Bit by bit the incantations drew her in; sounds came from her mouth; prayers flowed between her and those troubled eyes that fixed hers. She swam into an ecstasy as rare as one of those perfect dances of her youth when she used to swing in a whirl of music, a swirl of bodies, a circling of lights, floated out of her mortal frame, alone in the arms that embraced her.

Suddenly it all exploded. One of the four respites of the night had halted the prayers. The massed pilgrims relaxed. She looked blearily about her, no longer disjunct. Her guts rumbled. She looked at the old man beside her. She smiled at him and he at her.

'My poor old knees are crucified,' he grinned.

'You should have the skirts,' she grinned back.

They were all going out to stretch in the cool, and now dry, air, or to snatch a smoke. The amber windows of the church shivered in a pool of water. A hearty-voiced young woman leaning on the balustrade lit a match for her. The match hissed into the invisible lake lapping below.

'The ould fag,' said the young woman, dragging deep on her cigarette, 'is a great comfort. 'Tis as good as a man.'

'I wonder,' she said, 'what would Saint Patrick think if he saw women smoking on his island?'

'He'd beat the living lights out of the lot of us.'

She laughed aloud. She must tell him that. ... She began to wander through the dark crowds in search of him. He had said something that wasn't true and she would answer him. She went through the crowds down to the boat slip. He was standing there, looking out into the dark as if he had not stirred since she saw him there before midnight. For a moment she regarded him, frightened by the force of the love that gushed into her. Then she approached him.

'Well, Mr. Worldly Wiseman? Enjoying your boathouse bed?'

'I'm doing the vigil,' he said smugly.

'You sound almighty pleased with yourself.'

He spoke eagerly now:

'Jenny, we mustn't quarrel. We must understand one another. And understand this place. I'm just beginning to. An island. In a remote lake. Among the mountains. Night-time. No sleep. Hunger. The conditions of the desert. I was right in what I said to you. Can't you see how the old hermits who used to live here could swim off into a trance in which nothing existed but themselves and their visions? I told you a man can renounce what he calls the Devil, but not the flesh, not the world. They thought, like you, that they could throw away the flesh and the world, but they were using the flesh to achieve one of the rarest experiences in the world! Don't you see it?'

'Experiences! The next thing you'll be talking about is symptoms.'

'Well, surely, you must have observed?' He peered at the luminous dial of his watch. 'I should say that about four o'clock we will probably begin to experience a definite sense of dissociation. After that a positive alienation. ...'

She turned furiously from him. She came back to say:

'I would much prefer, Bobby, if you would have the decency to go away in the morning. I can find my own way home. I hope we don't meet again on this island. Or out of it!'

'The magic working?' he laughed.

After that she made a deliberate effort of the mind to mean and to feel every separate word of the prayers—which is a great foolishness since prayers are not poems to be read or even understood; they are an instinct; to dance would be as wise. She thought that if she could not feel what she said how could she mean it, and so she tried to savour every word, and, from trying to mean each word, lagged behind the rest, sank into herself, and ceased to pray. After the second respite she prayed only to keep awake. As the first cold pallor of morning came into the windows her heart rose again. But the eastern hills are high here and the morning holds off stubbornly. It is the worst hour of the vigil, when the body ebbs, the prayers sink to a drone, and the night seems to have begun all over again.

At the last respite she emerged to see pale tents of blue on the

55

hills. The slow cumulus clouds cast a sheen on the water. There is no sound. No birds sing. At this hour the pilgrims are too awed or too exhausted to speak, so that the island reverts to its ancient silence in spite of the crowds.

By the end of the last bout she was calm like the morning lake. She longed for the cup of black tea. She was unaware of her companions. She did not think of him. She was unaware of herself. She no more thought of God than a slave thinks of his master, and after she had drunk her tea she sat in the morning sun outside the women's hostel like an old blind woman who has nothing in life to wait for but sleep.

The long day expired as dimly as the vapour rising from the water. The heat became morbid. One is said to be free on this second day to converse, to think, to write, to read, to do anything at all that one pleases except the one thing everybody wants to do—to sleep. She did nothing but watch the clouds, or listen to the gentle muttering of the lake. Before noon she heard some departing pilgrims singing a hymn as the great ferryboats pushed off. She heard their voices without longing; she did not even desire food. When she met him she was without rancour.

'Still here?' she said, and when he nodded: 'Sleepy?'

'Sleepy.'

'Too many chocolates, probably.'

'I didn't eat them. I took them out of my pockets one by one as I leaned over the balustrade and guessed what centre each had—coffee, marshmallow, nut, toffee, cream—and dropped it in with a little splash to the holy fishes.'

She looked up at him gravely.

'Are you really trying to join in this pilgrimage?'

'Botching it. I'm behindhand with my rounds. I have to do five circuits between today and tomorrow. I may never get them done. Still, something is better than nothing.'

'You dear fool!'

If he had not walked away then she would have had to; such a gush of affection came over her at the thought of what he was doing, and why he was doing it—stupidly, just like a man; sceptically, just like a man; not admitting it to himself, just like a man; for all sorts of damn-fool rational reasons, just like a man; and not at all for the only reason that she knew was his real reason: because she was doing it, which meant that he loved her. She sat back, and closed her eyes, and the tears of chagrin oozed between her lids as she felt her womb stir with desire of him.

When they met again it was late afternoon.

'Done four rounds,' he said so cheerfully that he maddened her.

'It's not golf, Bobby, damn you!'

'I should jolly well think not. I may tell you my feet are in such a condition I won't be able to play golf for a week. Look!'

She did not look. She took his arm and led him to the quietest corner she could find.

'Bobby, I am going to confess something to you. I've been thinking about it all day trying to get it clear. I know now why I came here. I came because I know inside in me that some day our apple will have to fall off the tree. I'm forty. You are nearly fifty. It will have to happen. I came here because I thought it right to admit that some day, if it has to be, I am willing to give you up.'

He began to shake all over with laughter.

'What the hell are you laughing at?' she moaned.

'When women begin to reason! Listen, wasn't there a chap one time who said, "O God, please make me chaste, but not just yet"?'

'What I am saying is "now," if it has to be, if it can be, if I can make it be. I suppose,' she said wildly, 'I'm really asking for a miracle, that my husband would die, or that you'd die, or something like that that would make it all come right!'

He burst into such a peal of laughter, that she looked around her apprehensively. A few people near them also happened to be laughing over something and looked at them indulgently.

'Do you realize, Bobby, that when I go to confession here I will have to tell all about us, and I will have to promise to give you up?'

'Yes, darling, and you won't mean a single word of it.'

'But I always mean it!'

He stared at her as if he were pushing curtains aside in her.

'Always? Do you mean you've been saying it for six years?'

'I mean it when I say it. Then I get weak. I can't help it, Bobby. You know that!' She saw the contempt in his eyes and began to talk rapidly, twisting her marriage ring madly around her finger. He kept staring into her eyes like a man staring down the long perspective of a railway line waiting for the engine to appear. 'So you see why there wasn't any sense in asking me yesterday why I come now and not at some other time, because with me there isn't any other time, it's always *now*, I meet you *now*, and I love you *now*, and I think it's not right *now*, and then I think, "No, not *now*," and then I say I'll give you up *now*, and I mean it every time until we meet again, and it begins all over again, and there's never any end to it until some day I can say, "Yes, I used to know him

57

once, but not now," and then it will be a *now* where there won't be
any other *now* any more because there'll be nothing to live for.'

The tears were leaking down her face. He sighed:

'Dear me! You have got yourself into a mess, haven't you?'

'O God, the promises and the promises! I wish the world would
end tonight and we'd both die together!'

He gave her his big damp handkerchief. She wiped her eyes and
blew her nose and said:

'You don't mean to go to confession, do you?'

He chuckled sourly.

'And promise? I must go and finish a round of pious golf. I'm
afraid, old girl, you just want to get me into the same mess as
yourself. No, thank you. You must solve your own problems in your
own way, and I in mine.'

That was the last time she spoke to him that day.

She went back to the balustrade where she had smoked with the
hearty girl in the early hours of the morning. She was there again.
She wore a scarlet beret. She was smoking again. She began to talk,
and the talk flowed from her without stop. She had fine broad
shoulders, a big mobile mouth, and a pair of wild goat's eyes. After
a while it became clear that the woman was beside herself with
terror. She suddenly let it all out in a gush of exhaled smoke.

'Do you know why I'm hanging around here? Because I ought to
go into confession and I'm in dread of it. He'll tear me alive. He'll
murdher me. It's not easy for a girl like me, I can promise you!'

'You must have terrible sins to tell?' she smiled comfortingly.

'He'll slaughter me, I'm telling you.'

'What is it? Boys?'

The two goat's eyes dilated with fear and joy. Her hands shook
like a drunkard's.

'I can't keep away from them. I wish to God I never came here.'

'But how silly! It's only a human thing. I'm sure half the people
here have the same tale to tell. It's an old story, child, the priests
are sick of hearing it.'

'Oh, don't be talking! Let me alone! I'm criminal, I tell yeh! And
there are things you can't explain to a priest. My God, you can
hardly explain 'em to a doctor!'

'You're married?'—looking at her ring.

'Poor Tom! I have him wore out. He took me to a doctor one
time to know would anything cure me. The old foolah took me
temperature and gave me a book like a bus guide about when it's

safe and when it isn't safe to make love, the ould eedjut! I was
pregnant again before Christmas. Six years married and I have six
kids; nobody could stand that gait o' going. And I'm only
twenty-four. Am I to have a baby every year of my life? I'd give me
right hand this minute for a double whiskey.'

'Look, you poor child! We are all in the same old ferryboat here.
What about me?'

'You?'

'It's not men with me, it's worse.'

'Worse? In God's name, what's worse than men?'

The girl looked all over her, followed her arm down to her hand,
to her third finger.

'One man.'

The tawny eyes swivelled back to her face and immediately
understood.

'Are you very fond of him?' she asked gently, and taking the
unspoken answer said, still more pityingly, 'You can't give him up?'

'It's six years now and I haven't been able to give him up.'

The girl's eyes roved sadly over the lake as if she were surveying
a lake of human unhappiness. Then she threw her butt into the
water and her red beret disappeared into the maw of the church
porch.

She saw him twice before the dusk thickened and the day grew
cold again with the early sunset. He was sitting directly opposite
her before the men's hostel, smoking, staring at the ground between
his legs. They sat facing one another. They were separated by their
identities, joined by their love. She glimpsed him only once after
that, at the hour when the sky and the hills merge, an outline
passing across the lake. Soon after she had permission to go to her
cubicle. Immediately she lay down she spiralled to the bottom of a
deep lake of sleep.

She awoke refreshed and unburthened. She had received the
island's gift: its sense of remoteness from the world, almost a
sensation of the world's death. It is the source of the island's
kindness. Nobody is just matter, poor to be exploited by rich, weak
to be exploited by the strong; in mutual generosity each recognizes
the other only as a form of soul; it is a brief, harsh Utopia of
equality in nakedness. The bare feet are a symbol of that nakedness
unknown in the world they have left.

The happiness to which she awoke was dimmed a little by a
conversation she had with an Englishman over breakfast—the usual

black tea and a piece of oaten bread. He was a city man who had arrived the day before, been up all night while she slept. He had not yet shaved; he was about sixty-two or three; small and tubby, his eyes perpetually wide and unfocusing behind pince-nez glasses.

'That's right,' he said, answering her question. 'I'm from England. Liverpool. I cross by the night boat and get here the next afternoon. Quite convenient, really. I've come here every year for the last twenty-two years, apart from the war years. I come on account of my wife.'

'Is she ill?'

'She died twenty-two years ago. No, it's not what you might think—I'm not praying for her. She was a good woman, but, well, you see, I wasn't very kind to her. I don't mean I quarrelled with her, or drank, or was unfaithful. I never gambled. I've never smoked in my life.' His hands made a faint movement that was meant to express a whole life, all the confusion and trouble of his soul. 'It's just that I wasn't kind. I didn't make her happy.'

'Isn't that,' she said, to comfort him, 'a very private feeling? I mean, it's not in the Ten Commandments that thou shalt make thy wife happy.'

He did not smile. He made the same faint movement with his fingers.

'Oh, I don't know! What's love if it doesn't do that? I mean to say, it is something godly to love another human being, isn't it? I mean, what does "godly" mean if it doesn't mean giving up everything for another? It isn't human to love, you know. It's foolish, it's a folly, a divine folly. It's beyond all reason, all limits. I didn't rise to it,' he concluded sadly.

She looked at him and thought, 'A little fat man, a clerk in some Liverpool office all his life, married to some mousy little woman, thinking about love as if he were some sort of Greek mystic.'

'It's often,' she said lamely, 'more difficult to love one's husband, or one's wife, as the case may be, than to love one's neighbour.'

'Oh, much!' he agreed without a smile. 'Much! Much more difficult!'

At which she was overcome by the thought that inside ourselves we have no room without a secret door; no solid self that has not a ghost inside it trying to escape. If I leave Bobby I still have George. If I leave George I still have myself, and whatever I find in myself. She patted the little man's hand and left him, fearing that if she let him talk on even his one little piece of sincerity would prove to be a fantasy, and in the room that he had found behind his own room she would open other doors leading to other obsessions. He had told her something true about her own imperfection, and about the nature of love, and she wanted to share it while it was still true. But she could not find him, and there was still one more circuit to do before the ferryboat left. She did meet Goat's Eyes. The girl clutched her with tears magnifying her yellow-and-green irises and gasped joyously:

'I found a lamb of a priest. A saint anointed! He was as gentle! "What's your husband earning?" says he. "Four pounds ten a week, Father," says I. "And six children?" says he. "You poor woman," says he, "you don't need to come here at all. Your Purgatory is at home." He laid all the blame on poor Tom. And, God forgive me, I let him do it. "Bring him here to me," says he, "and I'll cool him for you." God bless the poor innocent priest, I wish I knew as little about marriage as he does. But,' and here she broke into a wail, 'sure he has me ruined altogether now. He's after making me so fond of poor Tommy I think I'll never get home soon enough to go to bed with him.' And in a vast flood of tears of joy, of relief, and of fresh misery: 'I wish I was a bloomin' nun!'

It was not until they were all waiting at the ferryboat that she saw him. She managed to sit beside him in the boat. He touched her hand and winked. She smiled back at him. The bugler blew his bugle. A tardy traveller came racing out of the men's hostel. The boatload cheered him, the bugler helped him aboard with a joke about people who can't be persuaded to stop praying, and there was a general chaff about people who have a lot to pray about, and then somebody raised the parting hymn, and the rowers began to push the heavy oars, and singing they were slowly rowed across the summer lake back to the world.

They were driving back out of the hills by the road they had come, both silent. At last she could hold in her question no longer:

'Did you go, Bobby?'

Meaning: had he, after all his years of silence, of rebellion, of disbelief, made his peace with God at the price of a compact against her. He replied gently:

'Did I probe your secrets all these years?'

She took the rebuke humbly, and for several miles they drove on in silence. They were close, their shoulders touched, but between them there stood that impenetrable wall of identity that segregates every human being in a private world of self. Feeling it she realized at last that it is only in places like the lake-island that the barriers

61

of self break down. The tubby little clerk from Liverpool had been right. Only when love desires nothing but renunciation, total surrender, does self surpass self. Everybody who ever entered the island left the world of self behind for a few hours, exchanged it for what the little man had called a divine folly. It was possible only for a few hours—unless one had the courage, or the folly, to renounce the world altogether. Then another thought came to her. In the world there might also be escape from the world.

'Do you think, Bobby, that when people are in love they can give up everything for one another?'

'No,' he said flatly. 'Except perhaps in the first raptures?'

'If I had a child I think I could sacrifice anything for it. Even my life.'

'Yes,' he agreed. 'It has been known to happen.'

And she looked at him sadly, knowing that they would never be able to marry, and even if she did that she would never have children. And yet, if they could have married, there was a lake ...

'Do you know what I'm planning at this moment?' he asked breezily.

She asked without interest what it was.

'Well, I'm simply planning the meal we're going to eat tonight in Galway, at midnight.'

'At midnight? Then we're going on with this pilgrimage? Are we?'

'Don't *you* want to? It was your idea in the beginning.'

'All right. And what are we going to do until midnight? I've never known time to be so long.'

'I'm going to spend the day fishing behind Glencar. That will kill the hungry day. After that, until midnight, we'll take the longest possible road around Connemara. Then would you have any objections to mountain trout cooked in milk, stuffed roast kid with fresh peas and spuds in their jackets, apple pie and whipped cream, with a cool Pouilly Fuissé, a cosy 1929 claret, West of Ireland Pont l'Évêque, finishing up with Gaelic coffee and two Otards? Much more in your line, if I know anything about you, than your silly old black tea and hot salt water.'

'I admit I like the things of the flesh.'

'You live for them!'

He had said it so gently, so affectionately that, half in dismay, half with amusement, she could not help remembering Goat's Eyes, racing home as fast as the bus would carry her to make love to her Tommy. After that they hardly spoke at all, and then only of casual things such as a castle beside the road, the sun on the edging sea, a tinker's caravan, an opening view. It was early afternoon as they entered the deep valley at Glencar and he probed in second gear for an attractive length of stream, found one and started eagerly to put his rod together. He began to walk up against the dazzling bubble of water and within an hour was out of sight. She stretched herself out on a rug on the bank and fell sound asleep.

It was nearly four o'clock before she woke up, stiff and thirsty. She drank from a pool in the stream, and for an hour she sat alone by the pool, looking into its peat-brown depth, as vacantly contented as a tinker's wife to live for the moment, to let time wind and unwind everything. It was five o'clock before she saw him approaching, plodding in his flopping waders, with four trout on a rush stalk. He threw the fish at her feet and himself beside them.

'I nearly ate them raw,' he said.

'Let's cook them and eat them,' she said fiercely.

He looked at her for a moment, then got up and began to gather dry twigs, found Monday's newspaper in the car—it looked like a paper of years ago—and started the fire. She watched while he fed it. When it was big enough in its fall to have made a hot bed of embers he roasted two of the trout across the hook of his gaff, and she smelled the crisping flesh and sighed. At last he laid them, browned and crackly, on the grass by her hand. She took one by its crusted tail, smelled it, looked at him, and slung it furiously into the heart of the fire. He gave a sniff-laugh and did the same with his.

'Copy cat!' she said.

'Let's get the hell out of here,' he said, jumping up. 'Carry the kit, will you?'

She rose, collected the gear, and followed him saying:

'I feel like an Arab wife. "Carry the pack. Go here. Go there".'

They climbed out of the glens onto the flat moorland of the Easky peninsula where the evening light was a cold ochre gleaming across green bogland that was streaked with all the weedy colours of a strand at ebb. At Ballina she suggested that they should have tea.

'It will be a pleasant change of diet!' he said.

When they had found a café and she was ordering the tea he said to the waitress:

'And bring lots of hot buttered toast.'

'This,' she said, as she poured out the tea and held up the milk jug questioningly, 'is a new technique of seduction. Milk?'

'Are you having milk?'

'No.'

'No, then.'

'Some nice hot buttered toast?'

'Are you having toast?' he demanded.

'Why the bloody hell should it be up to me to decide?'

'I asked you a polite question,' he said rudely.

'No.'

'No!'

They looked at one another as they sipped the black tea like two people who are falling head over heels into hatred of one another.

'Could you possibly tell me,' he said presently, 'why I bother my head with a fool of a woman like you?'

'I can only suppose, Bobby, that it is because we are in love with one another.'

'I can only suppose so,' he growled. 'Let's get on!'

They took the longest way round he could find on the map, west into County Mayo, across between the lakes at Pontoon, over the level bogland to Castlebar. Here the mountains walled in the bogland plain with cobalt air—in the fading light the land was losing all solidity. Clouds like soapsuds rose and rose over the edges of the mountains until they glowed as if there was a fire of embers behind the blue ranges. In Castlebar he pulled up by the post office and telephoned to the hotel at Salthill for dinner and two rooms. When he came out he saw a poster in a shop window and said:

'Why don't we go to the pictures? It will kill a couple of hours.'

'By rights,' she said, 'you ought to be driving me home to Dublin.'

'If you wish me to I will.'

'Would you if I asked you?'

'Do you want me to?'

'I suppose it's rather late now, isn't it?'

'Not at all. Fast going we could be there about one o'clock. Shall we?'

'It wouldn't help. George is away. I'd have to bring you in and give you something to eat, and ... Let's go to the blasted movies!'

The film was *Charley's Aunt*. They watched its slapstick gloomily. When they came out, after nine o'clock, there was still a vestigial light in the sky. They drove on and on, westward still, prolonging the light, prolonging the drive, holding off the night's decision. Before Killary they paused at a black-faced lake, got out, and stood beside its quarried beauty. Nothing along its stony beach but a few wind-torn rushes.

'I could eat you,' he said.

She replied that only lovers and cannibals talk like that.

They dawdled past the long fiord of Killary where young people on holiday sat outside the hotel, their drinks on the trestled tables. In Clifden the street was empty, people already climbing to bed, as the lights in the upper windows showed. They branched off on the long coastal road where the sparse whitewashed cottages were whiter than the foam of waves that barely suggested sea. At another darker strand they halted, but now they saw no foam at all and divined the sea only by its invisible whispering, or when a star touched a wave. Midnight was now only an hour away.

Their headlights sent rocks and rabbits into movement. The heather streamed past them like kangaroos. It was well past eleven as they poured along the lonely land by Galway Bay. Neither of them had spoken for an hour. As they drove into Salthill there was nobody abroad. Galway was dark. Only the porch light of the hotel showed that it was alive. When he turned off the engine the only sound at first was the crinkle of contracting metal as the engine began to cool. Then to their right they heard the lisping bay. The panel button lit the dashboard clock.

'A quarter to,' he said, leaning back. She neither spoke nor stirred. 'Jenny!' he said sharply.

She turned her head slowly and by the dashboard light he saw her white smile.

'Yes, darling?'

'Worn out?' he asked, and patted her knee.

She vibrated her whole body so that the seat shook, and stretched her arms about her head, and lowering them let her head fall on his shoulder, and sighed happily, and said:

'What I want is a good long drink of anything on earth except tea.'

These homing twelve o'clockers from Lough Derg are well known in every hotel all over the west of Ireland. Revelry is the reward of penance. The porter welcomed them as if they were heroes returned from a war. As he led them to their rooms he praised them, he sympathized with them, he patted them up and he patted them down, he assured them that the ritual grill was at that moment sizzling over the fire, he proffered them hot baths, and he told them where to discover the bar. 'Ye will discover it ...' was his phrase. The wording was exact, for the bar's gaiety was muffled by dim lighting, drawn blinds, locked doors. In the overheated room he

65

took off his jacket and unloosed his tie. They had to win a corner of the counter, and his order was for two highballs with ice in them. Within two minutes they were at home with the crowd. The island might never have existed if the barmaid, who knew where they had come from, had not laughed: 'I suppose ye'll ate like lions?'

After supper they relished the bar once more, sipping slowly now, so refreshed that they could have started on the road again without distaste or regret. As they sipped they gradually became aware of a soft strumming and drumming near at hand, and were told that there was a dance on in the hotel next door. He raised his eyebrows to her. She laughed and nodded.

They gave it up at three o'clock and walked out into the warm-cool of the early summer morning. Gently tipsy, gently tired they walked to the little promenade. They leaned on the railing and he put his arm about her waist, and she put hers around his, and they gazed at the moon silently raking its path across the sea towards Aran. They had come, she knew, to the decisive moment. He said:

'They have a fine night for it tonight on the island.'

'A better night than we had,' she said tremulously.

After another spell of wave fall and silence he said:

'Do you know what I'm thinking, Jenny? I'm thinking that I wouldn't mind going back there again next year. Maybe I might do it properly the next time?'

'The next time?' she whispered, and all her body began to dissolve and, closing her eyes, she leaned against him. He, too, closed his eyes, and all his body became as rigid as a steel girder that flutters in a storm. Slowly they opened their love-drunk eyes, and stood looking long over the brightness and blackness of the sea. Then, gently, ever so gently, with a gentleness that terrified her he said:

'Shall we go in, my sweet?'

She did not stir. She did not speak. Slowly turning to him she lifted her eyes to him pleadingly.

'No, Bobby, please, not yet.'

'Not yet?'

'Not tonight!'

He looked down at her, and drew his arms about her. They kissed passionately. She knew what that kiss implied. Their mouths parted. Hand in hand they walked slowly back to the hotel, to their separate rooms.

6. FOUR POEMS

DONAGH MACDONAGH

What of poetry?

Yeats died in 1939. During his lifetime and for at least a decade after it his titan figure dominated Irish letters. This did not make it easy for younger poets to establish their distinctive vision. Three or four poets, however, soon made a contribution completely their own.

The ballad is a living art-form with a long ancestry in Ireland and Donagh MacDonagh (1912–68), son of one of the executed leaders of 1916, also a poet, is a master of it. His bilingual rearing, moreover, allows him to draw freely on Gaelic as well as English folk tradition. "The Day set for our Wedding" catches the mood of the old warrior laments and moves easily forward to the savage imagery of the last stanza and the crude vernacular of the final cursing. "Going to Mass Last Sunday" expresses with gentle irony a lighter mood. In "Dublin Made Me" and "A Warning to Conquerors" the brooding sense of race, history and countryside, never far below the surface in any Irish writer, is caught up once more.

Donagh MacDonagh

FOUR POEMS

THE DAY SET FOR OUR WEDDING
(After the Irish)

The day set for our wedding
The town was full of horses,
There were priests and brothers murmuring
The words of the marriage service,
The feast upon the table,
The harp and charming fiddle,
Little the bridesmaids thought then
That they'd lay out my darling.

Take tidings to my people
That the sea has widowed me
And that my love who lightened
The air at any meeting,
Who would have been well mated
With the King of France's daughter
Is heavy on the bed
They decked out for our bridal.

The monsters have his eyes
And crabs the mouth that kissed me,
His two, bright, white hands
Devoured by the great salmon,
His curls tangled with salt
Are all the sea has spared me—
And may they rot, the botches
Who built the boat that drowned him.

GOING TO MASS LAST SUNDAY

(Tune: The Lowlands of Holland)

Going to Mass last Sunday my true love passed me by,
I knew her mind was altered by the rolling of her eye;
And when I stood in God's dark light my tongue could word no
    prayer
Knowing my saint had fled and left her reliquary bare.

Sweet faces smiled from holy glass, demure in saintly love,
Sweet voices ripe with Latin grace rolled from the choir above;
But brown eyes under Sunday wear were all my liturgy
How can she hope for heaven who has so deluded me?

When daffodils were altar gold her lips were light on mine
And when the hawthorn flame was bright we drank the year's new
    wine;
The nights seemed stained-glass windows lit with love that paled
    the sky,
But love's last ember perishes in the winter of her eye.

Drape every downcast day now in purple cloth of Lent,
Smudge every forehead now with ash, that she may yet repent,
Who going to Mass last Sunday could pass so proudly by
And show her mind was altered by the rolling of an eye.

Donagh MacDonagh

DUBLIN MADE ME

Dublin made me and no little town
With the country closing in on its streets
The cattle walking proudly on its pavements
The jobbers the gombeenmen and the cheats

Devouring the fair day between them
A public-house to half a hundred men
And the teacher, the solicitor and the bank-clerk
In the hotel bar drinking for ten.

Dublin made me, not the secret poteen still
The raw and hungry hills of the West
The lean road flung over profitless bog
Where only a snipe could nest

Where the sea takes its tithe of every boat.
Bawneen and curragh have no allegiance of mine,
Nor the cute self-deceiving talkers of the South
Who look to the East for a sign.

The soft and dreary midlands with their tame canals
Wallow between sea and sea, remote from adventure,
And Northward a far and fortified province
Crouches under the lash of arid censure.

I disclaim all fertile meadows, all tilled land
The evil that grows from it and the good,
But the Dublin of old statutes, this arrogant city,
Stirs proudly and secretly in my blood.

A WARNING TO CONQUERORS

This is the country of the Norman tower,
The graceless keep, the bleak and slitted eye
Where fear drove comfort out; straw on the floor
Was price of conquering security.

They came and won, and then for centuries
Stood to their arms; the face grew bleak and lengthened
In the night vigil, while their foes at ease
Sang of the stranger and the towers he strengthened.

Ragweed and thistle hold the Norman field
And cows the hall where Gaelic never rang
Melodiously to harp or spinning wheel.
Their songs are spent now with the voice that sang;

And lost their conquest. This soft land quietly
Engulfed them like the Saxon and the Dane—
But kept the jutted brow, the slitted eye;
Only the faces and the names remain.

7. THREE SHORT POEMS AND "THE GREAT HUNGER"

PATRICK KAVANAGH

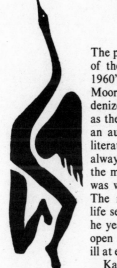

The poet Patrick Kavanagh (1905–67) was a phenomenon of the Dublin of the late 1930's until his death in the 1960's. Educated writers, Yeats, Lady Gregory, George Moore, Synge, had looked with sentimental eyes at the denizens of the Irish countryside, regarding the peasantry as the heirs of an unsullied national tradition. In O'Casey an autodidact from the Dublin slums had emerged into literature. But here was the rough countryman himself, always looking as if he had tramped in yesterday from the muddy fields of his native Monaghan. Sometimes he was what they expected of him, more often he was not. The rancour and unhappiness of Kavanagh's personal life seem to stem from the fact that while in the country he yearned for the society of those who would sometimes open a book, he found city intellectuals spurious and felt ill at ease among them.

Kavanagh is a religious poet. His is a pantheistic vision.

The very early, simple poems he wrote for the local newspaper, of which "Ploughman" is an example, express his fresh communion with nature. In middle life he came close to death in a severe illness and when he eventually emerged from hospital, wrote such poems as "Canal Bank Walk", which achieve a serenity and repose his intervening work lacks.

But his finest and unique poem, though it is only fair to mention that he himself repudiated it in later years, is "The Great Hunger", which first appeared in 1942. This is a searing vision of country life in Ireland at a particular period in her history. Maguire is one of our famous Irish bachelors (one quarter of the Irish population in these years never married), and we witness his sin-obsessed sexual frustration, meet his venomous, domineering old mother, "tall, hard as a Protestant spire", and his sister in her "purgatory of middle-aged virginity". When he himself comes to years there is a terrible irony in the contrast between his inner torment and the fact that his younger neighbours now look up to him as

> ... a man who could give advice
> To foolish young fellows.

And so to the loneliness of his grave in the man-hungry clay. No apology is needed for reprinting the whole of this long poem in this anthology. There is nothing similar in modern literature.

In case the vivid pen-portrait of Maguire's mother seem autobiographical, it may be contrasted with the gentle tribute of "In Memory of My Mother", which concludes this section. Kavanagh had in fact a close and rather touching relationship with his mother. He was the only one of her family she allowed pare her corns.

PLOUGHMAN

I turn the lea-green down
Gaily now,
And paint the meadow brown
With my plough.

I dream with silvery gull
And brazen crow.
A thing that is beautiful
I may know.

Tranquillity walks with me
And no care.
O, the quiet ecstasy
Like a prayer.

I find a star-lovely art
In a dark sod.
Joy that is timeless! O heart
That knows God!

CANAL BANK WALK

Leafy-with-love banks and the green waters of the canal
Pouring redemption for me, that I do
The will of God, wallow in the habitual, the banal,
Grow with nature again as before I grew.
The bright stick trapped, the breeze adding a third
Party to the couple kissing on an old seat,
And a bird gathering materials for the nest for the Word
Eloquently new and abandoned to its delirious beat.
O unworn world enrapture me, encapture me in a web
Of fabulous grass and eternal voices by a beech,
Feed the gaping need of my senses, give me ad lib
To pray unselfconsciously with overflowing speech
For this soul needs to be honoured with a new dress woven
From green and blue things and arguments that cannot be proven.

Patrick Kavanagh

THE GREAT HUNGER

I

Clay is the word and clay is the flesh
Where the potato-gatherers like mechanised scarecrows move
Along the side-fall of the hill—Maguire and his men.
If we watch them an hour is there anything we can prove
Of life as it is broken-backed over the Book
Of Death? Here crows gabble over worms and frogs
And the gulls like old newspapers are blown clear of the hedges,
    luckily.
Is there some light of imagination in these wet clods?
Or why do we stand here shivering?
                                    Which of these men
Loved the light and the queen
Too long virgin? Yesterday was summer. Who was it promised
    marriage to himself
Before apples were hung from the ceilings for Hallowe'en?
We will wait and watch the tragedy to the last curtain,
Till the last soul passively like a bag of wet clay
Rolls down the side of the hill, diverted by the angles
Where the plough missed or a spade stands, straitening the way.

A dog lying on a torn jacket under a heeled-up cart,
A horse nosing along the posied headland, trailing
A rusty plough. Three heads hanging between wide-apart
Legs. October playing a symphony on a slack wire paling.
Maguire watches the drills flattened out
And the flints that lit a candle for him on a June altar
Flameless. The drills slipped by and the days slipped by
And he trembled his head away and ran free from the world's
    halter,
And thought himself wiser than any man in the townland
When he laughed over pints of porter
Of how he came free from every net spread
In the gaps of experience. He shook a knowing head
And pretended to his soul
That children are tedious in hurrying fields of April
Where men are spanging across wide furrows.

76

Lost in the passion that never needs a wife—
The pricks that pricked were the pointed pins of harrows.
Children scream so loud that the crows could bring
The seed of an acre away with crow-rude jeers.
Patrick Maguire, he called his dog and he flung a stone in the air
And hallooed the birds away that were the birds of the years.

Turn over the weedy clods and tease out the tangled skeins.
What is he looking for there?
He thinks it is a potato, but we know better
Than his mud-gloved fingers probe in this insensitive hair.

'Move forward the basket and balance it steady
In this hollow. Pull down the shafts of that cart, Joe,
And straddle the horse,' Maguire calls.
'The wind's over Brannagan's, now that means rain.
Graip up some withered stalks and see that no potato falls
Over the tail-board going down the ruckety pass—
And *that's* a job we'll have to do in December,
Gravel it and build a kerb on the bog-side. Is that Cassidy's ass
Out in my clover? Curse o' God—
Where is that dog?
Never where he's wanted.' Maguire grunts and spits
Through a clay-wattled moustache and stares about him from the
     height.
His dream changes again like the cloud-swung wind
And he is not so sure now if his mother was right
When she praised the man who made a field his bride.

Watch him, watch him, that man on a hill whose spirit
Is a wet sack flapping about the knees of time.
He lives that his little fields may stay fertile when his own body
Is spread in the bottom of a ditch under two coulters crossed in
     Christ's Name.

He was suspicious in his youth as a rat near strange bread,
When girls laughed; when they screamed he knew that meant
The cry of fillies in season. He could not walk
The easy road to destiny. He dreamt
The innocence of young brambles to hooked treachery.
O the grip, O the grip of irregular fields! No man escapes.
It could not be that back of the hills love was free

And ditches straight.
No monster hand lifted up children and put down apes
As here.
                                        'O God if I had been wiser!'
That was his sigh like the brown breeze in the thistles.
He looks towards his house and haggard. 'O God if I had been
      wiser!'
But now a crumpled leaf from the whitethorn bushes
Dart like a frightened robin, and the fence
Shows the green of after-grass through a little window,
And he knows that his own heart is calling his mother a liar
God's truth is life—even the grotesque shapes of its foulest fire.

The horse lifts its head and cranes
Through the whins and stones
To lip late passion in the crawling clover.
In the gap there's a bush weighted with boulders like morality,
The fools of life bleed if they climb over.

The wind leans from Brady's, and the coltsfoot leaves are holed
      with rust,
Rain fills the cart-tracks and the sole-plate grooves;
A yellow sun reflects in Donaghmoyne
The poignant light in puddles shaped by hooves.

Come with me, Imagination, into this iron house
And we will watch from the doorway the years run back,
And we will know what a peasant's left hand wrote on the page.
Be easy, October. No cackle hen, horse neigh, tree sough, duck
      quack.

II

Maguire was faithful to death:
He stayed with his mother till she died
At the age of ninety-one.
She stayed too long,
Wife and mother in one.
When she died

The knuckle-bones were cutting the skin of her son's backside
And he was sixty-five.
O he loved his mother
Above all others.
O he loved his ploughs
And he loved his cows
And his happiest dream
Was to clean his arse
With perennial grass
On the bank of some summer stream;
To smoke his pipe
In a sheltered gripe in the middle of July—
His face in a mist
And two stones in his fist
And an impotent worm on his thigh.

But his passion became a plague
For he grew feeble bringing the vague
Women of his mind to lust nearness,
Once a week at least flesh must make an appearance.

So Maguire got tired
Of the no-target gun fired
And returned to his headland of carrots and cabbage
To the fields once again
Where eunuchs can be men
And life is more lousy than savage.

III

Poor Paddy Maguire, a fourteen-hour day
He worked for years. It was he that lit the fire
And boiled the kettle and gave the cows their hay.
His mother tall hard as a Protestant spire
Came down the stairs barefoot at the kettle-call
And talked to her son sharply: 'Did you let
The hens out, you?' She had a venomous drawl
And a wizened face like moth-eaten leatherette.
Two black cats peeped between the banisters

And gloated over the bacon-fizzling pan.
Outside the window showed tin canisters.
The snipe of Dawn fell like a whirring stone
And Patrick on a headland stood alone.

The pull is on the traces, it is March
And a cold black wind is blowing from Dundalk.
The twisting sod rolls over on her back—
The virgin screams before the irresistible sock.
No worry on Maguire's mind this day
Except that he forgot to bring his matches.
'Hop back there Polly, hoy back, woa, wae,'
From every second hill a neighbour watches
With all the sharpened interest of rivalry.
Yet sometimes when the sun comes through a gap
These men know God the Father in a tree:
The Holy Spirit is the rising sap,
And Christ will be the green leaves that will come
At Easter from the sealed and guarded tomb.

Primroses and the unearthly start of ferns
Among the blackthorn shadows in the ditch,
A dead sparrow and an old waistcoat. Maguire learns
As the horses turn slowly round the which is which
Of love and fear and things half born to mind.
He stands between the plough-handles and he sees
At the end of a long furrow his name signed
Among the poets, prostitute's. With all miseries
He is one. Here with the unfortunate
Who for half-moments of paradise
Pay out good days and wait and wait
For sunlight-woven cloaks. O to be wise
As Respectability that knows the price of all things
And marks God's truth in pounds and pence and farthings.

IV

April, and no one able to calculate
How far is it to harvest. They put down

The seeds blindly with sensuous groping fingers,
And sensual sleep dreams subtly underground.
To-morrow is Wednesday—who cares?
'Remember Eileen Farrelly? I was thinking
A man might do a damned sight worse ...' That voice is blown
Through a hole in a garden wall—
And who was Eileen now cannot be known.

The cattle are out on grass,
The corn is coming up evenly.
The farm folk are hurrying to catch Mass:
Christ will meet them at the end of the world, the slow and
    speedier.
But the fields say: only Time can bless.

Maguire knelt beside a pillar where he could spit
Without being seen. He turned an old prayer round:
'Jesus, Mary and Joseph pray for us
Now and at the Hour.' Heaven dazzled death.
'Wonder should I cross-plough that turnip-ground.'
The tension broke. The congregation lifted its head
As one man and coughed in unison.
Five hundred hearts were hungry for life—
Who lives in Christ shall never die the death.
And the candle-lit Altar and the flowers
And the pregnant Tabernacle lifted a moment to Prophecy
Out of the clayey hours
Maguire sprinkled his face with holy water
As the congregation stood up for the Last Gospel.
He rubbed the dust off his knees with his palm, and then
Coughed the prayer phlegm up from his throat and sighed: Amen.

Once one day in June when he was walking
Among his cattle in the Yellow Meadow
He met a girl carrying a basket—
And he was then a young and heated fellow.
Too earnest, too earnest! He rushed beyond the thing
To the unreal. And he saw Sin
Written in letters larger than John Bunyan dreamt of.
For the strangled impulse there is no redemption.
And that girl was gone and he was counting
The dangers in the fields where love ranted

81

Patrick Kavanagh

He was helpless. He saw his cattle
And stroked their flanks in lieu of wife to handle.
He would have changed the circle if he could,
The circle that was the grass track where he ran.
Twenty times a day he ran round the field
And still there was no winning-post where the runner is cheered
   home.
Desperately he broke the tune,
But however he tried always the same melody crept up from the
   background,
The dragging step of a ploughman going home through the
   guttery
Headlands under an April-watery moon.
Religion, the fields and the fear of the Lord
And Ignorance giving him the coward's blow,
He dare not rise to pluck the fantasies
From the fruited Tree of Life. He bowed his head
And saw a wet weed twined about his toe.

V

Evening at the cross-roads—
Heavy heads nodding out words as wise
As the rumination of cows after milking.
From the ragged road surface a boy picks up
A piece of gravel and stares at it—and then
He flings it across the elm tree on to the railway.
It means nothing,
Not a damn thing.
Somebody is coming over the metal railway bridge
And his hobnailed boots on the arches sound like a gong
Calling men awake. But the bridge is too narrow—
The men lift their heads a moment. That was only John,
So they dream on.

Night in the elms, night in the grass.
O we are too tired to go home yet. Two cyclists pass
Talking loudly of Kitty and Molly—

82

Horses or women? wisdom or folly?
A door closes on an evicted dog
Where prayers begin in Barney Meegan's kitchen;
Rosie curses the cat between her devotions;
The daughter prays that she may have three wishes—
Health and wealth and love—
From the fairy who is faith or hope or compounds of.

At the cross-roads the crowd had thinned out:
Last words are uttered. There is no to-morrow;
No future but only time stretched for the mowing of the hay
Or putting an axle in the turf-barrow.

Patrick Maguire went home and made cocoa
And broke a chunk off the loaf of wheaten bread;
His mother called down to him to look again
And make sure that the hen-house was locked. His sister grunted
    in bed.
The sound of a sow taking up a new position.
Pat opened his trousers wide over the ashes
And dreamt himself to lewd sleepiness.
The clock ticked on. Time passes.

VI

Health and wealth and love he too dreamed of in May
As he sat on the railway slope and watched the children of the
    place
Picking up a primrose here and a daisy there—
They were picking up life's truth singly. But he dreamt of the
    Absolute envased bouquet—
All or nothing. And it was nothing. For God is not all
In one place, complete
Till Hope comes in and takes it on his shoulder—
O Christ, that is what you have done for us:
In a crumb of bread the whole mystery is.

He read the symbol too sharply and turned
From the five simple doors of sense

83

To the door whose combination lock has puzzled
Philosopher and priest and common dunce.
Men build their heavens as they build their circles
Of friends. God is in the bits and pieces of Everyday—
A kiss here and a laugh again, and sometimes tears,
A pearl necklace round the neck of poverty.

He sat on the railway slope and watched the evening,
Too beautifully perfect to use,
And his three wishes were three stones too sharp to sit on,
Too hard to carve. Three frozen idols of a speechless muse.

VII

'Now go to Mass and pray and confess your sins
And you'll have all the luck,' his mother said.
He listened to the lie that is a woman's screen
Around a conscience when soft thighs are spread.
And all the while she was setting up the lie
She trusted in Nature that never deceives.
But her son took it as literal truth.
Religion's walls expand to the push of nature. Morality yields
To sense—but not in little tillage fields.

Life went on like that. One summer morning
Again through a hay-field on her way to the shop—
The grass was wet and over-leaned the path—
And Agnes held her skirts sensationally up,
And not because the grass was wet either.
A man was watching her, Patrick Maguire.
She was in love with passion and its weakness
And the wet grass could never cool the fire
That radiated from her unwanted womb
In that country, in that metaphysical land
Where flesh was a thought more spiritual than music
Among the stars—out of reach of the peasant's hand.

Ah, but the priest was one of the people too—
A farmer's son—and surely he knew

The needs of a brother and sister.
Religion could not be a counter-irritant like a blister,
But the certain standard measured and known
By which man might re-make his soul though all walls were down
And all earth's pedestalled gods thrown.

VIII

Sitting on a wooden gate,
Sitting on a wooden gate,
Sitting on a wooden gate
He didn't care a damn.
Said whatever came into his head,
Said whatever came into his head,
Said whatever came into his head
And inconsequently sang.
While his world withered away,
He had a cigarette to smoke and a pound to spend
On drink the next Saturday.
His cattle were fat
And his horses all that
Midsummer grass could make them.

The young women ran wild
And dreamed of a child
Joy dreams though the fathers might forsake them
But no one would take them,
No one would take them;
No man could ever see
That their skirts had loosed buttons,
O the men were as blind as could be.
And Patrick Maguire
From his purgatory fire
Called the gods of the Christian to prove
That this twisted skein
Was the necessary pain
And not the rope that was strangling true love.

But sitting on a wooden gate

Sometime in July
When he was thirty-four or five
He gloried in the lie:
He made it read the way it should,
He made life read the evil good
While he cursed the ascetic brotherhood
Without knowing why.
Sitting on a wooden gate
All, all alone
He sang and laughed
Like a man quite daft,
Or like a man on a channel raft
He fantasied forth his groan.
Sitting on a wooden gate,
Sitting on a wooden gate,
Sitting on a wooden gate
He rode in day-dream cars.
He locked his body with his knees
When the gate swung too much in the breeze.
But while he caught high ecstasies
Life slipped between the bars.

IX

He gave himself another year,
Something was bound to happen before then—
The circle would break down
And he would curve the new one to his own will.
A new rhythm is a new life
And in it marriage is hung and money.
He would be a new man walking through unbroken meadows
Of dawn in the year of One.

The poor peasant talking to himself in a stable door—
An ignorant peasant deep in dung.
What can the passers-by think otherwise?
Where is his silver bowl of knowledge hung?
Why should men be asked to believe in a soul
That is only the mark of a hoof in guttery gaps?

A man is what is written on the label.
And the passing world stares but no one stops
To look closer. So back to the growing crops
And the ridges he never loved.
Nobody will ever know how much tortured poetry he pulled weeds
   on the ridge wrote
Before they withered in the July sun,
Nobody will ever read the wild, sprawling, scrawling mad
   woman's signature,
The hysteria and the boredom of the enclosed nun of his thought.
Like the afterbirth of a cow stretched on a branch in the wind
Life dried in the veins of these women and men:
The grey and grief and unlove,
The bones in the backs of their hands,
And the chapel pressing its low ceiling over them.

Sometimes they did laugh and see the sunlight,
A narrow slice of divine instruction.
Going along the river at the bend of Sunday
The trout played in the pools encouragement
To jump in love though death bait the hook.
And there would be girls sitting on the grass banks of lanes.
Stretch-legged and lingering staring—
A man might take one of them if he had the courage.
But 'No' was in every sentence of their story
Except when the public-house came in and shouted its piece.

The yellow buttercups and the bluebells among the whin bushes
On rocks in the middle of ploughing
Was a bright spoke in the wheel
Of the peasant's mill.
The goldfinches on the railway paling were worth looking at—
A man might imagine then
Himself in Brazil and these birds the birds of paradise
And the Amazon and the romance traced on the school map lived
   again.

Talk in evening corners and under trees
Was like an old book found in a king's tomb.
The children gathered round like students and listened
And some of the saga defied the draught in the open tomb
And was not blown.

Patrick Kavanagh

X

Their intellectual life consisted in reading
Reynolds News or the *Sunday Dispatch*,
With sometimes an old almanac brought down from the ceiling
Or a school reader brown with the droppings of thatch.
The sporting results or the headlines or war
Was a humbug profound as the highbrow's Arcana.
Pat tried to be wise to the abstraction of all that
But its secret dribbled down his waistcoat like a drink from a
    strainer.
He wagered a bob each way on the Derby,
He got a straight tip from a man in a shop—
A double from the Guineas it was and thought himself
A master mathematician when one of them came up
And he could explain how much he'd have drawn
On the double if the second leg had followed the first.
He was betting on form and breeding, he claimed,
And the man that did that could never be burst.
After that they went on to the war, and the generals
On both sides were shown to be stupid as hell.
If he'd taken *that* road, they remarked of a Marshal,
He'd have ... O they know their geography well.
This was their university. Maguire was an undergraduate
Who dreamed from his lowly position of rising
To a professorship like Larry McKenna or Duffy
Or the pig-gelder Nallon whose knowledge was amazing.
'A treble, full multiple odds. ... That's flat porter ...
My turnips are destroyed with the blackguardly crows. ...
Another one. ... No, you're wrong about that thing I was telling
    you. ...
Did you part with your filly, Jack? I heard that you sold her. ...'
The students were all savants by the time of pub-close.

XI

A year passed and another hurried after it
And Patrick Maguire was still six months behind life—
His mother six months ahead of it;

His sister straddle-legged across it:—
One leg in hell and the other in heaven
And between the purgatory of middle-aged virginity—
She prayed for release to heaven or hell.
His mother's voice grew thinner like a rust-worn knife
But it cut venomously as it thinned,
It cut him up the middle till he became more woman than man,
And it cut through to his mind before the end.

Another field whitened in the April air
And the harrows rattled over the seed.
He gathered the loose stones off the ridges carefully
And grumbled to his men to hurry. He looked like a man who
    could give advice
To foolish young fellows. He was forty-seven,
And there was depth in his jaw and his voice was the voice of a
    great cattle-dealer,
A man with whom the fair-green gods break even.
'I think I ploughed that lea the proper depth,
She ought to give a crop if any land gives. ...
Drive slower with the foal-mare, Joe.'
Joe, a young man of imagined wives,   ,
Smiles to himself and answered like a slave:
'You needn't fear or fret.
I'm taking her as easy, as easy as ...
Easy there Fanny, easy, pet.'

They loaded the day-scoured implements on the cart
As the shadows of poplars crookened the furrows.
It was the evening, evening. Patrick was forgetting to be lonely
As he used to be in Aprils long ago.
It was the menopause, the misery-pause.

The schoolgirls passed his house laughing every morning
And sometimes they spoke to him familiarly—
He had an idea. Schoolgirls of thirteen
Would see no political intrigue in an old man's friendship.
Love
The heifer waiting to be nosed by the old bull.

The notion passed too—there was the danger of talk
And jails are narrower than the five-sod ridge

And colder than the black hills facing Armagh in February.
He sinned over the warm ashes again and his crime
The law's long arm could not serve with 'time'.

His face set like an old judge's pose:
Respectability and righteousness,
Stand for no nonsense.
The priest from the altar called Patrick Maguire's name
To hold the collecting-box in the chapel door
During all the Sundays of May.
His neighbours envied him his holy rise,
But he walked down from the church with affected indifference
And took the measure of heaven angle-wise.

He still could laugh and sing,
But not the wild laugh or the abandoned harmony now
That called the world to new silliness from the top of a wooden
    gate
When thirty-five could take the sparrow's bow.
Let us be kind, let us be kind and sympathetic:
Maybe life is not for joking or for finding happiness in—
This tiny light in Oriental Darkness
Looking out chance windows of poetry or prayer.

And the grief and defeat of men like these peasants
Is God's way—maybe—and we must not want too much
To see.
The twisted thread is stronger than the wind-swept fleece.
And in the end who shall rest in truth's high peace?
Or whose is the world now, even now?
O let us kneel where the blind ploughman kneels
And learn to live without despairing
In a mud-walled space—
Illiterate, unknown and unknowing.
Let us kneel where he kneels
And feel what he feels.

One day he saw a daisy and he thought it
Reminded him of his childhood—
He stopped his cart to look at it.
Was there a fairy hiding behind it?
He helped a poor woman whose cow

90

Had died on her;
He dragged home a drunken man on a winter's night;
And one rare moment he heard the young people playing on the
    railway stile
And he wished them happiness and whatever they most desired
    from life.

He saw the sunlight and begrudged no man
His share of what the miserly soil and soul
Gives in a season to a ploughman.
And he cried for his own loss one late night on the pillow
And yet thanked the God who had arranged these things.

Was he then a saint?
A Matt Talbot of Monaghan?

His sister Mary Anne spat poison at the children
Who sometimes came to the door selling raffle tickets
For holy funds.
'Get out, you little tramps!' she would scream
As she shook to the hens an armful of crumbs,
But Patrick often put his hand deep down
In his trouser-pocket and fingered out a penny
Or maybe a tobacco-stained caramel.
'You're soft,' said the sister; 'with other people's money
It's not a bit funny.'

The cards are shuffled and the deck
Laid flat for cutting—Tom Malone
Cut for trump. I think we'll make
This game, the last, a tanner one.
Hearts. Right. I see you're breaking
Your two-year-old. Play quick, Maguire,
The clock there says it half-past ten—
Kate, throw another sod on that fire.
One of the card-players laughs and spits
Into the flame across a shoulder.
Outside, a noise like a rat
Among the hen-roosts. The cock crows over
The frosted townland of the night.
Eleven o'clock and still the game
Goes on and the players seem to be

91

Drunk in an Orient opium den.
Midnight, one o'clock, two.
Somebody's leg has fallen asleep.
What about home? Maguire, are you
Using your double-tree this week?
Why? do you want it? Play the ace.
There's it, and that's the last card for me.
A wonderful night, we had. Duffy's place
Is very convenient. Is that a ghost or a tree?
And so they go home with dragging feet
And their voices rumble like laden carts.
And they are happy as the dead or sleeping ...
I should have led that ace of hearts.

XII

The fields were bleached white,
The wooden tubs full of water
Were white in the winds
That blew through Brannagan's Gap on their way from Siberia;
The cows on the grassless heights
Followed the hay that had wings—
The February fodder that hung itself on the black branches
Of the hill-top hedge.
A man stood beside a potato-pit
And clapped his arms
And pranced on the crisp roots
And shouted to warm himself.
Then he buck-leaped about the potatoes
And scooped them into a basket.
He looked like a bucking suck-calf
Whose spine was being tickled.
Sometimes he stared across the bogs
And sometimes he straightened his back and vaguely whistled
A tune that weakened his spirit
And saddened his terrier dog's.
A neighbour passed with a spade on his shoulder
And Patrick Maguire bent like a bridge
Whistled—good morning under his oxter,

And the man the other side of the hedge
Champed his spade on the road at his toes
And talked an old sentimentality
While the wind blew under his clothes.

The mother sickened and stayed in bed all day,
Her head hardly dented the pillow, so light and thin it had worn,
But she still enquired after the household affairs.
She held the strings of her children's Punch and Judy, and when a
    mouth opened
It was her truth that the dolls would have spoken
If they hadn't been made of wood and tin—
'Did you open the barn door, Pat, to let the young calves in?'
The priest called to see her every Saturday
And she told him her troubles and fears:
'If Mary Anne was settled I'd die in peace—
I'm getting on in years.'
'You were a good woman,' said the priest,
'And your children will miss you when you're gone.
The likes of you this parish never knew,
I'm sure they'll not forget the work you've done.'
She reached five bony crooks under the tick—
'Five pounds for Masses—won't you say them quick.'
She died one morning in the beginning of May
And a shower of sparrow-notes was the litany for her dying.
The holy water was sprinkled on the bed-clothes
And her children stood around the bed and cried because it was
    too late for crying.
A mother dead! The tired sentiment:
'Mother, Mother' was a shallow pool
Where sorrow hardly could wash its feet. ...
Mary Anne came away from the deathbed and boiled the calves
  · their gruel.
O what was I doing when the procession passed?
Where was I looking?
Young women and men
And I might have joined them.
Who bent the coin of my destiny
That it stuck in the slot?
I remember a night we walked
Through the moon of Donaghmoyne,
Four of us seeking adventure,

It was midsummer forty years ago.
Now I know
The moment that gave the turn to my life.
O Christ! I am locked in a stable with pigs and cows for ever.

XIII

The world looks on
And talks of the peasant:
The peasant has no worries;
In his little lyrical fields
He ploughs and sows;
He eats fresh food,
He loves fresh women,
He is his own master
As it was in the Beginning
The simpleness of peasant life.
The birds that sing for him are eternal choirs,
Everywhere he walks there are flowers.
His heart is pure,
His mind is clear,
He can talk to God as Moses and Isaiah talked—
The peasant who is only one remove from the beasts he drives.
The travellers stop their cars to gape over the green bank into his
    fields:—

There is the source from which all cultures rise,
And all religions,
There is the pool in which the poet dips
And the musician.
Without the peasant base civilisation must die,
Unless the clay is in the mouth the singer's singing is useless.
The travellers touch the roots of the grass and feel renewed
When they grasp the steering wheels again.
The peasant is the unspoiled child of Prophecy,
The peasant is all virtues—let us salute him without irony
The peasant ploughman who is half a vegetable—
Who can react to sun and rain and sometimes even

Regret that the Maker of Light had not touched him more
    intensely.
Brought him up from the sub-soil to an existence
Of conscious joy. He was not born blind.
He is not always blind: sometimes the cataract yields
To sudden stone-falling or the desire to breed.

The girls pass along the roads
And he can remember what man is,
But there is nothing he can do.
Is there nothing he can do?
Is there no escape?
No escape, no escape.

The cows and horses breed,
And the potato-seed
Gives a bud and a root and rots
In the good mother's way with her sons;
The fledged bird is thrown
From the nest—on its own.
But the peasant in his little acres is tied
To a mother's womb by the wind-toughened navel-cord
Like a goat tethered to the stump of a tree—
He circles around and around wondering why it should be.
No crash,
No drama.
That was how his life happened.
No mad hooves galloping in the sky,
But the weak, washy way of true tragedy—
A sick horse nosing around the meadow for a clean place to die.

XIV

We may come out into the October reality, Imagination,
The sleety wind no longer slants to the black hill where Maguire
And his men are now collecting the scattered harness and baskets.
The dog sitting on a wisp of dry stalks
Watches them through the shadows.
'Back in, back in.' One talks to the horse as to a brother.

Maguire himself is patting a potato-pit against the weather—
An old man fondling a new-piled grave:
'Joe, I hope you didn't forget to hide the spade,
For there's rogues in the townland. Hide it flat in a furrow.
I think we ought to be finished by to-morrow.'
Their voices through the darkness sound like voices from a cave,
A dull thudding far away, futile, feeble, far away,
First cousins to the ghosts of the townland.

A light stands in a window. Mary Anne
Has the table set and the tea-pot waiting in the ashes.
She goes to the door and listens and then she calls
From the top of the haggard-wall:
'What's keeping you
And the cows to be milked and all the other work there's to do?'
'All right, all right,
We'll not stay here all night.'

Applause, applause,
The curtain falls.
Applause, applause
From the homing carts and the trees
And the bawling cows at the gates.
From the screeching water-hens
And the mill-race heavy with the Lammas floods curving over the
     weir.
A train at the station blowing off steam
And the hysterical laughter of the defeated everywhere.
Night, and the futile cards are shuffled again.
Maguire spreads his legs over the impotent cinders that wake no
     manhood now
And he hardly looks to see which card is trump.
His sister tightens her legs and her lips and frizzles up
Like the wick of an oil-less lamp.
The curtain falls—
Applause, applause.

Maguire is not afraid of death, the Church will light him a candle
To see his way through the vaults and he'll understand the
Quality of the clay that dribbles over his coffin.
He'll know the names of the roots that climb down to tickle his
     feet.

And he will feel no different than when he walked through
    Donaghmoyne.
If he stretches out a hand—a wet clod,
If he opens his nostrils—a dungy smell;
If he opens his eyes once in a million years—
Through a crack in the crust of the earth he may see a face
    nodding in
Or a woman's legs. Shut them again for that sight is sin.

He will hardly remember that life happened to him—
Something was brighter a moment. Somebody sang in the distance.
A procession passed down a mesmerised street.
He remembers names like Easter and Christmas
By the colour his fields were.
Maybe he will be born again, a bird of an angel's conceit
To sing the gospel of life
To a music as flightily tangent
As a tune on an oboe.
And the serious look of the fields will have changed to the leer of a
    hobo
Swaggering celestially home to his three wishes granted.
Will that be? will that be?
Or is the earth right that laughs haw-haw
And does not believe
In an unearthly law.
The earth that says:
Patrick Maguire, the old peasant, can neither be damned nor
    glorified:
The graveyard in which he will lie will be just a deep-drilled
    potato-field
Where the seed gets no chance to come through
To the fun of the sun.
The tongue in his mouth is the root of a yew.
Silence, silence. The story is done.

He stands in the doorway of his house
A ragged sculpture of the wind,
October creaks the rotted mattress,
The bedposts fall. No hope. No lust.
The hungry fiend
Screams the apocalypse of clay
    In every corner of this land.

Patrick Kavanagh

IN MEMORY OF MY MOTHER

I do not think of you lying in the wet clay
Of a Monaghan graveyard; I see
You walking down a lane among the poplars
On your way to the station, or happily

Going to second Mass on a summer Sunday—
You meet me and you say:
"Don't forget to see about the cattle—"
Among your earthiest words the angels stray.

And I think of you walking along a headland
Of green oats in June,
So full of repose, so rich with life—
And I see us meeting at the end of a town

On a fair day by accident, after
The bargains are all made and we can walk
Together through the shops and stalls and markets
Free in the oriental streets of thought.

O you are not lying in the wet clay,
For it is a harvest evening now and we
Are piling up the ricks against the moonlight
And you smile up at us—eternally.

8. SIX POEMS

AUSTIN CLARKE

"I load myself with chains, then try to get out of them" is how in an unguarded moment Austin Clarke (1896–1974) defined his verse. "Good Lord", exclaimed his American interlocutor, "You cannot have many readers." And for many years that was true. Over the last decade of his life, however, Clarke's reputation steadily grew, at least among the younger Irish poets and critics, if more slowly among the general public.

Clarke's life was a tormented one and he is a complex poet. In many respects his poetry counterpoints the prose of Sean O'Faolain in the search for a spiritual maturity to match the political independence Ireland achieved after 1922. For both men, the enemy was organized Irish Catholicism obsessed with its curious conviction that sexual indulgence was the only serious sin. In his auto-biography Clarke recalls that at his first confession at the age of seven, the priest questioned him about mastur-bation. Sexual frustration is the theme in "The Envy of Poor Lovers".

A more complex poem is "The Straying Student". This is based on the legend of the spoiled priest distracted by feminine charms from his studies at the seminary of Salamanca, where Irish clerics were trained during the days when priests were hunted men at home. But the poem opens to wider horizons. It would not be easy to analyse its sudden shifts in time and mood from the naturalistic opening to the satirical close, or the symbolism and wild yearning of the intermediate stanzas.

There is an exasperation in many of Clarke's later satires that recalls Swift, and he exhibits some of Swift's exaggeration as he assails not only the banning of contraception by church and state, their lack of charity to unmarried mothers, corporal punishment in school or popular belief in cures at Lourdes, but also more docile targets, such as the export of live horses to be slaughtered and eaten in continental Europe. But always there is verbal dexterity and toughness, such as we find in the two-line poem "The Thorn."

It would be a mistake to take Clarke for a Voltairean. Few poets have written so movingly of the miracle of grace in the Mass as he does in "Martha Blake". The fact that a later poem, "Martha Blake at Fifty-one", depicts the same spinster dying in an agony of despair in no way diminishes the mystery of the religious experience expressed.

Clarke had more than his share of personal unhappiness. After an unsatisfactory first marriage, he spent many years in poverty and self-imposed exile in England. The last poem in this group reflects the double sense of alienation he felt on his return to spend the last period of his life in Ireland.

SIX POEMS

THE ENVY OF POOR LOVERS

Pity poor lovers who may not do what they please
With their kisses under a hedge, before a raindrop
Unhouses it; and astir from wretched centuries,
Bramble and briar remind them of the saints.

Her envy is the curtain seen at night-time,
Happy position that could change her name.
His envy—clasp of the married whose thoughts can be alike,
Whose nature flows without the blame or shame.

Lying in the grass as if it were a sin
To move, they hold each other's breath, tremble,
Ready to share that ancient dread—kisses begin
Again—of Ireland keeping company with them.

Think, children, of institutions mured above
Your ignorance, where every look is veiled,
State-paid to snatch away the folly of poor lovers
For whom, it seems, the sacraments have failed.

Austin Clarke

THE STRAYING STUDENT

On a holy day when sails were blowing southward,
A bishop sang the Mass at Inishmore,
Men took one side, their wives were on the other
But I heard the woman coming from the shore:
And wild in despair my parents cried aloud
For they saw the vision draw me to the doorway.

Long had she lived in Rome when Popes were bad,
The wealth of every age she makes her own,
Yet smiled on me in eager admiration,
And for a summer taught me all I know,
Banishing shame with her great laugh that rang
As if a pillar caught it back alone.

I learned the prouder counsel of her throat,
My mind was growing bold as light in Greece;
And when in sleep her stirring limbs were shown,
I blessed the noonday rock that knew no tree:
And for an hour the mountain was her throne,
Although her eyes were bright with mockery.

They say I was sent back from Salamanca
And failed in logic, but I wrote her praise
Nine times upon a college wall in France.
She laid her hand at darkfall on my page
That I might read the heavens in a glance
And I knew every star the Moors have named.

Awake or in my sleep, I have no peace now,
Before the ball is struck, my breath has gone,
And yet I tremble lest she may deceive me
And leave me in this land, where every woman's son
Must carry his own coffin and believe,
In dread, all that the clergy teach the young.

MEDICAL MISSIONARY OF MARY

One blowy morning, Sister Michael,
A student of midwifery,
Fell, handlebarring from her cycle,
Her habit twisted around a pedal:
She suffered bruises on her riff,
Serious injury to the spine
And so, in hope of miracle,
Was brought, a stretcher case, to Lourdes
Out of the blue, above the shrining
Of snowy peaks: unchosen, uncured
Although she had made novena, kissed
The relics: worse than ever, came back
By London, lying on her back,
Saw there, thank Heaven, a specialist
And now is on the recovery list.

THE THORN

In your decline, when truth is bare,
The thorn is seen without its crown.

MARTHA BLAKE

Before the day is everywhere
And the timid warmth of sleep
Is delicate on limb, she dares
The silence of the street
Until the double bells are thrown back
For Mass and echoes bound
In the chapel yard, O then her soul
Makes bold in the arms of sound.

But in the shadow of the nave
Her well-taught knees are humble,
She does not see through any saint
That stands in the sun
With veins of lead, with painful crown;
She waits that dreaded coming,
When all the congregation bows
And none may look up.

The word is said, the Word sent down,
The miracle is done
Beneath those hands that have been rounded
Over the embodied cup,
And with a few, she leaves her place
Kept by an east-filled window
And kneels at the communion rail
Starching beneath her chin.

She trembles for the Son of Man,
While the priest is murmuring
What she can scarcely tell, her heart
Is making such a stir;
But when he picks a particle
And she puts out her tongue,
That joy is the glittering of candles
And benediction sung.

Her soul is lying in the Presence
Until her senses, one
By one, desiring to attend her,
Come as for feast and run
So fast to share the sacrament,
Her mouth must mother them:
"Sweet tooth grow wise, lip, gum be gentle,
I touch a purple hem."

Afflicted by that love she turns
To multiply her praise,
Goes over all the foolish words
And finds they are the same;
But now she feels within her breast
Such calm that she is silent,
For soul can never be immodest
Where body may not listen.

On a holy day of obligation
I saw her first in prayer,
But mortal eye had been too late
For all that thought could dare.
The flame in heart is never grieved
That pride and intellect
Were cast below, when God revealed
A heaven for this earth.

So to begin the common day
She needs a miracle,
Knowing the safety of angels
That see her home again,
Yet ignorant of all the rest,
The hidden grace that people
Hurrying to business
Look after in the street.

RETURN FROM ENGLAND

Though every office stair
I climbed there, left me poorer,
Night after night, my wants
Toil down each step in selfsame
Dream; night after night, enduring
Such failure, I cast away
My body, on fire to reach
Mail-boat or train-from-Euston,
Catch up at last with smoke.
But mind, pretending pity,
Unslaves me in like haste,
Only to take me closer,
With some new tale of wrong here,
Holy retreat of tongue.
When I brought my wife
And children, wave over wave,
From exile, could I have known
That I would sleep in England
Still, lie awake at home?

9. RADIO PLAY:
"THE BIG HOUSE"

BRENDAN BEHAN

The place of Brendan Behan (1923–64) in serious literature may seem open to question. His boisterous escapades in his native Dublin, his appearances drunk on British television, his clambering from auditorium to stage to sing and participate in a New York performance of of one of his own plays, made him an international legend, entertaining or scandalous according to the viewer's outlook, during his short lifetime. The first German audience to see a play in translation was not amused, but later foreign audiences generally proved more indulgent.

His play, *The Hostage*, which was highly successful in Joan Littlewood's version for the London stage, is thin to read. This play was first written as *An Giall* in Irish, and the original is shorter and starker without the concessions to music-hall slapstick. *The Quare Fellow* is stronger: a grim, though shot with comedy, account of the night in jail preceding a hanging. It is said to have played its part in Britain's decision by a free vote in parliament to abolish capital punishment, which was under debate at the time. *Borstal Boy* is a vivid account of the author's experience in a reformatory for juveniles where he was incarcerated for IRA activities in the 1940's.

The work given here, a radio play of 1957, is less well known. But as a self-contained piece it shows Behan's brilliant sense of craftsmanship, his alert ear for the vernacular that reveals character, his zestful, innocent enjoyment of the picaresque. Are there international equivalents for the London cockney, Angel, and his rascally Dublin accomplice, Chuckles Genockey, for the gullible Irish steward, Dionysius O'Looney, and the Anglo-Irish landlord and his English-born wife, Ananias and Boadicea Baldcock? The Big House is perhaps a familiar rural landmark in any country recently emerged from semi-feudalism. The action is set in the period at the end of the 1921–23 civil war, when many of the Anglo-Irish landlords who had stayed on, though impoverished since the land reforms of the 1880's, decided to leave Ireland for good.

107

Brendan Behan

THE BIG HOUSE
A play for radio

THE BIG HOUSE: *(Intones, slowly, majestically)* My bullocks, oh, my bullocks. My bullocks, my beeves, sheep, in flocks, in herds, they surround me. My people, too, in the ghosts of their generations. Old Baldcock built me. Three hundred years ago. Released from the stocks at Bristol on condition that he came to Ireland and assist in the civilising of this unhappy isle, he came and made a thriving business, swindling Cromwell's soldiery out of their grants of land. If old Baldcock did not win it by the sword, well he did a better thing. He won it off them that *did* win it by the sword. Those that live by the sword shall perish by the . . . .

A MOST TREMENDOUS EXPLOSION IS HEARD

MRS. BALDCOCK: *(She leaps up in bed)* Ananias! *(Screeches)* Ananias! Ananias! Wake up! We're blown up! Blow up! I mean, wake up!

ANANIAS BALDCOCK: Yes, yes, damn it, Boadicea, I'm woken up.

MRS. BALDCOCK: I shan't stand it a moment longer. I knew we'd be blown up.

ANANIAS: We haven't been blown up. Damn it, we're still here in bed. That explosion was a mile away.

MRS. BALDCOCK: Well you might have some sympathy for whoever's house it *was* that was blown up. Not that it was anyone that matters, I suppose. There is no country house left in the neighbourhood for miles around. Hoggitts, Blood-Gores, Ramsbottoms, Snowteses, Pug-Footes, Grimeses . . . . all the aristocratic names, all the grace and splendour and civilized living that the very syllables of those noble names recall . . . all . . . *(She sighs)* . . . . gone away.

ANANIAS: There is nobody left in the district worth blowing up.

MRS. BALDCOCK: *(Sadly)*. I'm afraid you're right, Ananias. As a matter of fact *(more happy)* it can only have been the Civic Guard barracks.

ANANIAS: Maybe some of them have been killed . . . . or horribly mangled.

MRS. BALDCOCK: At the risk of seeming bloody minded, I'd say it's just as well to keep the Irish occupied in killing each other rather than in killing us.

ANANIAS: You forget, Boadicea, that I am Irish. Like my ancestors before me, I was born here.

MRS. BALDCOCK: If an ass is born in a stable, does that make it a horse?

ANANIAS: You forget, too, that most of the new Civic Guard are merely the old Royal Irish Constabulary with their cap badges changed. Men who served their King and Country faithfully; and collaborated openly and defiantly in the North East, and discreetly but efficiently in the South and West.

MRS. BALDCOCK: Well, serve them right for joining the rebels in the end and working for the Free State.

ANANIAS: You don't understand, Boadicea, that the Free State is the surest and best way of *beating* the rebels. Even Lord Birkenhead says so. 'Doing England's work, with an economy of English lives' he describes it.

LOONEY: Mashter, sir, and Mishtress, Mashter, sir, and mishtress, mashter, sir.

OTHER VOICES . . . . THE HEAVY ACCENTS OF THE
CIVIC GUARDS ARE HEARD

SERGEANT: Tell them 'tis only till morning. Just a bit of a refuge for the night is all we want.

LOONEY: I will sergeant, I will surely.

KNOCKING ON DOOR

Mashter, sir, and Mishtress.

MRS. BALDCOCK: *(Exasperated)* There's old Looney at the door. What can he want?

ANANIAS: Dionysius O'Looney is a loyal old soul. They have been butlers here since the house was built. For three hundred years, as long as the Baldcocks have lived here, there has always been a Looney in Tonesollock House. They have . . .

KNOCKS AGAIN

LOONEY: Mashter, sir, and mishtress . . . .

MRS. BALDCOCK: Never mind his sterling qualities now. Ask him what he wants.

ANANIAS: What is it, Looney?

LOONEY: The Eye Orr Ah is after letting off a bum, sir.

109

ANANIAS: I know, I know, we heard it. But it wasn't anywhere near here.
LOONEY: No, sir, 'twas only the Guards barracks, sir, and mashter sir . . . .
SERGEANT: Tell them 'tis only till the morning.
LOONEY: Yes sergeant. *(Louder)* And mashter, sir, and mishtress, the sergeant wants to know if we can put him up for the night. They've no place to go till morning.
SERGEANT: 'Tis only till morning, your honour, and we could shake down any ould place that'd be a shelter for us out of the wet, till we get the telephone going to Dublin in the morning.
ANANIAS: Very well. You can use the loft or one of the grooms' places.
SERGEANT: Thanks, sir, and a bed in heaven to you, sir.
ANANIAS: The same to you, my good fellow.
SERGEANT: And a bed in heaven to your good lady too, and good night ma'm. We only wants a shake down in the straw.

THEY MOVE OFF AND HIS VOICE FADES

. . . sure what's wrong with us sleeping in straw. Wasn't Our Lord born in it?
MRS. BALDCOCK: They can have the whole of Tonesollock House for me. Ananias!
ANANIAS: *(Tired)* Yes, Boadicea?
MRS. BALDCOCK: I've been in this horrible country twenty years too long . . . but not a day longer. I'm going to Hereward and Tabitha in Ealing. A dull, London suburb but peaceful, without guns and bombs going off every night for five years . . . and Ealing is private . . . without the native militia coming as refugees to live with one. Irish hospitality, I suppose. But I've had enough of it. Ananias, you can please yourself. If you love Tonesollock more than you love me, you'll . . . .
ANANIAS: I love you the most, Boadicea.
MRS. BALDCOCK: Very well then. We'll go together. You go in tomorrow to your solicitors. He'll find an agent and send in the rents, such as they are, and the proceeds of all cattle sales, and we leave directly for England.
LOONEY: *(Having shown the Sergeant and Guard to their accommodation)* There yous are now, Sergeant dear, and Guard. It's where the Protestant minister sleeps when he comes here. Himself and the wife, in that very bed. He's a Protestant of course, but a very religious man. The moans and groans of him there, kneeling there on that very floor when he's saying his night prayers would go through you.

SERGEANT: *(Feeling the mattress)* Sure, that's a grand bed, Mr. Looney.

GUARD: We're very thankful to you, Mister Looney, to put up us two poor homeless wanderers.

SERGEANT: Aye, indeed, we are so, Mister Looney.

LOONEY: Is there anything more I could do for yous, now? Would you like a drop of anything to restore your shattered nerves?

GUARD: Ah, no thanks, Mr. Looney, haven't you done enough for us?

SERGEANT: Ah, sure, Mister Looney, sir, it'd be too much trouble going down for it.

LOONEY: Who said anything about going down for it? Don't I carry me little consolation prize with me? Bottle in this pocket, glasses in this . . .

SOUNDS OF GLASS CHINKING

SERGEANT: Well, Glory be to God.

GUARD: Mr. Looney, you're a magician.

LOONEY: I'm telling you, the Looneys is no fools. Here . . *(Handing glasses round)* get that down yous.

SERGEANT: Slawncha.

GUARD: Slawncha gus sale.

LOONEY: Slawncha gus sale agut. Health and wealth to you.

SERGEANT: Land without rent to you.

GUARD: The woman of your heart to you.

LOONEY: A child every year to you.

SERGEANT: Married or single.

GUARD: A stout heart.

LOONEY: A wet beak.

SERGEANT: A death in Ireland.

ALL: Slawncha!

THEY DRINK

SERGEANT: *(Smacking his lips)* A good sup, Mr. Looney.

GUARD: Mr. Looney, sir, the sergeant wouldn't mind me asking you.

SERGEANT: It's depending what you are going to ask Mr. Looney for.

GUARD: *(Shyly)* I was going to ask him to sing us a little bit of a song.

LOONEY: Ah, sure me dear decent man, think of the mashter and mishtress and the hour of the night it is.

GUARD: Ah, sure, with respects to them, they're that hard of sleeping they hardly heard the landmine. Sure a bitteen of a song won't wake them so easy.

LOONEY: Yes, but the time it is.

SERGEANT: *(Bold from the whiskey)* Yerra, 'tis early before twelve and early after twelve.

LOONEY: All right, so boys, sure a bit of a song would cheer us up anyway.

SINGS

THERE IS ANOTHER EXPLOSION AND A BURST OF
MACHINE GUN FIRE AND SHOUTING

FIRST SHOUT: God forgive them murderers!

SECOND SHOUT: I hates bad grammar. *(Laughs more or less maniacally).*

MACHINE GUN FIRE

MRS. BALDCOCK: *(Moans in her sleep)* Oh, *(to the tune of 'Galway Bay')* Oh, maybe some day, I'll go back again to Ealing . . . .

ANANIAS: What's that, dear?

MRS. BALDCOCK: I was asleep.

ANANIAS: I never heard of anyone singing in their sleep.

MRS. BALDCOCK: I shouldn't be surprised if I danced in my sleep before I get out of this horrible country.

ANANIAS: Good night, dear.

MRS. BALDCOCK: Good night, Ananias . . . tomorrow . . . .

ANANIAS: Tomorrow in Jerusalem . .

MRS. BALDCOCK: In where, dear?

ANANIAS: In Holyhead, dear.

TONESOLLOCK HOUSE. IT IS EARLY MORNING AND THE BIRDS ARE
SINGING. THEY KEEP ON TWEETING FOR A LITTLE BUT NOT SO
NOTICEABLY

LOONEY: Ah, good morning sergeant, isn't that a lovely morning? Glory be to God. A pity the mashter and mishtress didn't delay a few weeks more before they thought of going away to Ealing.

SERGEANT: 'Tis so, then Looney. Sure, if they had have waited a bit longer, only a few weeks, sure everything is back to normal. Sure we're having our first eviction since 1917 tomorrow.

LOONEY: D'you tell me that, now sergeant dear?

SERGEANT: I do, bedad. The first eviction in six years, and I'll be in charge of it.

LOONEY: Sure, it's just like ould times sergeant dear.

SERGEANT: And the I.R.A is bet, thank God. That De Valera fellow got out a proclamation yesterday. De Valera telling his gangs of rogues, rebels, robbers and wreckers that they're bet, and calling

112

them to give up. It's in the paper here .... *(Reads)* .... 'Soldiers of the Legion of the Rearguard, Bulwark of the Nation's Honour ....'

LOONEY: God help us all. Soldiers ... honour .. *(Spits)* ..... murderers and robbers would be more like it.

SERGEANT: What else would you call them? Lot of scum. But anyway, it means one thing; the trouble is over. That's the end of the Civil War.

LOONEY: A *civil* war, did you call it? Bedad, and if that's what you call a civil war, sergeant dear, I hope I never see an *uncivil* one.

ANGEL: Call that a war? I've seen worse rows in the canteen of a Saturday night over someone pinching a pint.

LOONEY: Did you so then, sir? It could be. I believe they manage things better across the other side. Sure God help the Irish, if it was raining soup, they'd be out with forks. But I didn't think you'd had a war over in England this long time.

ANGEL: No, we 'ad it in France mostly. We nearly always 'ave our wars in someone else's country.

SERGEANT: If it's no harm asking, now what might your business be around here?

ANGEL: It's every 'arm. I'm in a 'urry to do some business 'ere in Tonesollock 'ouse and I'm not doing with neither of you, so I'll be off. Ta, ta.

SERGEANT: What did he say 'Ta, ta' for? I didn't give him anything.

LOONEY: That's his English way of saying 'goodbye'.

SERGEANT: *(Ponderously)* Taah, taah.

LOONEY: Angel is his name. At least that's what Mister Chuckles calls him.

SERGEANT: Angel, that's a peculiar class of a name, more especially for a fellow the like of that. That's a fellow wouldn't lose his way in a jail, I'm telling you.

LOONEY: Angel is the name of the place in London he comes from. He's a great buddy of Mister Chuckles.

SERGEANT: Since Mister and Missus Baldcock went away over to England, I've heard nothing but 'Mister Chuckles' here, and 'Mister Chuckles' there. Who the hell is this Mister Chuckles, if it's no harm asking.

LOONEY: *(Lowers his voice)* Ah, sergeant dear, you may well ask. A Dublin jackeen be the name of Chuckles Genockey is all I know about him, from the tenement houses off of the North Circular Road.

113

SERGEANT: And what class of a man is that to leave to run an estate? What would the likes of him know about land or cattle?

LOONEY: 'Tis not what he knows about land at all, at all, sergeant dear, but he knows the world and all about cattle.

SERGEANT: And how could he know about cattle without knowing about land?

LOONEY: Ah, sergeant, 'tis not on the land but in the market the money's made. What poor farmer ever made a fortune and isn't it a common thing for buyers and blockers and every kind of trickster to maybe double their money at a fair without ever handling a beast only buying off a farmer cheap and selling to a foreign buyer dear?

SERGEANT: Indeed, 'tis true for you.

LOONEY: Till the women going into the butcher are paying for meat the way it would be as cheap for them to be eating gold.

SERGEANT: Musha, 'tis true for you Looney. I often saw my own father selling a beast to a robber of a buyer. *(Starts)* God bless us, what am I saying? Them men can't be classed as robbers. They are respectable with sons in the priesthood, and T.D.'s aye and landlord gentry like Mr. and Mrs. Baldcock. *(Reproachfully)* 'Tis a shame for you, Looney, to be leading me into the sin of criticisin' respectable men with motor cars and money.

LOONEY: I didn't mean it, sergeant.

SERGEANT: Do you know there's Royalty that deals in store cattle, and bishops. It's sinful, Looney, for us to talk like that.

LOONEY: I'm very sorry, sergeant.

SERGEANT: Ah, sure, I know you didn't mean any harm. And sure the Looneys were always known to be decent respectable people that knew their place and served their masters while there was life in their bodies. I often heard Mister Baldcock here saying: 'A Looney', says he, 'a Looney would work till he'd drop!'

LOONEY: It was only that I was trying to explain to you, sergeant, how the likes of Mr. Chuckles Genockey came to be agent here. He was always running round the cattle market from the time he was able to walk, and from doing messages for cattlemen, he rose up to be a class of a spy or a go-between from one buyer to another, and he used to do Mister Baldcock's business for him in the market and now he's taken over Tonesollock House and the estate as well. It's a bit queer to see a man from the slums of Dublin that never had as much land as would fill a window-box, doing the Lord and master over Tonesollock, but sure as you said sergeant, it doesn't do to be criticizing our betters.

SERGEANT: Oh, I didn't mean a bowsy the like of that. Sure, that fellow is an impostherer of low degree. Only meant that it's not every one that makes money is a robber. Most of them are not. The best rule is that them that had money previously are entitled to make more. Them that makes it for the first time are hill and dale robbers until they've had it for at least twenty years.

LOONEY: Well, you'd include Mister Chuckles with the hill and dale robbers.

SERGEANT: Injubettiddley. And that ruddy English Angel that came down to see him this morning.

LOONEY: He's a plumber. He came down to repair the roof. Look, the two of them is up there now.

ON THE ROOF. SEAGULLS SCREAMING AND ROOF NOISES GENERALLY

ANGEL: . . . Now, this bit of flashing 'ere . . . there'll be nearly a 'alf ton of bluey in that alone.

CHUCKLES: And how much is lead at the moment?

ANGEL: 'Alf a quid a 'alf 'undred. That's about what *we'll* get. But they must 'ave 'ad a bleedin' lead mine of their own the way they poured it on this 'ere roof. I suppose we should get a thousand quid for the lot.

CHUCKLES: That should buy a few loaves anyway.

ANGEL: 'Course it will take a few days to get it all into the city, so I reckon on starting right now.

CHUCKLES: You get it ripped off and shag it down off the roof, and I'll get some of the farm labourers to load it on the lorry and we'll be in to Dublin with the first load quick and speedy. I'll go below and collect them . . .

ANGEL: Right . . . . oh, I'll make a start anyway. *(Starts)*.

SOUNDS OF LEAD BEING RIPPED OFF ROOF

Uu . . uup you come. Eas . . . eesy does it. Hey, Chuckles!

CHUCKLES: Hell . . . oooh?

ANGEL: Shall I start flinging it dahn nahw?

CHUCKLES: When I shout up, 'Throw it down', you can begin. *(To Looney)* Hey . . . you.

LOONEY: Is it me, mashter Chuckles?

CHUCKLES: The very same. Tell that peeler there to get offside if he does not want a hundredweight of lead to come crashing down on his napper.

SERGEANT: Look at here, me good man . . . . .

LOONEY: Stand away now, sergeant dear, for mashter Chuckles.

CHUCKLES: *(Shouts)* right away there, Angel, throw it dow . . . wn!

LEAD CRASHES FROM ROOF TO GROUND

115

SERGEANT: Look at here, Mister Looney, is it mending that roof or destroying it they are? Lifting the lead off it. Ripping and robbing maybe.

CHUCKLES: Hey, sleep-in-your-skin.

LOONEY: Yes, mashter Chuckles?

CHUCKLES: Go down and get some of them bullocks' nurses up here to get that lead on to the lorry.

SERGEANT: Who did he say?

LOONEY: Bullocks' nurses he calls the cattle boys.

SERGEANT: *(Raising his voice to include Chuckles)* Before you go for anyone and before you put an ounce of lead up on that lorry, would it be any harm for me to be asking where its going and where you're bringing it to. *(Sarcastically)* That is, Mister Chuckles, if you don't mind.

CHUCKLES: I do mind .... and *you* mind ... mind your own bleedin' business.

SERGEANT: Look at here, me good man, I'm responsible for the protection of property in the district of Tonesollock.

CHUCKLES: And I'm responsible for the property of Tonesollock House and the estate and lands thereof, and our solicitors are Canby, Canby, and Dunne, Molesworth Street, near the Freemasons' Hall, and if you interfere with me, I'll call them on the telephone and tell them you're persecuting the ex-Unionist minority, and get a question asked in the Senate. The Minister of Justice will love you for that.

SERGEANT: *(In suppressed wrath, but just a little anxious)* I'll attend to you in a minute me man. *(To Looney)* What's this ex-Unionist minority? What does that mean, in plain English?

LOONEY: It means the gentry.

SERGEANT: And is that Dublin guttersnipe ... telling me ... telling me ... that *I'm* persecuting the gentry? Does he make out that he's one of them?

LOONEY: Well I suppose he means that he's running the estate for the master, and he's in the master's place like while the master is away.

SERGEANT: *(Sighs)* And God knows I was right. When I saw the dead lancers lying in O'Connell Street and heard the naval artillery pounding the Post Office, I said to myself, something is going to happen, and when I heard the crash of the ....

TERRIFIC NOISE AS ANOTHER LOAD OF LEAD CRASHES TO GROUND

SERGEANT: *(Roars)* hey, you, up there, hey! ...

ANGEL: Hey you down there, want to get a 'undredweight of lead on your noggin?

SERGEANT: You just mind . . . . .

CHUCKLES: You just get to hell out of here. You're on private land. If something falls on your cabbage head, you needn't come looking to us for compensation.

SERGEANT: *(Indignant and despairing)* Look at here Mister Looney, will you tell that impiddent bowsy who I am?

LOONEY: *(In distress)* Oh, sergeant dear, it's not *my* fault and don't go bringing me into it. I don't want to lose me situation that I've been in this fifty years.

CHUCKLES: Hey you. Go-be-the-wall-and-tiddle-the-bricks.

LOONEY: Do you hear the way he calls me out of me name? The old respected name of Looney that was here before the Danes. How would I be trying to get that fellow to give respect to you when I can't get it for myself?

SERGEANT: *(Sighs)* I'll be off for now, Mister Looney, but when Mister Baldcock comes back . . . I'll have a something or two to say to him.

LOONEY: Aye, *when* Mister Baldcock comes back. I'll be as dead as poor Black Joe waiting for him.

CHUCKLES: Hey, you Step-and-fetch-it, do you not hear me calling?

LOONEY: Yes, Mister Chuckles, sir, I hear you calling me, sir, but what you call me, sir, is not my name.

CHUCKLES: Never you mind what I'm calling you.

LOONEY: I am a Looney, sir, and descended from a long line of Looneys, and I got a medal from the Royal Dublin Society at the Horse Show. . . .

CHUCKLES: What as . . . a prize goat?

LOONEY: For fifty years' service sir to the one family. The Baldcocks that own this estate.

CHUCKLES: I don't give a God's curse if you were here since Judas was in the Fire Brigade, and I won't give a damn if you're not here five minutes more. I'd be just as well pleased to be rid of you and a few more of them valleys and footmen up in the house, and maids and housekeepers . . . . *(Thoughtfully)* . . . No, I'd keep the maids, except the old one.

LOONEY: The housekeeper you mean sir. Miss Gilltrap.

CHUCKLES: Yes, the one with a face like a plateful of mortal sins.

LOONEY: A most respected and superior class of woman, sir.

CHUCKLES: She looks it. But anyway, get some of them fellows up

117

here and have that lead loaded on the lorry for us. Myself and the plumber have to be going into Dublin, directly.

LOONEY: *(Resignedly)* I'll go and get them, sir. *(Moves off mike muttering to himself)* Curse a God on you, you low Dublin jackeen. You'd sack Miss Giltrap, would you? But you'd keep the young maids, you would. *(Mutters and snuffles off)*

LORRY STARTS AND MOVES OFF

ANGEL: I thought they'd never get 'er bleedin' loaded. You know, it's a funny thing but the Irish over 'ere in Ireland, they ain't a bit like the Irish over at 'ome in England. Over 'ere they'd stand around all day, if they was let.

CHUCKLES: The fellows out on the farm and looking after the beasts are all right. They'll do a bit of a fiddle with me when we're taking cattle to the market. It's those butlers and valleys that I don't like.

ANGEL: Specially that old Looney. 'E gives me the creeps 'e does.

CHUCKLES: Ah well, I'll have the whole lot cleared out in another week.

ANGEL: I know business is business, Chuckles, and we'll have it off for a few thousand nicker each but don't you feel like, well old Baldcock trusted you a lot?

CHUCKLES: Of course, he trusted me a lot. How the hell could we've arranged the job at all if he didn't trust me? This is not like screwing some gaff along the Tottenham Court Road . . . a rapid creep in, blow the peter and then scarper and read about it in the papers next morning. This is plundering a whole estate. Cattle, horse, sheep, pigs, even let the grazing. The furniture, pictures, the delph, glassware, all that I've had crated with old Baldcock's address in England stencilled on the sides so as they all think he's having it sent to him in England. Now there's the lead and tomorrow or the day after I'm bringing a geezer out to value the doors.

ANGEL: When he comes back, he'll come back to a ruin.

CHUCKLES: That's it.

ANGEL: I'm only asking mind, do you not feel in a way, it's a bit rough on them?

CHUCKLES: How is it? They got a picture of the old man that built the house. It's in books in the library and the Baldcocks boast about it that Cromwell's soldiers croaked about two villagefuls of people to get that land. And old Baldcock got the land off Cromwell's soldiers by using his loaf . . . the same as I'm using mine.

ANGEL: Well, you can 'ardly blame the old man for what happened years ago.

CHUCKLES: I'm not blaming anyone. I don't go in for this lark 'on our side was Erin and virtue, on their side the Saxon and guilt'. I just don't see why old Baldcock should have a lot of lolly and live in a big house while I go out to graft every morning and come home to a rat trap.

ANGEL: Well, you're a Communist, that's what you are.

CHUCKLES: I'm not a Communist, I'm too humble and modest. The Communists want to free all the workers of the world. I'm content to make a start and free one member of it at a time ... myself.

ANGEL: You're just a tealeaf, then.

CHUCKLES: That's right, I'm a thief, same as you, and same as Mister and Mrs. Baldcock. Only as they inherited their lolly, they are really receivers. And they say the receiver is worse than the thief. And now we're coming towards our own fence. Mister Eyes of Green, Marine Dealer.

ANGEL: What sort of a bleeding name is 'Eyes of Green'?

CHUCKLES: I don't know; it's just what everyone else calls him around the Liberty. I suppose they call him 'Eyes of Green' because he's an Irish Jew from Dublin City.

ANGEL: We never 'eard of Irish Jews in London.

CHUCKLES: Well you don't notice, I suppose. Most Dublin Jews have an accent like mine, only a bit worse.

NOISE OF LORRY SLOWING UP AND STOPPING

ANGEL: 'Ere 'e is, anyway. Mind if I see if 'e answers to his name? Hallo, Mister Eyes of Green.

EYES OF GREEN: Hello, you Black and Tan.

CHUCKLES: Listen, Eyes, nark the patriotism just now. We want to do a little business.

ANGEL: We've got a lot of bluey to sell you, Mister Eyes of Green, so don't be so leery.

EYES OF GREEN: All right I'll get it over here and weigh it.

LORRY BACKED OVER BESIDE SCALES AND LEAD WEIGHED

ANGEL: That's the lot then.

EYES OF GREEN: Eighty quid, that's right?

ANGEL: No, it's not right.

CHUCKLES: Do you know, if you gave up being a Jew, you could be a jockey. You've a neck as hard as a jockey's rump.

EYES OF GREEN: What's the difference?

119

ANGEL: You're not even going by your own scales. And that's good lead.

EYES OF GREEN: Where did you get it and when are you going to give it back?

CHUCKLES: We got it from the estate I'm managing, and I'll show you the papers and give a proper receipt for the proper price.

EYES OF GREEN: I say eighty, what's the difference?

CHUCKLES: A score of pounds.

EYES OF GREEN: Split it. I'll give you ninety.

CHUCKLES: Done, and I hope the odd ten nicker chokes you.

EYES OF GREEN: That's real decent of you. *(Counts money)* Here you are. And many thanks for your Christian sentiments.

CHUCKLES: Shalom alechim, Eyes of Green.

EYES OF GREEN: Slawn latt, Chuckles.

CHUCKLES: Start her up, Angel, and we'll get over to the Northside for a drink.

LORRY STARTS AGAIN AND OFF. STOPS
PUBLIC HOUSE. SOUNDS OF BOTTLES, GLASSES. HUM OF
CONVERSATION. WHEN CHUCKLES AND ANGEL ENTER, THERE ARE
SHOUTS OF WELCOME, MALE AND FEMALE

SHOUTS: Me hard man, Chuckles Genockey. Ah, Chuckles, is it yourself that's in it? Musha, me tight Chuckles. You're more nor welcome.

CHUCKLES: Shut up and give us a chance to order a drink for the people.

MALE SHOUT: Silence there for the decent man.

BARMAN: Yes, Chuckles, and what will it be?

CHUCKLES: *(Looks round counting)* One, two, three, four . . . It'd be cheaper to buy the pub. Well, make that . . . er . . . sixteen half ones of malt and chasers.

BARMAN: Certainly, Chuckles . . . . *(Shouts)* sixteen small whiskeys and sixteen bottles of stout.

GRANNY GROWL: There you are, Mrs. Grunt, that's yours.

GRANNY GRUNT: Thank you, Mrs. Growl.

GRANNY GROWL: Don't thank me, thank Chuckles.

GRANNY GRUNT: Thank you, Mister Chuckles, sir, and slawncha.

GRANNY GROWL: Slawncha, Chuckles.

GRANNY GRUNT: Slawncha, Chuckles.

MALE AND FEMALE SHOUTS: Shancha, Chuckles, the flower of the flock; the heart of the roll. Slawncha, and slawncha, again and again.

ANGEL: They don't 'alf like their wallop. Especially the old dears.

Reminds me of 'ome. The Bricklayer's arms or the Elephant of a Saturday night.

CHUCKLES: Wait till they get rightly oiled. *(Shouts)* Hey, more gargle for the people.

GRANNY GRUNT: Me life on you, Chuckles, and the divil thump and thank the begrudgers.

GRANNY GROWL: Up the Republic and to hell with the rest. Give us a rebel song, Mrs. Grunt, ma'm, a real Fenian one, the one you got the six months for. Up Stallion!

GRANNY GRUNT: I will, allana, if you'll hand me that tumbler. *(She swallows a drink)* Thanks. *(Clears her throat)* *(Sings)*

GRANNY GRUNT AND CHORUS:

When I was young I used to be as fine a man as ever you'd
        see.
And the Prince of Wales, he says to me 'Come and join the
        British Army' . . .
Toora loora loora loo,
They are looking for monkeys in the zoo.
And if I had a face like you,
I'd join the British Army.

(Sings)

Nora Condon baked the cake, but 'twas all for poor Nell
        Slattery's sake,
I threw myself into the lake, pretending I was barmy.
Toora loora loora loo,
'Twas the only thing that I could do,
To work me ticket home to you,
And lave the British Army.

SHOUTING, MALE AND FEMALE, LIKEWISE SCREECHES AND
ROARS

SHOUT: Granny Grunt, your blood's worth bottling.

ROAR: Me life on you Granny Grunt.

SCREECH: A noble call, now, you have ma'm.

CHUCKLES: Granny Grunt, nominate your noble call.

GRANNY GRUNT: I call on the Granny Growl. Mrs. Growl, ma'm, Maria Concepta, if I call you be your first name.

GRANNY GROWL: *(With dignity)* Certingly, Teresa Avila, to be sure.

CHUCKLES: Get something to lubricate your tonsils first. *(Shouts)* More gargle, there!

GRANNY GROWL: God bless you, me son.

GRANNY GRUNT: May the giving hand never falter.

121

FIRST VOICE: Up the Republic!
SECOND VOICE: Up Everton!
THIRD VOICE: Up the lot of yous.
                    DRINKS ARE HANDED ROUND
CHUCKLES: Did everyone get their gargle?
                    SHOUTS OF ASSENT
CHUCKLES: Well, Granny Growl, give us your song. Carry on with
the coffin . . . the corpse'll walk.
GRANNY GROWL AND CHORUS: *(Sings)*
Get me down me petticoat and hand me down me shawl,
Get me down me petticoat, for I'm off to the Linen Hall,
He was a quare one, fol de doo ah gow a dat
He was a quare one, I tell you.

If you go to the Curragh Camp, ask for Number Nine,
You'll see three squaddies standing there,
An' the best looking one is mine
He was a quare one, fol de doo ah gow a dat,
He was a quare one, I tell you.

If he joined the Army under a false name,
To do me for me money,
It's his ould one's all to blame.
He was a quare one, fol de doo a gow a dat
He was a quare one, I tell you.

If you put them to the war, out there to fight the Boers,
Will you try and hould the Dublins back,
See the Bogmen go before.
He was a quare one, fol de doo a gow a dat
He was a quare one, I tell you.

Me love is on the ocean and me darling's on the sea,
Me love he was a darling chap,
Though he left me fixed this way.
He was a quare one, fol de doo a gow a dat
He was a quare one, I tell you.

So . . . get me down me petticoat and hand me down me shawl,
Get me down me petticoat for I'm off to the Linen Hall
With your he was a quare one, fol de doo ah gow a dat,
He was a quare one, I tell you.
GRANNY GROWL: *(Sobs a bit)* Me tired husband, poor ould
Paddins, he was shot in the Dardanelles.

122

GRANNY GRUNT: *(Sympathetically)* And a most paintful part of the body to be shot.

GRANNY GROWL: And me first husband was et be the Ashantees. All they found of him was a button and a bone.

GRANNY GRUNT: God's curse to the hungry bastards.

GRANNY GROWL: But still and all ma'm what business had he going near them? Me second husband had more sense. He stopped in the militia, and never went further than the Curragh for a fortnight.

GRANNY GRUNT: Maria Concepta, do you remember when he used to wait on them coming off of the train at Kingsbridge and they after getting their bounty money, and waiting in on the station to be dismissed.

GRANNY GROWL: 'Deed and I do, Teresa Avila, and me provoked sergeant, he was an Englishman, would let a roar that'd go through you.

ANGEL: *(An N.C.O.'s roar)* 'Ri ... ght'! To yore respective workhouses, pore'ouses, and 'ore 'ouses ... d .. iss, . miss'!

GRANNY GRUNT: That's the very way he used to shout. It used to thrill me through me boozem.

GRANNY GROWL: Poor ould Paddins me tired husband ....

CHUCKLES: Granny Growl, never mind your husband for a minute. *(Raises his voice)* How would yous all like to come to a house cooling?

MALE AND FEMALE SHOUTS: We'd love to.

GRANNY GROWL: Teresa Avila, what's a house cooling?

GRANNY GRUNT: The opposite to a house warming I suppose. Like an American wake, when someone is going away. Chuckles is going away tonight, I heard them saying. But anyway there will be gargle on the job.

GRANNY GROWL: Oh begod, I'm game ... game for anything! *(She raises her voice to a shout)* ... Game for anything. Bottle or draught!

CHUCKLES: All get settled in the lorry. All out to the lorry. The ladies gets in first and settles themselves and the men carries out the drink. Hey there, put up the gargle on the counter for the men to carry out to the lorry. Ten dozen of stout and ten bottles of whiskey.

OUTSIDE IN THE LORRY

GRANNY GRUNT: Are you right there, Teresa Avila?

GRANNY GROWL: I'm great, Maria Concepta. At our age we enjoy a good ride. It's that seldom we get one.

123

MALE VOICES: Take up that parcel. Here mind the drink.

GRANNY GRUNT: Yous young women there at the end of the lorry take the gargle off of the men.

SOUNDS OF BOTTLES RATTLING AS THEY'RE PUT ABOARD THE TRUCK

MALE VOICES: Everything stored aboard, Chuckles.

ANGEL: *(From the cab)* Right, jump up behind and we're off.

LORRY STARTS OFF INTO THE NIGHT

BARMAN: *(Shouts from the door)* Good night, good night.

MALE AND FEMALE SHOUTS: Goodnight, goodnight, goodnight and good luck.

LORRY GATHERS SPEED

TONESOLLOCK HOUSE. THE LORRY APPROACHES DIMLY HEARD IN THE NIGHT

LOONEY: *(From his window)* Here they are back.

(CHORUS FROM THE LORRY, FAINT BUT GROWING SLOWLY AS THE LORRY COMES NEARER THE HOUSE). ...

'HE WAS A QUARE ONE' ...

LOONEY: Another drunken lot of scum, and old women amongst them. The dirty filthy lot. They'll be roaring and singing and cursing now till morning. Ah, Tonesollock House ...

IN THE HOUSE

GRANNY GROWL: Ah me tired husband, he was in the Boer war, and he was standing there in the middle of South Africa, in a big long line, thousands upon thousands of them, every man like a ramrod, stiff as pokers, not a man to move even when a comrade fell, stretched on the parade ground, prostituted from the heat, and up rides Lord Roberts.

GRANNY GRUNT: A lovely man. I seen him in the Park and a pair of moustaches on his face a yard long. Waxed and stiff, they went through me boozem.

GRANNY GROWL: He rides along half the length of the line till he comes to my Paddins, and lets a roar out of him that would move your bowels: 'Fuslier Kinsella!' he roars.

GRANNY GRUNT: God bless us!

GRANNY GROWL: 'Fuslier Kinsella', he shouts. Paddins steps forwards, smacks the butt of his rifle, and Lord Roberts looks down at him off his big white horse, and his moustache trembling with glory, 'Fuslier Kinsella', he roars, 'wipe your bayonet .. you've killed enough!

GRANNY GRUNT: My poor fellow, he was a ral, in the Fusiliers.

GRANNY GROWL: What's a ral, Maria Concepta?

124

GRANNY GRUNT: Well, it's either an admiral, a corporal or a general, but he was a ral, anyway. Pass us that bottle there, Teresa Avila, and we'll have a sup between us anyway. *(They drink)* Where's Chuckles and that English chap be the way?

UPSTAIRS

CHUCKLES: I suppose we better get down now to the others. I suppose most of them is laid out, be this time. What time is it, Angel?

ANGEL: It's a quarter to five. The sun is coming up.

CHUCKLES: Well, I've everything here. The money from the cattle, from the sale of the farm equipment, and the house fittings, five thousand quid . . . two for you . . . .

ANGEL: That'll be a help. D'you know the last honest graft I was in was the railway . . . thirty-five bob a week.

CHUCKLES: And three for me. We better go down and say goodbye to them down below.

THEY GO DOWNSTAIRS

GRANNY GRUNT: There you are, Chuckles.

CHUCKLES: We're off to the boat. We come down to bid yous goodbye.

GRANNY GROWL: Bedad and we'll give yous a send off. Rouse up there the lot of yous.

MALE AND FEMALE SHOUTS: Wake up there! Wake up there! And sing!

GRANNY GROWL: Wake up Teresa Avila, wake up! Pass a bottle round there, till we wish Chuckles 'Good Luck'.

MALE AND FEMALE SHOUTS: Good luck, Chuckles, Slawncha, Good Luck, and God go with you.

GRANNY GRUNT AND CHORUS: *(Sings)*

Hand me down me petticoat, hand me down me shawl,
Hand me down me petticoat, for I'm off to the Linen Hall.
He was a quare one, fol de doo ah gow a dat,
He was a quare one, I tell you.

HOLYHEAD STATION. RATTLE, ROAR, ETC., OF TRAINS.
WHEESH OF BRAKES

PORTER: This way for the Dublin boat. This way for the mail boat. This way for the Dublin boat.

MRS. BALDCOCK: You've seen about the luggage, Ananias?

ANANIAS: Yes, dear.

MRS. BALDCOCK: It will be nice to be home in dear old Ireland again.

ANANIAS: Yes, dear.

MRS. BALDCOCK: That horrid little house of Tabitha's, and Hereward so rude about you discharging your shotgun in the garden! And those awful, frightful, horrible children.

ANANIAS: Yes, dear, I knew you'd prefer to be back in Tonesollock.

MRS. BALDCOCK: It will be just like when first we wed, and you brought me there as a bride.

ANANIAS: Dear Boadicea.

MRS. BALDCOCK: Darling Ananey!

ANANIAS: Dearest, darlingest Boadey!

MRS. BALDCOCK: *(Greatly astonished)* Look, Ananias.

ANANIAS: Where, darling, at what, dear?

MRS. BALDCOCK: They're just coming out of the customs shed.

ANANIAS: *(A trifle impatient)* Who's coming out of the customs shed, darling?

MRS. BALDCOCK: The agent . . . your man of affairs . . . at home . . . at Tonesollock.

ANANIAS: Genockey, in England?

MRS. BALDCOCK: Wales, darling.

ANANIAS: *(Impatiently)* Whatever it is. Leaving that customs shed!

MRS. BALDCOCK: There he is there, don't you see him with another man, there, they're speaking to a porter.

ANANIAS: Why, bless my soul, so it is.

MRS. BALDCOCK: They're coming this way, dear, speak to him.

ANANIAS: Genockey, Genockey, I didn't hear you coming over. You didn't write.

ANGEL: *(Speaking politely)* I'm afraid you're making a mistake, sir, My employer does not speak English.

ANANIAS: Does not speak English? Ridiculous. Genockey was born and bred in the City of Dublin, where they speak the best English after Oxford.

ANGEL: I'm afraid you are mistaken, sir. This is Doctor Hohnhohn *(he makes for 'Hohnhohn', a sound indistinct but very French)* Professor of Celtic Studies at the Sorbonne . . . Belfast Celtic and Glasgow Celtic.

ANANIAS: I beg your pardon, sir.

ANGEL: *(To Chuckles)* Vous-etes le professeur Hohnhohn, ouis?

CHUCKLES: Ouis, je suis.

ANGEL: *(Speaking in his normal Cockney accent)* See, he says so 'imself. We got to catch this train for London . . . . Ta, lady, ta gov.

TRAIN MOVES OFF. GATHERS SPEED. FADES.

THE BIG HOUSE

THE BIG HOUSE: Through war, riot and civil commotion have I

126

stood, and have lived through bad times to see these good times. To get rid of common people and their noisy children and have back again, safe from the towns and cities, my dear horse-faced ladies, and my owners. Stout, redfaced men, and the next best thing to animals, and best of all, the land, for the horse, sheep and bullock, which my people even come to resemble in the end .... my beeves, oh my beeves, my sheep, my horses, and oh my bullocks, my bullocks, my bullocks ......

10. ONE-ACT PLAY: "ON THE OUTSIDE"

TOM MURPHY

Two forms of provincial entertainment flourished in the Ireland of the 1950's: amateur theatricals and the dance-hall. The former had a respectable pedigree harking back to the days when little Johnny Cassidy and his brother would hire a disused stables in Dublin's slumland for a shilling a night to charge their audiences a penny a head to see the future Sean O'Casey play Richard the Third, and further back to Dion Boucicault and *The Colleen Bawn*. The dance-hall was more recent. The priests had frowned on the cross-road dancing of the 1920's and later the spread of the motor-car made the old family-style dance in the farmhouse kitchen unmanageable. By the 1950's visitors to rural Ireland were amazed at the enormous dance-palaces erected in out-of-the-way places.

Tom Murphy's first short play, *On the Outside*, written in collaboration with Noel O'Donoghue, unites both traditions and is an accurate document of the times. It won a manuscript competition in Athlone in 1962, was played once by an amateur group in Cork, then forgotten. When it was first performed professionally at the Project Arts Centre in 1974, Ireland had changed so rapidly that much of its dialogue made it a period piece, but it proved all the more successful for that. It was the hit of the Dublin Theatre Festival that year. A new affluence had come to rural Ireland, but the dead-end frustration it records remained a contemporary issue.

A full-length play of Tom Murphy's, *The Sanctuary Lamp*, ran successfully at the Abbey Theatre in 1975.

129

Tom Murphy

ON THE OUTSIDE

Characters

Kathleen

Anne
Joe
Frank
Drunk
Mickey Ford
First Man
Girl
Bouncer
Second Man

The time is 1958, and the place
outside a country dancehall

A quiet country road outside a dancehall. The dancehall, in the background, is an austere building suggesting, at first glance, a place of compulsory confinement more than one of entertainment. Then, through a small window, high up on the wall, can be seen the glow of the ballroom lights, and, occasionally, to complement the more romantic numbers, a revolving crystal ball, tantalising and tempting to anyone on the outside without the wherewithal to gain admission. Popular music of the time (late fifties) played badly by the band, continues throughout the play; except, from time to time when a dance ends. Then follows some half-hearted applause; and this, in turn is followed by the faint buzz of voices. The usual dancehall noises.
A placard is placed somewhere against the dancehall wall, and

130

*its message reads: "I.N.T.O. DANCE TONIGHT, 8–12. MUSIC
BY THE MARVELTONES ORCHESTRA. ADMISSION 6/-."*

*There are two girls on the stage when the lights come up:
Kathleen and Anne. Anne is the younger, about twenty, very naive
and anxious to be conventional. She is sincere but rather stupid;
and the words of a popular song are the true expression of the
human spirit. Kathleen, on the other hand is two years older and
more sophisticated. She has, perhaps, worked in Dublin or England
for a time. She has less romantic illusions, is more neutral and even
cynical at times. But that is not to say that she is unromantic. She
simply has a better idea than Anne of what it is all in aid of.*

*When we first see them, Anne is rather dejected, but still looking
off towards the main road half-hopefully. Kathleen is walking up
and down. She has a cardigan pulled tightly over her shoulders.
They have obviously been waiting for a long time. Kathleen stops
and looks at Anne.*

KATHLEEN It's late. *(Pause)*. Well, don't you think you've waited
long enough? After all, we're here I-don't-know-how-
long.

ANNE Just another few minutes.

KATHLEEN *(To herself)* Just another few ... It's late!

ANNE He'll be here any second now. I'm sure of it.

KATHLEEN Yes, when the dance is over, I suppose. And that won't
be very long at all now. Lord, I'm frozen.

ANNE It's not that cold.

KATHLEEN And I left off that heavy vest too. I hope my mother
doesn't find it under the pillow. And will you look at
the cut of my shoes! Oh, come on in. It's silly waiting
any longer.

ANNE Ah, Kathleen, a few seconds more.

KATHLEEN He's not coming.

ANNE But why? He said he would. It was he wanted to. He
said to meet him here outside the hall.

KATHLEEN *(Impatiently)* yes—yes, but he's kind of late, isn't he?
(There is a short pause; KATHLEEN *sees she is having
no effect)*. What's his name anyway, Frank what?

ANNE But he's very nice though.

KATHLEEN Are you sure his first name is Frank even? ... What
does he do? What kind of job has he?

ANNE Ah, Kathleen.

KATHLEEN Oh, you never can tell. I was going with a fella last

131

year in Dublin. Not bad looking either. And, of course, fool here was real struck. I liked him. Richard Egan. And then one night we met—yeh know Mary O'Brien nursing in the Mater? And later she took me aside. "Do you not know who he is?" she said. "No." "He's the porter at the hospital." The shagging porter. *And* his name wasn't Richard.

ANNE What was it?

KATHLEEN Declan ... I don't remember what he told me he was. The Civil Service I suppose. Taught me a lot I can tell you ... What did this Frank tell you he was?

ANNE He said he was—he didn't say.

KATHLEEN What?

ANNE He isn't like that. He really is very nice.

KATHLEEN Tck!

ANNE We—talked to each other.

KATHLEEN Talk! They're all the same *(Moving to a better vantage point)* ... Wait on: Someone coming now.

ANNE Is it him?

KATHLEEN I can't make him out so well. It might be.

ANNE Oh, what'll I say? What'll I do?

KATHLEEN Up near the car park.

ANNE Come on in, Kathleen. We're going in. We're not waiting a second longer. Come on.

KATHLEEN *(Still looking off R)* Oh, it's not him at all. He's gone up the other way.

ANNE *(Disappointed)* Are you sure?

KATHLEEN Some old drunk. They're everywhere. Well, we might as well go in so.

ANNE Ah, Kathleen.

KATHLEEN What's wrong with you now? You were mad to go in a few seconds ago.

ANNE I can't understand it.

KATHLEEN He's forgotten, he's with someone else, he's drinking. In some pub.

ANNE I don't like men who drink.

KATHLEEN The dance is half-over—

ANNE I asked him and he smokes alright—

KATHLEEN He isn't coming—

ANNE But he doesn't drink, he said.

KATHLEEN You're only a fool.

ANNE ... But why?

KATHLEEN For god's sake, don't take him so seriously: You've
only seen him once before ... Look, I'm sure he's very
nice, but he'll hardly come tonight now. There's
thousands of them in there! Maybe you'll meet
someone with a car.

ANNE *(Childishly)* I don't want a car ... I don't agree ... I
don't care what he does.

KATHLEEN *(Giving up)* I don't know, I'm a worse fool to be
waiting here with you at all. *(Pause)*

ANNE Do you think ... could he ... have come, maybe, and
didn't see us here and gone in, thinking, maybe, I
wasn't coming?

KATHLEEN *(To herself)* In the name of—! *(Seeing her chance)*
Yes. That's what happened. We'll go in and see. Come
on. Well, come on.

ANNE *(Reluctantly)* Alright.

KATHLEEN *(As they exit)* Good job you brought your own money
with you.

The stage is empty. There is a short pause. Then JOE
comes in. He looks at the hall entrance.

For the record, JOE *is about twenty-two and employed
as an apprentice to some trade, as indeed is* FRANK.
He is immature and irresponsible but not bad.

JOE *(Calling softly off)* Alright, sham, they're gone.
FRANK *enters. He is a stronger personality than* JOE.
Same age as JOE *and works at the same trade. He is
old enough, however, to be aware of the very rigid
class distinctions that pervade a small, urban-rural
community and resents "them" with the cars and
money because he has not got the same. It is hard to
say how far he is really bad and how far he is only an
intelligent product of his environment.*

JOE Blazes, I thought they'd never go. I've cramps all over
from being stuck back there.

FRANK What did you think of her? Not bad, is she?

JOE Not too bad for this hole, I suppose.

FRANK Ah, she's alright now.

133

JOE Wait'll you see the one I'll get. *(Starts to move towards door)*

FRANK Stall, sham, take it easy a while. We don't want to land in right after them.

JOE Hey, what are you going to say to her? ... You kept her waiting all night ... Tell her you're an automatic scientist and you were ducking communists all night. If she's a bit innocent, she'll swallow anything.

FRANK Stall it, stall it.

JOE Tell her the truth so. I was hiding behind the wall all night watching you because I hadn't got the price of two tickets. That'll go down well.

FRANK Pity I didn't work the see-you-inside act, but she thinks I'm loaded. The car we came in broke down and we only got here now.

JOE And she'll say: "Who did you come with?" And you'll say—oh, Mickey Ford or someone. And she'll say: "Oh, de Mickey de Ford or someone: we saw de Mickey de Ford going in at nine o'clock." What's all the fuss about this one for anyway, she's only a mul.

FRANK I just want something she'll believe. I wouldn't mind hanging on to her for a while. What would you tell her?

JOE Slap her down.

FRANK I'll tell her what I like and she'll believe me. And I'll be narked she didn't wait for me.

(FRANK breaks into song. JOE dances, then stops when he sees the poster)

JOE Hey!

FRANK What?

JOE How much is this dance tonight, did you say?

FRANK Four bob.

JOE *(Points at poster)* Look. The poster. Admission six bob.

FRANK Six *what!*

JOE Six shillings. You and your four bob dance. Where did you get that from?

FRANK It's robbery. *(Laughing)* Six bob!

JOE Just because there's no other dance on around here tonight.

FRANK Well, we'll just have to pay up since we came this far. Give us two bob till Friday.

JOE *(Laughs)* What? And how do you think I'm fixed?

FRANK You'll get it back Friday.

JOE Give you hell. I've four and six. Four and a lousy kick. And I borrowed that just before I came out here.

FRANK Are you coddin' me?

JOE Where would I get it?

FRANK Great, that's great, that's just deadly now. I've just the bare four bob. *(Pause)* The quare one in the box-office?

JOE Will I give her a twirl? (or "try her"). Give us your money.

FRANK Offer her half-a-dollar apiece first: we might get in for four then.

JOE *(Adjusting his tie)* We might get in for choicer *(nothing)* yet.

FRANK Okay, Elvis, go to it.

(JOE *moves up the steps into the hall.* FRANK *takes out his cigarettes immediately* JOE *has disappeared, and lights one. Noises are heard off stage and the* DRUNK *enters. ... He is a small, labouring man, aged about fifty. He shuffles on stage, sees* FRANK *and approaches him.* FRANK *treats him in a very off-hand manner)*

DRUNK Excuse me. Excuse me—Sir! (FRANK *ignores him)* Excuse me. Give us a light, will you? *(He has a cigarette in his hand.* FRANK *still ignores him)* Could you oblige a gentleman with a light, Sir? (FRANK *gives him a light)* Thanks. Much obliged. Thank you. *(Notices music in background)* What's on?

FRANK Dance.

DRUNK Hah? A dance? Oh, a dance! ... Who's playing it? Who's playing the music?

FRANK Marveltones.

DRUNK Marbletones—Mar—Marvel *(Laughs)* I thought you said the Marvel—Marble—tones. *(He laughs)* How much is it?

FRANK Six bob.

DRUNK Hah?

FRANK Six bob. Six shillings.

135

DRUNK *(Still unaware of* FRANK'S *annoyance)* Hah?

FRANK One, two, three, four, five, six shillings.

DRUNK *(Looking at him seriously for a second in silence)* No need to be smart, young fellah. No need at all. You can answer a civil question when it's put to you.

FRANK Go away.

DRUNK No need for that. No need.

FRANK *(Controlling himself)* Right, no need. Now will you clear before I call the guards or something. Go home to your wife. Go home.

DRUNK Home? Anything but the death! *(He grins)*

FRANK *(Looks at him for a moment, then walks away)* ... Look, don't be annoying me.

DRUNK And I've no wife. I'm single. No one in the world but me. No one cares. I don't care! ... Why did you say—

FRANK Okay, okay, you've no wife. Now will you go.

DRUNK Where?

FRANK Anywhere.

(JOE *comes out of the hall*)

FRANK Any good?

JOE No good, no luck, no cut: six bob.

FRANK Bitch.

JOE If the hall was empty they'd be damn glad to take it.

FRANK Bloody crowd of robbers.

DRUNK What's up lads?

JOE We might try her again later on though.

DRUNK What's up lads?

JOE Who's the sham?

DRUNK How ya goin' on, young fellah?

FRANK Oh, my pardon. Ten thousand, one hundred and eighteen pardons! This gentleman here is Mr. Narrow-Neck.

JOE How yeh, Mr. Narrow-Neck!

DRUNK Hah? No—no, I said—I said—

FRANK You didn't? Sorry about that, sham. I thought the name suited him, didn't you? *(They laugh)*

DRUNK No, I said—

JOE Little-Back, he said. Delighted.

DRUNK No, I said—

FRANK No, you didn't. Are you drunk or something?

136

JOE You'd better watch out, Mr. Little-Back, or you'll be seeing gollies next: Waw—waw—aw! ...

DRUNK *(Quickly)* I said Jim Daly. Jim Daly. Seamus O'Dálaigh.

(FRANK *and* JOE *laugh*)

FRANK Ah, of course. I knew I'd seen you before. Muscles himself: Mr. Universe of 1958. Well, Mr. Daly, meet my friend here (*Points to* JOE) Bill Bottle and goodbye now. Scram, do you understand? Scram. Scram.

(JOE *takes* DRUNK'S *cap and throws it deftly at dancehall door.* DRUNK *follows his cap and exits to hall.* JOE *laughs then becomes silent*)

JOE Well he's in and we're here.

FRANK Was she anyway promising at all? *(Nodding towards box-office)* Boxy.

JOE We'll try her again in a while.

FRANK Who do they think they are with their little post-office books and two and a half per cent, per annum.

JOE Anno Domini, Annie get your gun.

FRANK This one ass place.

JOE And she got her gun. *(Then suddenly)* We're the asses to come out here miles Six bob! And the floor like galvanize in there.

FRANK Lord, I'd love to be independent. ... I have to get in.

JOE You won't see me paying six bob.

FRANK What do you think?

JOE Could we get pass-outs maybe?

FRANK Yeh ... *(To himself)* Yeh, cadge and cadge again.

JOE There's a good crowd in there. There's bound to be someone leaving soon: jiggy-jiggy in the passion wagons.

(*While* JOE *is saying the last line above,* MICKEY FORD *comes out of the dancehall. He is about the same age as* FRANK *and* JOE. *His suit is better than theirs, and he wears a loud American-style tie. He is well off, having a car and no lack of money. He is a tradesman of some kind or at any rate he has a good job. Nevertheless, he is adolescent in many ways. He likes to talk about himself and boast of his exploits in a*

137

> *rather naive way. This smugness and boasting make*
> *him very self-confident and lead to an appalling*
> *triviality in his conversation. Naturally, neither*
> FRANK *nor* JOE *can bear him since he represents all*
> *that they are not and all that they resent. It should be*
> *mentioned that he affects a* slight *American accent*
> *whenever he thinks of it.* FRANK *and* JOE *watch him go*
> *up the road)*

FRANK Oh, look out: there's Handsome himself! Whid *(look*
      at) the tie he has on.

JOE How yeh, Mick!

MICKEY Hi, fellahs! Are you going in?

FRANK

JOE Yeh.

MICKEY *(Exiting to a shop off)* See you inside. *(They laugh*
      quietly at his disappearing back)

JOE Think would he—would he be any good for the touch?

FRANK No.

JOE Well, we can't wait for someone to come along and
      say, "here, lads, here's three-and-six for ye".

FRANK And he'll tell half the hall inside we touched him. His
      money, you know, is real special. He's loaded to the
      nockers with threepenny bits—legacy stakes.

JOE Well, I'm going to try him when he comes back. If he
      tells anyone we touched him we won't give him the
      money back: Law three hundred and six in the
      touchers' rule book.

FRANK Do you see him at all driving round the town always
      with one arm sticking out the window? Hail, rain or
      snow the elbow is out. I don't know how he doesn't get
      paralyzed with the cold. I'm going to write to Henry
      Ford.

JOE Yeh?

FRANK And tell him to invent a car—great idea—with an
      artificial arm fixed on and sticking out the window.
      The hard man car they'll call it. Then fellahs like
      Mickey can still be dog tough without exposing
      themselves. Get me?
      (They laugh)

JOE Stall it. Brilliantino is coming back.

FRANK Are you happy at your work?

(JOE *whistles furiously in reply.* MICKEY FORD *enters, eating an apple*)

JOE Oh, there y'are, Mick!

(FRANK *nods*)

MICKEY Hi fellahs! *(He comes over to them)*

JOE What's the dance like, Mick?

MICKEY Not bad. The band's not bad.

JOE Much women inside?

MICKEY Loaded, stacked, powerful talent, deadly. Best I've seen for a long while.

FRANK *(Dryly)* I bet you've squared already, Mick?

MICKEY I've my eye on a few but I don't know which I'll bother with yet. There's a Jane in there that's nursing in England home on holidays. What a woman! Full of your arms, you know. *(He winks)*

JOE There's nothing like them ones that spend a while in England. Them are the ones to get.

FRANK And the Protestants.

MICKEY And she's all talk too. Ah, but I don't think I'll bother.

FRANK *(Innocently)* Jay, and I bet you'd be sound there too, sham.

MICKEY Sure I know, but there's a few others I'm sort of watching.

FRANK Yeh?

MICKEY There's a Kelly one in there from round here. I had—

JOE Anne Kelly?

MICKEY Do you know her, Joe?

JOE *(Looks at FRANK)* Sort of.

MICKEY I had a dance or two with her. I was thinking about her but—I don't know.

JOE Why?

MICKEY Ah—there's not an awful lot of her in it. Do you know her, Frank?

FRANK *(Nods)* How's the car going, Mick?

MICKEY A bird.

JOE Any accidents or anything?

MICKEY No, but do you know, I was coming home from work the other evening. Monday. Well you know me—boot down all the time.

FRANK *(Dryly)* You were doing over fifty, I suppose?

MICKEY Fifty? Sixty-five, seventy. I was flying along. All of a sudden I felt the pull to the right. Like a flash, I

139

	changed down and slapped on the brakes. The front tyre was gone.
FRANK	*(Whistles)* Wheeew!
MICKEY	They're tubeless, you know.
FRANK	Go on!
JOE	Jay!
MICKEY	Well, you know yourselves when you're speeding like that and you get a blow-out, the car could go anywhere. Heaven, hell, anywhere. You just want to stay cool and act fast. It's easy enough to get killed nowadays.
JOE	That's if you're not fast enough like you were?
MICKEY	Gee, guys, you want to be fast alright.
FRANK	That's for a blow?
MICKEY	For any emergency, and a blow-out too. Which reminds me, I'd better blow. *(All laugh)* I've a real nice bit asked for the next dance.
JOE	Good man, Mick—Oh, Mick, a second! You see we're kind of stuck, like, and—
MICKEY	Aw jay, lads, the car is full!
JOE	No. We're stuck for a few shillings.
MICKEY	Aw jay, lads—
JOE	Three and six—
MICKEY	Aw jay, lads—
JOE	Till Friday night—Friday dinner time.
MICKEY	I couldn't. I've—I've only five bob on me and I've to get a gallon of juice for the bus going home. And it might be a roundabout way too. *(He smiles slyly but gets no response)*
JOE	Maybe you'd manage without the petrol?
MICKEY	I couldn't, honest. She's very low. I had five and sevenpence and I bought the apple. The good stuff costs five bob a gallon.
JOE	If you give us three and six we'll borrow it inside for you. There's a crowd from home in there.
MICKEY	Aw, I couldn't risk it.
JOE	We'd be sure to get it! There's no risk.
MICKEY	Aw, it's too chancey. Look, I'd like to help you but I can't. I've a few odd pence here if that's any use to—
FRANK	Okay.
MICKEY	Jay, sorry now, fellahs.
	(JOE *is about to try again*)

FRANK Okay!

JOE Okay, sham.

MICKEY Sorry. I'd better go in. Be seeing you.

(He goes into the hall)

JOE You have your glue. Twilix. *(He joins* FRANK*)* Where did he get that accent. "Hi, fellahs".

FRANK He has an uncle in America and they get letters at home from him. .... He'll be all double basses and carburettors and ignition keys inside now with the women.

JOE And they seem to fall for that kind of bull too. He squares a lot—

FRANK I don't know, does he square that many? A lot of the women he gets are very thick anyway. The car helps him. ... He mustn't give anything up at home at all.

JOE By God, it's not so with me. The auld fellow would break my back.

FRANK How much do you give up?

JOE Half ... How much do you give up? (FRANK *sighs*) ... But they need it.

FRANK *(Pause)* And what do you do with the other half? A pound!

JOE Spend it! *(They laugh)*

FRANK Aw but—Jesus!—this bumming around from one end of the week to the other is terrible! Jesus, look at us now! Look at us in that auld job with Dan Higgins. The fags we get out of him—just from soft-soaping an imbecile. Ah, yes, we all get a big laugh but—I don't know.

JOE Did you see Dan Higgins today going into the boss's office? *(Laughs)* He nearly tore the head off himself pulling off his cap.

FRANK But again it's not so funny. No, serious, sham. This old job. Do you know what I think? Do you know what the job is like? Serious, sham.

JOE *(Laughing)* What?

FRANK The bosses are gods and we're only—

JOE *(Laughing)* Carney, the transport boss—

FRANK No, but the job. You know, it's like a big tank. The whole town is like a tank. At home is like a tank. A

141

huge tank with walls running up, straight up. And
we're at the bottom, splashing around all week in their
Friday night vomit, clawing at the sides all around.
And the bosses—and the big-shots—are up around the
top, looking in, looking down. You know the look?
Spitting. On top of us. And for fear we might climb
out someway—Do you know what they're
doing?—They smear grease around the walls.
(They laugh. Pause)

FRANK It's pushing on. We'd better do something quick.

JOE Will I try Mary Jane in the office again?

FRANK I don't think so.

JOE What?

FRANK ... Joe.

JOE Yeh?

FRANK It's no good standing out here. If one of us went in he
could borrow money for the other.

JOE Or if he had a date inside he could go off with her.

FRANK Look, sham, give us two bob and I'll get it for you
inside. This Anne Kelly—look, sham, if I don't get in
there I'm finished with her.

JOE So what?

FRANK I'll get the money for you inside.

JOE Who'll give it to you?

FRANK I'll get it.

JOE Do you think I'm going to be standing around out
here, frozen, on my tod?

FRANK I'll only be a second.

JOE No.

FRANK It's the only chance we have. Listen I have to go in
there: You heard Ford yourself. He has his eye on her.

JOE Alright so. I'll go in and borrow the money for you.
Give me one and six.

FRANK No, I've a better chance.

JOE I don't see that. *(He exits for a few moments to
investigate the possibility of getting in by means of a
back way. Noises and voices arguing are heard from
the box-office.* JOE *returns)*

JOE Hey, what's up?

FRANK It must be a ladies' choice: the women are charging
Ford!

JOE It's a bull and cow! *(A row)*

142

(They move to a better vantage position as dancehall door opens and BOUNCER *appears pushing* DRUNK *out of the hall)*

BOUNCER Out! Out!

DRUNK Come out, come out! Come on out, you and all the other bastards in there!

BOUNCER You watch your language around here now, Daly.

(He exits returning to dancehall)

DRUNK I want my bottle back! No one takes anything from me and gets away with it! I'll show yeh! *(To himself)* Mr. Tough. God, I'd kill him. Steal their lousy booze. *(He sees* FRANK *and* JOE*)* Did you see that? I'm telling you he's lucky I didn't—Did you see that?

FRANK I thought you'd tear him to pieces.

DRUNK I would too. *(Shouts)* And I will!

JOE What were you going on with the girl for anyway?

DRUNK Hah? What girl? There was no girls.

JOE At your age, too, McGoo.

DRUNK No, no, the booze was—

FRANK What were you doing to her?

DRUNK It was the booze.

JOE Come off it!

DRUNK No! I had a bottle of stout in my pocket and I was just having a quiet slug when up comes Tough. Mr. Big Tough comes up and says I stole it. I didn't. 'Twasn't me.

JOE Stole what? Your bottle?

DRUNK Naw! The band's booze. Someone stole it, all of it—the whole case of it! But 'twasn't me. They blamed me. They put me out and said it was me.

FRANK That band is failing alright.

DRUNK *(Puzzled)* Hah?

FRANK Right, we'll see you tomorrow.

(They ignore DRUNK. DRUNK *begins to move away. He tugs up his trousers and money rattles.* FRANK *and* JOE *look at each other quickly)*

FRANK Oh, Jim?

143

DRUNK Hah?

FRANK That chucker-out wants his ears pinned back alright.

DRUNK And I told him. I told him I never set eyes on it.

FRANK Sure ...

DRUNK I'm not one for drinking that much—a case of it!

JOE Sure.

FRANK Jim, old stock, you know the three of us should stick together. Pals.

DRUNK *(Smiling)* Pals.

FRANK Joe, that chucker-out can't get away with insulting people like that. I'll tell you, we'll go in and get stuck in him.

JOE Cripes, we will. Come on. Oh, how much is the dance?

DRUNK I don't know. I paid—

FRANK It's six bob.

JOE I've only four and six.

FRANK Wait a minute. *(Pretends to search his pockets)* Four lousy bob.

JOE We're only short three and six. Just three and six.

FRANK That's all that's stopping us from Chucker-head. A lousy three and six.

DRUNK Short of cash, lads?

JOE Three and six.

DRUNK Lousy three and six. *(Mournfully)*

FRANK A friend is what we need now.

DRUNK Well, I'm your pal, amn't I?

JOE Sure!

DRUNK Well, I'm your pal, amn't I?

FRANK The best, Jim. You won't see us stuck.

DRUNK I wo'not. How much do ye want?

JOE Three and six.

DRUNK Three and six. *(He takes some coins from his pocket and hands them to JOE)* Here.

FRANK *(To JOE)* How much is in it?

JOE Hang on.

DRUNK Here's more. Take it. *(Handing more coins)*

FRANK How much is in it?

JOE Hang on.

DRUNK Here's more. Take it. *(Handing more coins)*

FRANK How much is in it?

JOE *(To DRUNK)* Is that all you have? *(To FRANK)* Sixpence halfpenny.

FRANK What?

DRUNK *(Still searching)* That's all. All gone now, pals. Have
ye enough? Then don't worry. We'll get him. We'll
wait here till Mr. Tough comes out after the dance to
get him.

FRANK Go home.

DRUNK Hah?

JOE Get home!

DRUNK *(As he exits)* Home. Scram. Pals. Well, I'm not going
home. ...

JOE *(Turns to look after* DRUNK) Jays, like a stray dog! ...
What brought us out here? What clown told you it was
a four bob dance?

FRANK Stall—Wait—two coming out now.

*(A couple, man and a girl, anywhere between twenty
and thirty years of age, come out from dance and start
to move off. They have been given passes by the
BOUNCER inside, in case they want to go back again)*

GIRL I thought we were going to the shop?

MAN I just want to get something in the car for a minute.

JOE Hey, any pass-outs?

MAN No. Not a soul fainted. *(He grins proudly. The girl
laughs)*

FRANK Haw-haw! Funny man! Big joke! Pity about your
and JOE face! Makum joke for squaw! Waw! Buff! The wit!
Half wit!

FRANK Great old fun wasn't he?

JOE God bless him.

*(FRANK begins to whistle idly. JOE rattles the money
in his pocket and idly takes out a box of matches, looks
at them and quickly replaces them. He moves up and
down giving an occasional kick to the ground)*

JOE Oh, to have a lickle house, to own the hearth and stool
and all; in the dear little, sweet little emerald Isle, in
the county of Mayo.

(Pause)

Break down the bridge six warriors rushed,
and the storm was shot and they shat in the storm.

145

FRANK And Sarsfield strung up by the nockers behind them!
   (Pause) Look, let me go in and borrow the money for
   you.
JOE Now don't start that again.
FRANK It's the only sensible thing to do.
JOE Will I try the quare one in the office again.
FRANK I'll try her.

(FRANK *exits into hall.* JOE *takes out cigarettes and
lights one quickly. He takes several deep pulls
furiously in order to make the cigarette smaller. The
couple (that exited on p. 31) re-enter, the girl in a
minor huff adjusting her clothing. At the same time,*
BOUNCER *appears in dancehall doorway, ejecting*
FRANK)

BOUNCER Out! Out!
FRANK No need to break my effing arm!
BOUNCER What's that?
FRANK *(Walking away)* No, okay. Jim.
BOUNCER You watch your filthy tongue and keep away from
   here if you know what's good for you.

(Couple and BOUNCER *exit to hall)*

JOE What happened?
FRANK Boxy in the office got ratty and called the bouncer.
   Jim. *(Roughly)* Give us a fag.
JOE Its only a butt, I had, sham.

(FRANK *gropes in his pockets and produces a butt. A
second couple come out of the hall. The girl is*
KATHLEEN. JOE *runs over to them)*

JOE Are you going back again?
SECOND *(Curtly)* No.
 MAN
JOE Any chance of your pass-outs?—We'll buy them.
KATHLEEN That your friend over there?
JOE Yeh.
KATHLEEN Is he Frank?
JOE *(Doubtfully)* Yes.

KATHLEEN I was with a girl tonight who was waiting for him.

JOE Is that—ah—so? *(He does not know how to handle the situation)* Frank! Come here, a minute, sham. This here is a friend of Anne Kelly's.

FRANK Oh, hello. Oh yes.

THIRD MAN What's up?

KATHLEEN Just a minute. (*To* FRANK) She was very disappointed when you didn't come.

FRANK Yes? Is that so? You see, we were held up. I was disappointed too. Is she inside?

KATHLEEN She waited an awful long time for you.

FRANK Yeh? Well. She shouldn't have waited so long.

JOE In the cold too.

FRANK I hope she wasn't mad at me.

KATHLEEN I don't know. Maybe *she'll* understand. You're going in aren't you?
(Slight pause)

JOE Well, if you give us the—

FRANK *(Cutting in quickly)* We were playing a football match. Oh, only a sort of a street league, you know. But they take that kind of thing so seriously, you see? And the match started late too. I was vexed but what could I do—you know?—togged out there—I just couldn't—you know?

JOE And it was nearly eight o'clock when—

FRANK *(Cutting in again)* Yeh. And then to crown it all—you know how before a match you've no right place to put your clothes—and I gave my money to one of the crowd to hold for me and—well, the match finishing so late I just fired on my clothes and dashed out here and forgot all about the money. I knew Anne would be waiting and I didn't want to keep her that long so—

KATHLEEN Then you haven't any—

FRANK Oh, any other time, you know—you couldn't forget to collect a thing like that—but it was so late and it never entered my head and I didn't want to keep Anne so long.

KATHLEEN So you haven't any money?

JOE That's why we want pass-outs.

SECOND MAN Well, you can have ours *(He gives them to* JOE)

JOE Thanks.

147

FRANK Thanks very much. I hate to—
SECOND That's alright. So long. *(He's trying to get away)*
MAN
KATHLEEN Oh, you'd better hurry.
FRANK Yes?
KATHLEEN Competition.
FRANK Me? Who?
KATHLEEN Bye.
SECOND Bye.
MAN

(KATHLEEN *and* SECOND MAN *exit*)

JOE So long.
FRANK So I've competition.
JOE Wonder who it is.
FRANK Ford. Well, we'll soon take care of that. Come on.
Give me one of those passes. Act casual-like now, like
as if you were in before.

*(They go into the hall. The stage is empty. Slight
pause)*
JOE'S
VOICE We were in before!
BOUNCER'S
VOICE Get out! You weren't in before!
FRANK'S
VOICE We were!
BOUNCER'S
VOICE Outside the two of you! Quick now! I've had enough of
you all night.

(BOUNCER, FRANK *and* JOE *appear at the door*)

FRANK *(Holding up his pass-out)* And what are these things
meant to be for?
BOUNCER You watch your filthy tongue!
JOE What are pass-outs for?
BOUNCER Give them to me. (*Takes* JOE'S) They're not
transferable.
FRANK *(Pleads)* Aw, Jim. We'll slip you eight bob.

148

BOUNCER You don't know me, don't use my name, therefore.
         (Pushes them away) Now clear.

JOE   *(An undertone)* Now clear before Johnny MacBrown
         swallows his false tooth.

BOUNCER What? ... Did you pass a remark? ... (*To* JOE) Are
         you a good man? ... (*To* FRANK) Are you? ...
         Maybe you're two good men, hah? ... Townies ...
         Clear. *(His challenge not accepted, he exits to hall)*

JOE   ... Will we blow?

FRANK   These buffers will soon object to us walking on the
         roads. He wouldn't be so tough in town.

JOE   I thought earlier the pass-outs wouldn't work.

FRANK   Yeh-yeh-yeh-yeh-yeh, you knew it all. (FRANK *regrets
         the remark, he takes out his last two cigarettes; he
         would like to smoke one and give the other to* JOE: *the
         futility of it. He puts cigarettes back in his pocket*)
         God, these buffers! (MICKEY FORD *enters. They do not
         see him*) Like as if we were dirt.

JOE   ... Will we blow?

MICKEY   Hi, fellahs.

JOE
FRANK   Hi!

MICKEY   Gee, guys, hot in there. Girl inside talking about you,
         Frank. Anne Kelly.

FRANK   Yeh?

MICKEY   You had a—sort of date with her.

FRANK   Sort of?

MICKEY   Are you thinking of going with her?

FRANK   What business is that of yours?

MICKEY   I mean—She knows you're out here.

FRANK   How does she know? Did you—

MICKEY   I didn't tell her. I—

FRANK   Mouth! Listen Ford, no one else would have told her.

MICKEY   I didn't—I just came out to—

FRANK   Ah, shut up. You'd better keep well away from me
         from now on, because I'd love to hurt that handsome
         face.

MICKEY   God, I'd give you more than you'd want anytime.
         (FRANK *gives a short derisive laugh*) But I have my
         brothers inside tonight—

FRANK   Your brothers—Your big brothers—The crankshaft

149

family! You give me a pain in my royal differential arse!

MICKEY They're inside. And you remember you have a long way to go home.

FRANK And you remember they're only home on holidays, and in a week or two nice little Mickey-bags will go home some night with his Florida Beach tie all blood. *(He grabs at* MICKEY'S *tie and gives it a quick tug)*

MICKEY God, you won't try anything like that on with me. Think back what happened with you and your auld drunken auld layabout auld fella last year: Oh, didn't quiet, cunning Frank stand beside him kicking in the shop window, and stand beside him wanting to take on the town. The priest saved you from being arrested, but he mightn't bother a second time.

FRANK How many girls have you squared tonight, sham?

MICKEY I've Anne Kelly squared. Do you think she'd have anythin' to do with you now?

(FRANK *moves towards him*)

MICKEY You'd better to stay where you are.

FRANK Pity about his head—isn't it, Joe?

MICKEY I'll be out in a—

FRANK Tell us about the blow-out again, sham.

MICKEY I'll be out in a minute with her. If you know what's good for you, you'll—well, you know what's best to do. Remember, my brothers will be just inside the door. *(Exits quickly into hall)*
(Pause)

FRANK I'll get him. I'll get him.

JOE Not tonight, Frank.

FRANK I'll get him. I'll kick the day-lights out of him.

JOE Take it easy.

FRANK I'll make him sorry.

JOE The brothers. Four of them.

FRANK I'm not an eejit. They'll be back in England in a week or two.

JOE What's so special about this Kelly one anyway.

FRANK ... Ah, she can go to hell. I'm not sticking around here much longer. England. I'm bailing out of that lousy job. Lousy few bob a week. Twenty-two years old and

150

where does it get me? Yes, sir—I'm a pig, sir—if you
say so, sir! *(Suddenly)* Well, he's not getting away
with her that easy.

JOE   But—

FRANK   Don't worry—don't worry.

JOE   But he'll call the brothers—

FRANK   No. By now, he'll have told her how hard a man he
is—how he can break a fellah's back with a spit. I'll
chat her up when she comes out. *(He stands watching
the door)*

JOE   Let's blow, sham.

(DRUNK *enters*)

FRANK   (*To* DRUNK *intensely*) You! Keep away from me!

JOE   (*To* FRANK) You want to chat her up? Here she is.

(MICKEY *and* ANNE *come out*)

FRANK   Anne. Anne. (ANNE *stops*)

MICKEY   *(Nervously)* Leave her alone.

FRANK   I can explain. Honest to God, I was playing football.
Honest to—No. I hadn't the money. Am I leaving you
home?

MICKEY   What about all the lies you told her? Pick on someone
your own class now.

FRANK   Ford, there's nothing surer but I'll get you.

MICKEY   Now, Miss Kelly—there's Frank Mooney. What do
you think of him? (ANNE *is crying now*)

FRANK   Am I taking you home? Anne? *(Slight pause)*

ANNE   ... You're only a liar. I wouldn't have anything to do
with you. *(As she exits)* Are you coming, Mickey?

(MICKEY *exits after her*)

FRANK   *(Quietly)* ... Shout at them.

JOE   What?

FRANK   Shout, shout, shout at them!

JOE   *(Roars)* Spark-plug face! Handsome! Glue-bags!

FRANK   Torn mouth!

JOE   Carburettor head! Cop on yank!

FRANK   Torn mouth! — Torn mouth! — Torn mouth!

151

(Laughing harshly, drawing DRUNK *into their
company)* Wait, he's in top gear now!—She's not
tickin' over so good. Valve timing out. I'd say
condenser is faulty. Going round a corner, bootin' her
to the last, doin' seventy three and a half miles an hour
and do you know what happened him?—Do you know
what happened to him? A cock of hay fell on top of
him! *(They laugh harshly)* Oh, this—this damn place,
this damn hall, people, those lousy women! I could — I
could —

*(He rushes over to the poster and hits it hard with his
fist. He kicks it furiously)*

JOE Come on out of here to hell.

(They exit. The band plays on. DRUNK *gives a few
impotent kicks to the poster as the lights fade)*

11. OPENING OF NOVEL: "AT SWIM-TWO-BIRDS"

FLANN O'BRIEN

Humour is notoriously the most national and least exportable of literary genres, the most difficult to 'explain'. If, despite this, one risks an attempt to define Irish comic writing, it might be said to consist of passages of earthy matter-of-fact detail interspersed by flights of extreme imaginative fantasy. This is the quality that makes Joyce's *Ulysses* an immensely funny book and which in Beckett's *Waiting for Godot* keeps audiences constantly amused during an essentially serious enquiry into man's metaphysical situation. So it is with Flann O'Brien. The excerpt here should illustrate the point.

At Swim-Two-Birds, published in 1939, is also one of Ireland's few, though distinguished, contributions to experimental form in literature. The theories propounded by the seedy Dublin Oblomov who constitutes the book's hero foreshadow Robbe-Grillet and the French anti-novelists of a decade later.

Foreign readers may be curious to know a little more about the wayward genius who was the book's author and who is rapidly following in the steps of Joyce, Yeats and Beckett as a topic for Ph.D. theses. Brian O'Nolan, his real name, was born in 1911 of Catholic parents in the Northern border town of Strabane. After the family moved to Dublin in 1923, all the sons, as they came of age, attended the National University of Ireland, where one is a professor today. Various relatives in fact were distinguished scholars in Latin, Greek, Theology and Irish, and it was against this background that Brian honed his wits. He entered the Irish civil service on leaving university, and precariously remained there till his death in 1966. His drinking and his caustic pen found him frequent enemies among the establishment, but he also had unsuspected admirers in high places who shielded him, when they could, from retribution.

The appearance under pseudonym of *At Swim-Two-Birds* with its unique mixture of erudition and fantasy secured its standing among Dublin's student *avant-garde*, though the outbreak of the European war eclipsed its success elsewhere. Flann O'Brien's other masterpiece, *The Third Policeman*, was written soon afterwards; but for reasons no one has

153

convincingly explained this manuscript disappeared until it was published posthumously in 1967. Meanwhile, under yet another pseudonym, Myles na Gopaleen, O'Nolan's newspaper column in *The Irish Times* had made him a household word, so that friends meeting on the bus going to work would greet each other with: "Did you see what Myles said today?" It must be the first and so far the only occasion on which an Irish writer of genius, while making no concessions to the public philistinism, in fact the contrary, received that public's acclamation.

From
AT SWIM-TWO-BIRDS

Having placed in my mouth sufficient bread for three minutes' chewing, I withdrew my powers of sensual perception and retired into the privacy of my mind, my eyes and face assuming a vacant and preoccupied expression. I reflected on the subject of my spare-time literary activities. One beginning and one ending for a book was a thing I did not agree with. A good book may have three openings entirely dissimilar and inter-related only in the prescience of the author, or for that matter one hundred times as many endings.

Examples of three separate openings—the first: The Pooka MacPhellimey, a member of the devil class, sat in his hut in the middle of a firwood meditating on the nature of the numerals and segregating in his mind the odd ones from the even. He was seated at his diptych or ancient two-leaved hinged writing-table with inner sides waxed. His rough long-nailed fingers toyed with a snuff-box of perfect rotundity and through a gap in his teeth he whistled a civil cavatina. He was a courtly man and received honour by reason of the generous treatment he gave his wife, one of the Corrigans of Carlow.

The second opening: There was nothing unusual in the appearance of Mr John Furriskey but actually he had one distinction that is rarely encountered—he was born at the age of twenty-five and entered the world with a memory but without a personal experience to account for it. His teeth were well-formed but stained by tobacco, with two molars filled and a cavity threatened in the left canine. His knowledge of physics was moderate and extended to Boyle's Law and the Parallelogram of Forces.

The third opening: Finn MacCool was a legendary hero of old

155

Ireland. Though not mentally robust, he was a man of superb physique and development. Each of his thighs was as thick as a horse's belly, narrowing to a calf as thick as the belly of a foal. Three fifties of fosterlings could engage with handball against the wideness of his backside, which was large enough to halt the march of men through a mountain-pass.

I hurt a tooth in the corner of my jaw with a lump of the crust I was eating. This recalled me to the perception of my surroundings.

It is a great pity, observed my uncle, that you don't apply yourself more to your studies. The dear knows your father worked hard enough for the money he is laying out on your education. Tell me this, do you ever open a book at all?

I surveyed my uncle in a sullen manner. He speared a portion of cooked rasher against a crust on the prongs of his fork and poised the whole at the opening of his mouth in a token of continued interrogation.

Description of my uncle: Red-faced, bead-eyed, ball-bellied. Fleshy about the shoulders with long swinging arms giving ape-like effect to gait. Large moustache. Holder of Guinness clerkship the third class.

I do, I replied.

He put the point of his fork into the interior of his mouth and withdrew it again, chewing in a coarse manner.

Quality of rasher in use in household: Inferior, one and two the pound.

Well faith, he said, I never see you at it. I never see you at your studies at all.

I work in my bedroom, I answered.

Whether in or out, I always kept the door of my bedroom locked. This made my movements a matter of some secrecy and enabled me to spend an inclement day in bed without disturbing my uncle's assumption that I had gone to the College to attend to my studies. A contemplative life has always been suitable to my disposition. I was accustomed to stretch myself for many hours upon my bed, thinking and smoking there. I rarely undressed and my inexpensive suit was not the better for the use I gave it, but I found that a brisk application with a coarse brush before going out would redeem it somewhat without quite dispelling the curious bedroom smell which clung to my person and which was frequently the subject of humorous or other comment on the part of my friends and acquaintances.

Aren't you very fond of your bedroom now, my uncle continued. Why don't you study in the dining-room here where the ink is and where there is a good book-case for your books? Boys but you make a great secret about your studies.

My bedroom is quiet, convenient and I have my books there. I prefer to work in my bedroom, I answered.

My bedroom was small and indifferently lighted but it contained most of the things I deemed essential for existence—my bed, a chair which was rarely used, a table and a washstand. The washstand had a ledge upon which I had arranged a number of books. Each of them was generally recognized as indispensable to all who aspire to an appreciation of the nature of contemporary literature and my small collection contained works ranging from those of Mr Joyce to the widely read books of Mr A. Huxley, the eminent English writer. In my bedroom also were certain porcelain articles related more to utility than ornament. The mirror at which I shaved every second day was of the type supplied gratis by Messrs Watkins, Jameson and Pim and bore brief letterpress in reference to a proprietary brand of ale between the words of which I had acquired considerable skill in inserting the reflection of my countenance. The mantelpiece contained forty buckskin volumes comprising a Conspectus of the Arts and Natural Sciences. They were published in 1854 by a reputable Bath house for a guinea the volume. They bore their years bravely and retained in their interior the kindly seed of knowledge intact and without decay.

I know the studying you do in your bedroom, said my uncle. Damn the studying you do in your bedroom.

I denied this.

Nature of denial: Inarticulate, of gesture.

12. STORY: "A GREAT GOD'S ANGEL STANDING"

BENEDICT KIELY

Benedict Kiely (b. 1919) is another Northern humorous writer, erudite also, but in a more classic mould. The story given here from his 1973 collection *A Ball of Malt and Madame Butterfly* might find a parallel in Boccaccio or Chaucer, but its setting is unmistakably Irish and of its time. Classic too is the blending of wry, dry humour with compassion for the human condition.

159

Benedict Kiely

A GREAT GOD'S ANGEL STANDING

Pascal Stakelum, the notorious rural rake, and Father Paul, the ageing Catholic curate of Lislap, met the two soldiers from Devon by the bridge over the Camowen River and right beside the lunatic asylum. It was a day of splitting sunshine in the year of the Battle of Dunkirk. Pascal and the priest were going to visit the lunatic asylum, Father Paul to hear confessions, Pascal to bear him company and to sit at a sealed distance while the inmates cudgelled what wits they had and told their sins. The two soldiers, in battledress and with heavy packs on their backs, were on their way home from Dunkirk, not home to Devon exactly but to Sixmilecross, to the house of two sisters they had married in a hurry before they set off for France. It was, as you may have guessed, six miles from our garrison town of Lislap to the crossroads village where the two sisters lived, and it was a very warm day. So every one of the four, two in thick khaki, two in dull black, was glad to stop and stand at ease and look at the smooth gliding of the cool Camowen.

The bridge they rested on was of a brownish grey stone, three full sweeping arches and, to the sides, two tiny niggardly arches. In a blue sky a few white clouds idled before a light wind, and beyond a wood at an upstream bend of the river a two-horse mowing-machine ripped and rattled in meadow grass. The stone of the bridge was cut from the same quarry as the stone in the high long wall that circled the lunatic asylum and went for a good half-mile parallel with the right bank of the river.

—In France it was hot, said the first soldier.

—He means the weather was hot, said the second soldier.

The four men, priest and rake and soldiers two, laughed at that: not, Pascal says, much of a laugh, not sincere, no heartiness in it.

—Hot as hell, said the second soldier. Even the rivers was hot.

—Boiling, said the first soldier. That canal at Lille was as hot as a hot bath.

160

—Ruddy mix-up, said the second soldier. The Guards, they fired at the Fusiliers, and the Fusiliers, they fired at the Guards. Nobody knew who was what. Ruddy mix-up.

They took the cigarettes Pascal offered.

—Boiling hot and thirsty, said the second soldier. Never knew such thirst.

Father Paul said: You could have done with some Devon cider.

—Zider, said the first soldier. There were zomething.

—Zomerset you are, said the second soldier.

They all laughed again. This time it was a real laugh.

The Camowen water where it widened over gravel to go under the five stone arches was clear and cool as a mountain rockspring. Upstream, trout rings came as regularly as the ticks of a clock.

The two soldiers accepted two more cigarettes. They tucked them into the breast-pockets of their battledress. They hitched their packs, shook hands several times and knelt on the motorless roadway for Father Paul's blessing. They were not themselves Arcees, they said, but in camp in Aldershot in England they had been matey with an Arcee padre, and they knew the drill. Blessed after battle, they stood up, dusted their knees as carefully as if they'd never heard of mud or blood and, turning often to wave back, walked on towards the two sisters of Sixmilecross.

—Virginia, Father Paul said, was the best place I ever saw for cider.

Just to annoy him, Pascal said: Virginia, County Cavan, Ireland.

They were walking together on a narrow footwalk in the shadow of the asylum wall.

—Virginia, U.S.A., Paul said. The Old Dominion. Very well you know what Virginia I mean. They had great apple orchards there, and fine cider presses, around a little town called Fincastle under the shadow of the Blue Ridge Mountains. That was great country, and pleasant people and fine horses, when I was a young man on the American mission.

It was a period out of his lost youth that Paul frequently talked about.

In those days of his strange friendship with Pascal he was thin and long-faced and stoop-shouldered with the straining indignant stoop that is forced on tall people when the years challenge the power to hold the head so high. That day the sun had sucked a little moisture out of his pale cheeks. He had taken off his heavy black hat to give the light breeze a chance to ruffle and cool his thin grey hair, but the red line the hat rim had made was still to be seen and, above the red line, a sullen concentration of drops of sweat. He was though, as Pascal so often said, the remains of a mighty handsome man and with such dignity, too, and stern faith and such an eloquent way in the pulpit that it was a mystery to all of us what the bishop of the diocese had against him that he had never given him the honour, glory and profit of a parish of his own.

—In the mood those two boyos are in, Pascal said, it will take them no time at all walking to the sisters at Sixmilecross.

That was the way Pascal, in accordance with his animal nature, thought; and Sixmilecross was a village in which, as in every other village in our parts, Pascal had had some of the rural adventures that got him his dubious reputation, and that made us all marvel when we'd see a character like him walking in the company of a priest. In Burma, I once heard an old sweat say, adulterers kill a pig to atone for their crime, so it was only apt and proper, and even meet and just, that Pascal should be a pork butcher. When he went a-wooing in country places he'd never walk too far from his rattly old Morris Cowley without bringing with him a tyre lever or starting handle, for country girls were hell for having truculent brothers and if they didn't have brothers they had worse and far and away worse, male cousins, and neither brothers nor male cousins, least of all the male cousins, had any fancy for Pascal rooting and snorting about on the fringes of the family. That's Pascal, for you. But at the moment, Paul is speaking.

—A man hungers to get home, he said. The men from Devon won't count the time or the number of paces. Time, what's time? They've come a long walk from the dreadful gates of eternity. Once I told you, Pascal boy, you were such a rake and run-the-roads you'd have to live to be ninety, to expiate here on this earth and so dodge the devil.

Complacently Pascal said: The good die young.

—Ninety's a long time, Father Paul said. But what's time? Here in this part of my parish ...

They were walking in at the wide gateway. He waved his black wide-brimmed hat in a circle comprehending the whole place, as big almost as the garrison town itself, for all the crazy people of two counties, or those of them that had been detected and diagnosed, were housed there.

—This part of my parish, he said. As much happiness or unhappiness as in any other part of the parish. But one thing that doesn't matter here is time. As far as most of them know, time and eternity are the same thing.

162

They walked along a serpentine avenue, up sloping lawns to the main door. The stone in the walls of the high building was cut from the same quarry as the stone that bridged the river, as the stone in the encircling wall. The stone floor in the long cool corridor rang under their feet. They followed a porter along that corridor to a wide bright hospital ward. Unshaven men in grey shirts sat up in bed and looked at them with quick bright questioning eyes. The shining nervous curiosity of the ones who sat up disturbed Pascal. He preferred to look at the others who lay quietly in bed and stared steadily at points on the ceiling or on the opposite wall, stared steadily but seemed to see neither the ceiling nor the opposite wall, and sometimes mumbled to nobody words that had no meaning. A few men in grey suits moved aimlessly about the floor or sat to talk with some of the bright curious men in the beds. Beside the doorway a keeper in blue uniform dotted with brass buttons sat and smoked and read a newspaper, raised his head and nodded to the priest, then returned to his pipe and his newspaper.

Father Paul moved from bed to bed, his purple stole about his neck. The murmur of his voice, particularly when he was at the Latin, was distinctly audible. His raised hand sawed the air in absolution and blessing. Once in a while he said something in English in a louder voice and then the man he was with would laugh, and the priest would laugh, and the man in the next bed, if he was a bright-eyed man, would laugh, and another bright-eyed man several beds away would start laughing and be unable to stop, and a ripple of laughter would run around the room touching everybody except the staring mumbling men and the keeper who sat by the door.

Pascal sat beside an empty bed and read a paperbacked book about a doctor in Germany who was, or said he thought he was, two men, and had murdered his wife, who had been a showgirl, by bathing her beautiful body in nitric acid. That sinful crazy waste of good material swamped Pascal in an absorbing melancholy so that he didn't for a few moments even notice the thin hand gripping his thigh. There, kneeling at his feet, was a man in grey clothes, misled into thinking Pascal was a priest because Pascal wore, as did the gay young men of that place and period, a black suit with, though, extremely wide and unclerical trousers. Pascal studied, with recognition, the inmate's grey jacket, the scarce grey hair, the spotted dirty scalp. The kneeling man said: Bless me, father, for I have sinned.

163

—Get up to hell Jock Sharkey, Pascal said. I'm no priest. You're crazy.

He was, he says, crimson in the face with embarrassment. The keeper was peeking over his newspaper, laughing, saying Jock sure was crazy and that, in fact, was why he was where he was. The keeper also blew smoke-rings from thick laughing lips, an irritating fellow. He said: Fire away, Pascal. It'll keep him quiet. I hear him two or three times a week.

—It wouldn't be right, Pascal said.

He had theological scruples, the only kind he could afford.

Only once in my life, he was to say afterwards, did a man ever ask me to listen to him confessing his sins and, fair enough, the place should be a lunatic asylum and the man, poor Jock Sharkey, that was put away for chasing women, not that he ever overtook them or did anybody any harm. They walked quick, he walked quick. They walked slow, he walked slow. He was just simply fascinated, the poor gormless bastard, by the sound of their feet, the hobbled trot, the high heels, you know, clickety-click, thigh brushing thigh. Poor Jock.

—What he'll tell you, said the keeper, is neither right nor wrong. Who'd anyway be better judge than yourself, Pascal? Even Father Paul doesn't know one half of what you know. You, now, would know about things Paul never heard tell of.

The man on his knees said: I suppose you'll put me out of the confession box, father. I'm a terrible sinner. I wasn't at mass or meeting since the last mission.

—Why was that? said Pascal the priest.

—The place I'm working in, they won't let me go to mass.

—Then it's not your fault, said Pascal. No sin. Grievous matter, perfect knowledge, full consent.

He did, he said afterwards, remember from his schooldays that impressive fragment of the penny catechism of Christian doctrine: the stud-book, the form-book, the rules for the big race from here to eternity.

—But when I go to confession, father, I've a bad memory for my sins. Will you curse me, father, if I forget some of them?

—By no means, Jock. Just recite what you remember.

The keeper, more offensive as his enjoyment increased, said that Pascal wouldn't know how to curse, that he didn't know the language. The head of the kneeling man nodded backwards and forwards while he mumbled the rhythmical words of some prayer or prayers of his childhood. Now and again the names of saints came clearly out of the confused unintelligible mumble, like bubbles rising from a marshy bottom to the surface of a slow stream. Then he repeated carefully, like a child reciting, these words from an old rebel song: I cursed three times since last Easter Day. At mass-time I went to play.

Pascal was seldom given to visions except in one particular direction, yet he says that at that moment he did see, from his memory of school historical pageants, the rebel Irish boy, kneeling in all innocence or ignorance at the feet of the brutal red-coated captain whose red coat was, for the occasion, covered by the soutane of the murdered rebel priest.

The keeper said: You should sing that, Jock.

—I passed the churchyard one day in haste, Jock said, and forgot to pray for my mother's rest.

—You're sure of heaven, said the keeper, if that's the sum total of your sins. The Reverend Stakelum himself, or even Father Paul, won't get off so easy.

The penitent looked up at Pascal and Pascal looked down at stubbly chin, hollow jaws, sorrowful brown eyes. Poor Jock, Pascal thought, they put you away just for doing what I spend all my spare time, and more besides, at: to wit, chasing the girls. Only you never even seemed to want to catch up with them.

For poor Jock was never more than what we called a sort of a mystery man, terrifying the girls, or so they claimed, by his nightly wanderings along dark roads, his sudden sprints that ended as sharply and pointlessly as they began, his shouted meaningless words provoked perhaps by a whiff of perfume in his nostrils or by that provocative tap-tippity-tap of high hard heels on the metalled surface of the road. A child might awaken in the night and cry that there was a man's face at the window. A girl might run home breathless and say that Jock had followed her for half a mile, suiting his pace to hers, like a ghost or a madman. He couldn't be a ghost, although he was as thin and as harmless as any ghost. So we put him away for a madman.

He stared long and hard at Pascal. His thin right hand tightly grasped Pascal's knee.

—David Stakelum's son, he said. I'd know you anywhere on your father. Thank God to see you in the black clothes. Your father was a decent man and you'll give me the blessing of a decent man's son.

He bowed his head and joined his hands. Behind the newspaper the keeper was gurgling. Pascal said afterwards that his father wouldn't be too pleased to think that his hell's own special hell-raker of a son bore him such a resemblance that even a crazy man could see it. But if his blessing would help to make Jock content then Jock was welcome to it. So he cut the sign of the cross over the old crazy dirty head. He touched with the tips of the fingers of both hands the bald patch on the dome. He held out those fingers to be kissed. The most fervent young priest fresh from the holy oil couldn't have done a better job. Pascal had so often studied the simple style of Father Paul. The keeper was so impressed that he folded the newspaper and sat serious and quiet.

Father Paul walked slowly towards them, along the narrow passage between the two rows of beds. Walking with him came a fat red-faced grey-headed inmate. The fat inmate talked solemnly, gestured stiffly with his right hand. The priest listened, or pretended to listen, turning his head sideways, stretching his neck, emphasising the stoop in his shoulders. He said: Mr. Simon, you haven't met my young friend, Pascal.

The fat man smiled benevolently at Pascal but went on talking to the priest. As you know, sir, I am not of the Roman Catholic persuasion, yet I have always been intrigued by the theory and practice of auricular confession. The soul of man, being walled around and shut in as it is, demands some outlet for the thoughts and desires that accumulate therein.

He had, Pascal says, a fruity pansy voice.

—The child, he said, runs to its mother with its little tale of sorrow. Friend seeks out friend. In silence and secrecy souls are interchanged.

It was exactly, Pascal was to say, as if the sentences had been written on the air in the loops and lines of copper-plate. You could not only hear but see the man's talk: A Wesleyan I was born, sir, and so remain. But always have I envied you Roman Catholics the benefits of the confessional, the ease that open confession brings to the soul. What is the Latin phrase, sir?

Paul said: Ad quietam conscientiam.

—Ad quietam conscientiam, Simon repeated. There is peace in every single syllable. There is much wisdom in your creed, sir. Wesley knew that. You have observed the spiritual similarity between Wesley and Ignatius of Loyola.

The keeper said: Simon, Doctor Murdy's looking for you. Where in hell were you?

—He asks me where I have been, sir. Where in hell.

Father Paul said: He means no harm, Simon. Just his manner of speaking.

Simon was still smiling. From elbow to bent wrist and dangling hand, his right arm was up like a question mark. He said to Father Paul: Surveillance, sir, is a stupid thing. It can accomplish nothing, discover nothing. If I were to tell this fellow where I had been, how could he understand? On this earth I have been, and beyond this earth.

He shook hands with the priest but not with Pascal nor the keeper nor Jock Sharkey. He walked with dignity past the keeper and back down the ward.

—There goes a travelled man, Pascal said.

Father Paul was folding his purple stole. He said: There are times when religion can be a straitjacket.

—It's not Simon's time yet for the straitjacket, the keeper said. When the fit takes him he'll brain the nearest neighbour with the first handy weapon.

At the far end of the ward where Simon had paused for a moment, there was a sudden noise and a scuffling. The keeper said: Too much learning is the divil.

He thumped down the passage between the beds.

—Now for the ladies, Father Paul said. You'll be at home there, Pascal. They say all over the town that no man living has an easier way with the ladies.

Pascal was to report to myself and a few others that if Paul had wanted to preach him a sermon to make his blood run cold and to put him off the women for the rest of his life, he couldn't have gone about it in a better way.

Is it true that, as the poet said, you never knew a holy man but had a wicked man for his comrade and heart's darling? Was it part of Paul's plan to pick Pascal as his escort and so to make an honest boy out of him or, at least, to cut in on the time that he would otherwise spend rummaging and ruining the girls of town and country? The thing about Pascal was that, away from the companionship of Paul, he thought of nothing but women when, of course, he wasn't butchering pork, and perhaps he thought of women even then. Like many another who is that way afflicted he wasn't big, violent, handsome, red-faced or blustering. No, he went about his business in a quiet way. His hair was sparse, of a nondescript colour, flatly combed and showing specks of dandruff. He wore horn-rimmed spectacles. He was one of those white-faced

167

fellows who would, softly and secretly and saying nothing about it to their best friends, take advantage of their own grandmothers. The women were mad about him. They must have been. He kept himself in fettle and trim for his chosen vocation. When the two soldiers and Paul were, in the sunshine on the Camowen Bridge, talking of Devon cider, Pascal was thinking, he says, of sherry and raw eggs, and oysters, porter and paprika pepper.

On the day of Paul's funeral he said to me: A decent man and I liked him. But, my God, he had a deplorable set against the women or anybody that fancied the women.

—Except myself, he said. For some reason or other he put up with me.

—That day at the female ward, he said, at the geriatrics you call 'em, I cheated him, right under his nose, God forgive me. And may Paul himself forgive me, since he knows it all now.

Pascal stood at the threshold of this female ward while Father Paul, purple stole again around his neck, moved, listening and forgiving with God's forgiveness, from bed to bed. Pascal wasn't much of a theologian, yet looking at the females in that female ward he reckoned that it was God, not the females, who needed forgiveness. They were all old females, very old females, and as such didn't interest Pascal. He had nothing, though, against old age as long as it left him alone. His father's mother was an attractive, chubby, silver-haired female, sweet as an apple forgotten and left behind on a rack in a pantry, wrinkled, going dry, yet still sweet beyond description. But these sad old females, a whole wardful of them, were also mad and misshapen, some babbling like raucous birds, some silently slavering.

He couldn't make up his mind whether to enter the ward and sit down or to walk up and down the cool echoing corridor. He always felt a fool when walking up and down like a sentry, but then he also felt a fool when standing or sitting still. He was just a little afraid of those caricatures of women. This was the first time he had ever been afraid of women, and afraid to admit to himself that these creatures were made in exactly the same way as women he had known. He was afraid that if he went into the ward and sat down he would see them in even greater detail than he now did from the threshold. He was young. Outside the sun was shining, the Camowen sparkling under the sun, the meadow grass falling like green silk to make beds for country lovers. But here all flesh was grass and favour was deceitful and beauty was vain. It was bad enough looking at the men. To think what the mind could do to the body. But it was hell upon earth looking at the women. Jock Sharkey, like a million lovers and a thousand poets, had gone mad for beauty. This, in the ward before him, was what could happen to beauty.

He stepped, shuddering, back into the corridor and collided with a tall nurse. He apologised. He smelled freshly-ironed, starched linen and disinfectant, a provoking smell. A quick flurried glance showed him a strong handsome face, rather boyish, brick-red hair bursting out over the forehead where the nurse's veil had failed to restrain it. He apologised. He was still rattled by his vision in the ward. Contrary to his opportunist instinct he was even about to step out of the way. But the nurse didn't pass. She said: It is you, Pascal Stakelum, isn't it? Did they lock you up at last? A hundred thousand welcomes.

He had to do some rapid thinking before he remembered. There were so many faces in his memory and he was still confused, still a little frightened, by those faces in the ward. She didn't try to help. She stood, feet apart and solidly planted, and grinned at him, too boyish for a young woman but still fetching. She was, if anything, taller than he was. Her brother, then he remembered, had gone to school with us, a big fellow, as dark as she was red, very clever but capricious, making a mockery of things that he alone, perhaps, of all of us could understand and, in the end, throwing the whole thing up and running away and joining the Royal Air Force. So the first thing Pascal said, to show that he knew who she was, was to ask about the brother, and when would he be coming home. She said: He won't be coming home.

—Why for not?

She said he had been killed at Dunkirk.

Coming right after the prospect of the mad old women, that was a bit of a blow in the face, but at least, he told himself, clean death in battle was not madness, deformity, decay; and the moment gave Pascal the chance to sympathise, to get closer to her. He held her hands. He said he was sorry. He said he had always liked her brother. He had, too. They had, indeed, been quite friendly.

She said: It's war. He would always do things his own way.

She seemed proud of her brother, or just proud of having a brother dead at Dunkirk.

—This is no place to talk, Pascal said. And I'm with Father Paul. Meet me this evening at the Crevenagh Bridge.

That was the old humpy seventeenth-century bridge on the way to a leafy network of lovers' lanes and deep secret bushy ditches.

169

—Not this evening, she said. I'm on duty. But tomorrow.

—Eight o'clock on the dot, said Pascal.

That was his usual time during the summer months and the long warm evenings. And he was very punctual.

She walked away from him and towards Father Paul. He looked after her, no longer seeing the rest of the ward. She was a tall strong girl, stepping with decision and a great swing. Jock Sharkey would have followed her to the moon.

Father Paul, the shriving done, was again folding his stole. He joked with a group of old ladies. He told one of them that on his next visit he would bring her a skipping rope. He told another one he would bring her a powderpuff. He distributed handfuls of caramels to the whole crew. They cackled with merriment. They loved him. That was one bond between Pascal and himself. The women loved them both.

—But if he meant to preach to me that time, Pascal said to us, by bringing me to that chamber of horrors, I had the laugh on him.

In the sunshine on the lawn outside, the superintending doctor stood with his wife and his dogs, three Irish setters, one male, two female. The doctor and his wife stood, that is, and the setters ran round and round in erratic widening circles.

Those smart-stepping Devon men were by now approaching Sixmilecross, and the two sisters, and rest after battle and port after stormy seas.

The doctor was a handsome cheery fellow, even if he was bald. He wore bright yellow, hand-made shoes, Harris tweed trousers and a high-necked Aran sweater. The wife was small and dainty and crisp as a nut, and a new wife; and the two of them, not to speak of the three setters, were as happy as children. They talked—the doctor, the woman, Paul and Pascal—about the war, and about the two soldiers from Devon and their two women in Sixmilecross. Then Father Paul wished the doctor and his wife many happy days, and he and Pascal stepped off towards the town. At the gateway they met a group of thirty or forty uniformed inmates returning, under supervision, from a country walk. One of them was gnawing a raw turnip with which, ceasing to gnaw, he took aim at Pascal and let fly. Pascal fielded the missile expertly—in his schooldays he had been a sound midfield man—and restored it to the inmate who was still chewing and looking quite amazed at his own deed. All this, to the great amusement of the whole party, inmates and three keepers. But, oddly enough, Paul didn't join in the merriment. He stood, silent and abstracted, on the grass at the side of the driveway. He looked at the sky. His lips moved as though he were praying, or talking to himself.

Pascal gave away what cigarettes he had left to the hiking party and he and the priest walked on, Paul very silent, over the Camowen. When they were halfways to the town, Paul said: Some men can't live long without a woman.

Pascal said nothing. He remembered that there was a story that Paul had once beaten a loving couple out of the hedge with a blackthorn stick. He remembered that Paul came from a stern mountainy part of the country where there had been a priest in every generation in every family for three hundred years. He thought of the red nurse and the hedge ahead of her. So he said nothing.

—That new wife of his, Paul said, was American. Did you notice?

—She dressed American, Pascal said. But she had no accent.

—She comes from a part of the States and from a class in society where they don't much have an accent, Paul said. At least not what you in your ignorance would call an American accent.

Pascal said: The Old Dominion.

—You're learning fast, Paul said.

The town was before them.

—Three wives he had, Paul said. One dead. Irish. One divorced. English. And now a brand new one from Virginia. Some men can't go without.

Pascal made no comment. He contented himself with envying the bald doctor his international experience. He resolved to travel.

—Most men, said Paul, aren't happy unless they're tangled up with a woman. The impure touch. But the French are the worst. Their blood boiling with wine. From childhood. How could they keep pure?

Pascal hadn't the remotest idea. So he made no comment. He didn't know much about the French but he reckoned that just at that moment in history they had enough and to spare on their plates without also having to worry about purity.

—But pleasures are like poppies spread, Paul said.

He was a great man always to quote the more moralising portions of Robert Burns. Pascal heard him out: You seize the flower, its bloom is shed. Or like the snow falls in the river—a moment white, then melts forever. Or like the borealis race, that flit

171

ere you can point their place. Or like the rainbow's lovely form, evanishing amid the storm.

—Burns, said Father Paul, well knew what he was talking about. Those, Pascal, are the words of wisdom gained through sad and sordid experience.

Pascal agreed. He was remembering the nurse's dead brother who had been a genius at poetry. He could write parodies on anything that any poet had ever written.

When Pascal met the nurse at the Crevenagh Bridge on the following evening she was, of course, in mourning. But the black cloth went very well with that brilliant red hair. Or like the rainbow's lovely form. There was something about it, too, that was odd and exciting, like being out, he said, with a young nun. Yet, apart from the colour of her clothes, she was no nun. Although, come to think of it, who except God knows what nuns are really like?

Pascal, as we know, was also in black but he had no reason to be in mourning. It had rained, just enough to wet the pitch. Otherwise the evening went according to Operation Pascal. When he had first attacked with the knee for the warming-up process he then withdrew the knee and substituted the hand, lowering it through the band of her skirt, allowing it to linger for a playful moment at the bunker of the belly button. Thereafter he seemed to be hours, like fishermen hauling a net, pulling a silky slip out of the way before the rummaging hand, now living a life of its own, could negotiate the passage into her warm drawers. Pascal didn't know why he hadn't made the easier and more orthodox approach by laying the girl low to begin with and then raising skirt and slip, except it was that they were standing up at the time, leaning against a sycamore tree. The rain had passed but the ground was wet, and to begin his wooing by spreading his trenchcoat (Many's the fine rump, he boasted, that trenchcoat had kept dry, even when the snow was on the ground.) on the grass, seemed much too formal. Pascal Stakelum's days, or evenings or nights, were complex with such problems.

Later came the formal ceremonious spreading of the trenchcoat on a protective mattress of old newspapers, and the assuming by both parties, of the horizontal. By that time the big red girl was so lively that he swore she'd have shaken Gordon Richards, the King of them All, out of the saddle. She kept laughing and talking, too, so as to be audible, he reckoned, thirty yards away but fortunately he had chosen for the grand manoeuvre a secluded corner of the network of lanes and ditches. He had a veteran's knowledge of the terrain and he was nothing if not discreet.

He was not unmindful of the brother dead in faraway France. But then the brother had been such an odd fellow that even in Pascal's tusselling with his strong red sister he might have found matter for amusement and mockery. As Pascal bounced on top of her, gradually subduing her wildness to the rhythmic control of bridle and straddle and, in the end, to the britchen of his hands under her buttocks, he could hear her brother's voice beginning the schoolboy mockery of Shelley's soaring skylark: Hell to thee, blithe spirit. Pascal and the splendid panting red girl moved together to the poet's metre.

That was one brother Pascal did not have to guard against with starting handle or tyre lever. Working like a galley slave under the dripping sycamore he was in no fear of ambush.

Paul got his parish in the end, the reward of a well-spent life, he said wryly. He died suddenly in it before he was there for six months. That parish was sixty miles away from Lislap, in sleepy grass-meadow country where the slow River Bann drifts northwards out of the great lake. Pascal missed Paul's constant companionship more than he or anybody else would have believed possible and began, particularly after Paul's sudden death, to drink more than he had ever done before, and went less with the girls, which puzzled him as much as it did us. It worried him, too: for in the house of parliament or public house that we specially favoured, he asked me one day was he growing old before his time because he was growing fonder of drink and could now pass a strange woman on the street without wondering who and what she was.

—You're better off, Pascal, I said. What were you ever doing anyway but breaking them in for other men? You never stayed long enough with any one woman to be able in the long run to tell her apart from any other woman.

He was more hurt than I had imagined he would be. But he sadly agreed with me, and said that some day he hoped to find one real true woman with whom he could settle down.

—Like with poor Paul that's gone, he said. Some one woman that a man could remember to the last moment of his life.

—No, I'm not crazy, he said. Two days before his death I was with Paul in his parish, as you know. We went walking this evening after rain, by the banks of a small river in that heavy-grass country.

173

That was the last walk we had together. The boreen we were on went parallel with the river bank. We met an old man, an old bewhiskered codger, hobbling on a stick. So Paul introduced us and said to Methusaleh: What now do you think of my young friend from the big garrison town of Lislap?

—The old fellow, said Pascal, looked me up and looked me down. Real cunning country eyes. Daresay he could see through me as if I was a sheet of thin cellophane. But he lied. He said: Your reverence, he looks to me like a fine clean young man.

—That was an accurate description of me, Pascal Stakelum, known far and wide.

Pascal brooded. He said: A fine clean young man.

—Then that evening, he said, we sat for ages after dinner, before we knelt down to say the holy rosary with those two dry sticks of female cousins that did the housekeeping for him. One quick look at either of them would put you off women for time and eternity. There's an unnerving silence in the houses that priests live in: the little altar on the landing, you know, where they keep the sacrament for sick calls at night. Imagine, if you can, the likes of me on my bended knees before it, wondering would I ever remember the words when it came my turn to lead the prayers. But I staggered it. Closed my eyes, you might say, and took a run and jump at it, and landed on the other side word perfect. It would have been embarrassing for Paul if I hadn't been able to remember the words of the Paterandave in the presence of those two stern cousins. One evening one of them sat down opposite me in a low armchair and crossed her legs, poor thing, and before I could look elsewhere I had a view of a pair of long bloomers, passion-killers, that were a holy fright. You would't see the equal of them in the chamber of horrors. Six feet long and coloured grey and elastic below the knee. But when the two cousins were off to bed, and good luck to them, we sat and talked until all hours, and out came the bottle of Jameson, and Paul's tongue loosened. It could be that he said more than he meant to say: oh, mostly about Virginia and the Blue Ridge Mountains and the lovely people who always asked the departing stranger to come back again. Cider presses near Fincastle. Apple orchards. Dogwood trees in blossom. He went on like that for a long time. Then he got up, rooted among his books, came back with this one book covered in a sort of soft brown velvet with gold lettering and designs on the cover and, inside, coloured pictures and the fanciest printing you ever saw, in red and in black. He said to me: Here's a book, Pascal, you might keep as a memory of me when I'm gone.

—So I laughed at him, making light of his gloomy face, trying to jolly him up, you know. I said: Where, now, would you be thinking of going?

—Where all men go sooner or later, he said.

—That was the end of my laughing. That's no way for a man to talk, even if he has a premonition.

—Keep the book as a token, Paul said to me. You were never much for the poetry, I know. But your wife when you find her might be, or, perhaps, some of your children. You've a long road ahead of you yet, Pascal, all the way to ninety, and poetry can lighten the burden. That book was given to me long ago by the dearest friend I ever had. Until I met yourself, he said. Long ago in a distant country and the wench is dead.

—Those were the last words I ever heard Paul speak, excepting the Latin of the mass next morning, for my bus passed the church gate before the mass was rightly over, and I had to run for it. But bloody odd words they were to come from Paul.

—Common enough words, I said. Anybody could have said them.

—But you didn't see the book, Pascal said. I'll show it to you.

He did, too, a week later. It was an exquisite little edition, lost on Pascal, I thought with some jealousy, both as to the perfection of the bookmaker's art and as to the text, which was William Morris telling us, there in a public house in Lislap, how Queen Guenevere had defended herself against the lies of Sir Gauwaine, and a charge of unchastity. Fondling the book, I was not above thinking how much more suitable than Pascal I would have been as a companion for old Paul. So that I felt more than a little ashamed when Pascal displayed to me with what care he had read the poem, underlining here and there in red ink to match the rubric of the capitals and the running titles on the tops of the pages. It was, almost certainly, the only poem to which he had ever paid any particular attention, with the possible exception of that bouncing parody on Shelley's skylark.

—It's like a miniature mass book, he said. Red and black. Only it was by no means intended for using at the mass. See here.

He read and pointed with his finger as he read: She threw her wet hair backward from her brow, her hand close to her mouth touching her cheek.

—Coming from the swimming-pool, Pascal said, when the dogwoods were in blossom. You never knew that Paul was a champion swimmer in his youth. Swimming's like tennis. Brings out the woman in a woman. Arms wide, flung-out, breasts up. Oh, there

175

were a lot of aspects to Paul. And listen to this: Yet felt her cheek burned so, she must a little touch it. Like one lame she walked away from Gauwaine.

—Time and again, Pascal said, he had heard it said that lame women had the name for being hot. Once he had seen on the quays of Dublin a one-legged prostitute. The thought had ever afterwards filled him with curiosity, although at the time he wouldn't have risked touching her for all the diamonds in Kimberley.

—And her great eyes began again to fill, he read, though still she stood right up.

That red nurse, he remembered, had had great blue eyes, looking up at him like headlamps seen through mist.

—But the queen in this poem, he said, was a queen and no mistake. And in the summer it says that she grew white with flame, white like the dogwood blossoms and all for this Launcelot fellow, lucky Launcelot, and such a pansy name. One day, she says, she was half-mad with beauty and went without her ladies all alone in a quiet garden walled round every way, just like the looney bin where I met that nurse. And both their mouths, it says, went wandering in one way and, aching sorely, met among the leaves. Warm, boy, warm. Then there's odd stuff here about a great God's angel standing at the foot of the bed, his wings dyed with colours not known on earth, and asking the guy or girl in the bed, the angel has two cloths, you see, one blue, one red, asking them, or him or her, to guess which cloth is heaven and which is hell. The blue one turns out to be hell. That puzzles me.

It puzzled both of us.

—But you must admit, said Pascal, that it was a rare book for a young one to be giving a young priest, and writing on it, look here, for Paul with a heart's love, by the Peaks of Otter in Virginia, on a day of sunshine never to be forgotten, from Elsie Cameron. Usually the women give breviaries to the priests, or chalices, or amices, or albs, or black pullovers. She must have been a rare one, Elsie Cameron. Would you say now that she might have had a slight limp? It's a Scottish name. Paul was forever talking about what he called the Scots Irish in Virginia and the fine people they were. All I know is that Scottish women are reputed to be very hot. They're all Protestants and don't have to go to confession.

Pascal had known a man who worked in Edinburgh who said that all you had to do to set a Scotswoman off was to show her the Forth Bridge, the wide open legs of it. That man had said that the Forth Bridge had never failed him.

When I said to Pascal that all this about Paul could have been as innocent as a rose, he said he was well aware of that: he wasn't claiming that Paul had done the dirty on the girl and left her to mourn out her life by the banks of the James River. But that it may all have been innocent for Paul and Elsie only made it the more mournful for Pascal. Fond memories and memories, and all about something that never happened.

—Any day henceforth, Pascal said, I'll go on a journey just to see for myself those Blue Ridge Mountains. Were they ever as blue as Paul thought they were? Cider's the same lousy drink the world over. What better could the orchards or women have been in Virginia than in Armagh? You see he was an imaginative man was old Paul, a touch of the poet, and soft as putty and sentimental away behind that granite mountainy face. Things hurt him, too. He told me once that one day walking he met that mad Maguire one from Cranny, the one with the seven children and no husband, and tried to talk reason to her, and she used language to him the like of which he had never heard, and he turned away with tears in his eyes. He said he saw all women degraded and the Mother of God sorrowful in Nancy Maguire who was as bad as she was mad. An odd thought. He should have taken the stick to her the way I once heard he did to a loving couple he found under the hedge.

But pleasures are like poppies spread, as Paul would say, walking the roads with Pascal ad quietam conscientiam, looking at mad Nancy and listening to her oaths, seeing Elsie Cameron under the apple trees under the Blue Mountains in faraway Virginia. Once I wrote a story about him and it was printed in a small little-known and now defunct magazine. That story was all about the nobility of him and the way he used to chant the words of Burns; and then about how he died.

He came home to his parochial house that morning after reading the mass and sat down, one of the cousins said, at the breakfast table, and sat there for a long time silent, looking straight ahead. That wasn't like him. She asked him was he well. He didn't answer. She left the room to consult her sister who was fussing about in the kitchen. When she came back he had rested his head down on the table and was dead.

Looking straight ahead to Fincastle, Virginia, and seeing a woman white with flame when the dogwood blossomed, seeing the tall angel whose wings were the rainbow and who held heaven, a red cloth, in one hand, and hell, a blue cloth, in the other.

Benedict Kiely

There was no place in that story of mine for Pascal Stakelum, the rural rake.

13. ONE-ACT PLAY: "THE PADDY PEDLAR"

M. J. MOLLOY

Before leaving the topic of Irish humour, it seems fitting to include here M. J. Molloy's one-act folk drama, *The Paddy Pedlar*, based on macabre happenings in the past century a few miles from the playwright's home. Joe Molloy, as he is generally known, was born in 1917 outside Milltown in County Galway. His mother was a schoolteacher, his father a commercial traveller, ranging the countryside round with horse and side-car, collecting orders for distilled spirits and small groceries. In a biographical note, Molloy writes: "like Shakespeare, Shaw and Ibsen, he saw his family fall from prosperity to near poverty when his father died, leaving a family of eight to be reared on his widow's salary". Despite that, Joe was educated at the local college in Tuam, then spent two years training to enter the Catholic missions in the Far East. A tubercular knee led to abandoning that career, and he spent another two years in a sanatorium. With only brief forays to Dublin, and more rarely still further afield, he has lived at Milltown ever since.

History had fascinated him from an early age and college training opened up the worlds of Greek, Latin, philosophy and theology, interests to prove lasting. In his early twenties an evening at the Abbey Theatre captivated him for his life work and he began writing plays. The first was produced by fellow-patients at the sanatorium one Christmas.

The basis of Molloy's dialogue is similar to Synge's. Whether a play, as the example here, is set in the Ireland of long ago, or, as *The Wood of the Whispering* (1953), handles a contemporary social problem, Molloy uses the heightened ordinary speech of the people round him. A Sunday will find him cycling the roads of County Galway, notebook in pocket, to spend patient hours talking and listening at a cottage fireside. An evening may find him listening in the local pub to the small farmers' conversation about him. Picturesque local incident too goes into the plays. Thus a local policeman, whose zeal prompted him to prosecute his wife for riding a bicycle without a light, soon found himself on stage.

Molloy's first real success was *The King of Friday's Men*, which ran at

179

the Abbey in 1948 for several weeks, and achieved short runs subsequently in London and New York.

The Paddy Pedlar, written in 1949, was first produced by the Ballina players, directed by the playwright's brother, Gerard, in 1952. It won the All Ireland Amateur Drama Final in Athlone that year and was produced at the Abbey the following year.

THE PADDY PEDLAR

CHARACTERS

OOSHLA, A small farmer.

THADY, A farmer's son.

HONOR, Thady's sweetheart.

SIBBY, A farmer's wife.

MATTHIAS, Another farmer.

THE PADDY PEDLAR.

PRODUCTION NOTE.

Don't let any part of the "contents" of the pedlar's sack be seen by the audience; the "contents" are best left entirely to their imagination. The sack itself should never be let stand on its end, or held in any way likely to outline its "contents."

The play is most successful when produced at a good fast pace, and should not take more than 45 to 50 minutes.

The scene is the kitchen of a small straw-thatched cottage on the outskirts of a peasant village, in an out-of-the-way hilly part of the Galway-Mayo border country. The time is the autumn of the year 1840 during Ireland's Famine decade.

The furniture is rudimentary. There are no chairs, only a few rough home-made wooden stools. There is no table, and the dresser is small and empty save for one wooden mug with a wooden porridge spoon laid across it, one large knife, and a few eggshells arranged in order. On the right hand wall hangs a smoke-blackened cross consisting merely of two sticks nailed together. The dresser

181

*stands against the back wall, on the right from the actor's point of
view. On the left end of the back wall is the door opening on to the
road. In this wall also is the usual small window. Some sheaves of
straw stand in a corner. The fireplace is in the right hand wall, and
doors in the right hand and left hand walls lead to the two
bedrooms.*

*Ooshla Clancy lies fully dressed on his back on the floor, with
one leg across one of the stools, from which he had fallen in
drunken slumber. A small whiskey jar stands at his elbow on
another stool.*

*After the curtain goes up there is stillness for a few moments,
then a horseman can be heard riding by and driving a herd of
cattle, cracking his whip, and shouting at both cattle and dog as he
does so. "S-go on there! S-go on there!" [Loudly.] "Turn them out,
dog! Get before them! Easy there." And so, with much barking
from the dog, they move on out of earshot.*

*But the noise has awakened Ooshla, and he shifts uneasily, and
finally sits up. He clutches at his head and groans.*

OOSHLA: Oh, murther! My head is ruined for life and for ever! My
curse on the poteen, and the curse of the Seven Ganders that
plucked the grass off Solomon's grave! [*He turns over, sees the
jar at his elbow, growls in hatred.*] There you are still, and may
the Divil fly away with you! [*He hesitates a few moments,
weakening at every moment; then with a cry.*] 'Tis kill or cure,
and better be dead than the state I'm in. [*He grasps the jar in
both hands and takes a mighty swig. He rises, and sets out for
the door, a little shakily at first, but is soon himself again. He is
a well built man of fifty with the alert eye and quick speech of
the man who has contrived to live for many years on his wits and
by roguery. But there is nothing low, or mean looking, about
him. On the contrary there is a curious air of the gentleman; and
it appears in his seriousness, in his impressive gestures and walk
and carriage, in his clear cut speech, and in the way he waxes his
moustache ends. His clothes he contrives to wear with an air,
although they are old cast-offs. Yet all this seems to proceed not
from affectation, but from some kind of inner conviction. He
unbolts and opens the door, and looks upon the sunset for a few
moments. Suddenly he starts, closes the door hastily, puts the
poteen jar on the dresser and has just time to stretch on the
hearth simulating sleep when Thady and Honor come in. Honor
is about twenty, tall, slow moving and quiet, and good-looking,*

*too, in an unsophisticated country way. She is serious and silent,
and her look is abstracted. She seems a kind, sincere type of girl.*
[*Thady is a big, easy-going, good-humoured fellow in the late
twenties. His voice is very soft and low for so big a man. Before
speaking to, or replying to, anyone, he looks upon him a moment
or two, and then addresses him directly and confidentially as if
there was no one else in the room. His shrewd and tolerant eyes
look around upon all the world good-humouredly. He wears a hat
and he carries a stout blackthorn stick.*]

HONOR: He's sleeping yet. In the daytime he do sleep mostly, on
account the dark night is his safest time for stealing.

THADY: And is this all the bed he has?

HONOR: Not it. He has a fine feather bed back in the room. He
must be as drunk as a stick, or he'd not fall-off asleep here. [*She
sets to work to light the fire. Thady espies the jar of poteen on
the dresser, and duly sniffs at, and tastes it.*]

THADY: Prime poteen he has. D'ye think did he steal it the same as
he steals all his wants of spuds and oatmeal.

HONOR: Ooshla steals only spuds and oatmeal, enough to keep the
breath in him. A well-wisher gave him the poteen likely.

THADY: [*Looking into the bedroom on the right*]: 'Tis a fine lump of
a house, and as clean as a leaf. We wouldn't call the Queen our
Aunt if we were married in here.

HONOR: He's sure and certain to let us live here. He'd never have
squandered my fortune only his wife was after dying, and he had
no family, and he honestly meant to leave me his house and land
that'd be worth more than my twenty guineas fortune.

THADY: [*Crossing to look into the other room*]: Your father
behaved as silly as a duck to go giving Ooshla your fortune.
Didn't he know well that money is tempting?

HONOR: Sure my father was failing fast with the fever himself, so
he had to trust it to someone until I grew up. He knew my
mother was lighthearted, and sure to spend it. [*Pulling a loose
stone out of the wall.*] In here Ooshla had the guineas sleeping
before the Divil coaxed him to start spending them at last.

THADY: Maybe he hasn't it all spent yet. If I left my thumb on his
throat a while, maybe he'd own up to a few guineas saved. [*He
kneels beside Ooshla, and begins to push back his sleeves.*]

HONOR: He hasn't a brass farthing left. Once he commenced
spending he was a year taking his ease and pleasuring, and then
he had to go stealing for a living, for he had the habit of work
lost.

THADY: To go robbing a young orphan's fortune was a dirty turn. Rouse up, Ooshla Clancy, till we see will you act manful, and make the loss good. [*He pokes him in the ribs good-humouredly.*]

OOSHLA: Did I hear a stir? [*Sees Honor.*] Honor, is that yourself? [*Sees Thady.*] And who is the young man? [*He is affable; but serious and gentlemanly as usual.*]

HONOR [*Between whom and Ooshla there seems to be a strong bond of affection*]: Thady Durkin my bachelor that I was telling you about. Let ye be talking, and I'll ready your breakfast first, and join in the talk further on.

[*She is busy for some time now. She finds a dozen or so of warm roasted potatoes in the ashes, and places them upon a stool. She puts beside it a mug of water taken from a wooden bucket near the door. She finds a large piece of oaten cake in the dresser, and slices it up with the big knife displayed on the dresser. This also she leaves beside the potatoes. From time to time she pauses and watches the pair, listening in her silent way.*]

OOSHLA [*Quickly and anxiously*]: Tell me did you win your fight against your young brother?

THADY [*Cheerfully*]: Not me; I'm no match for him at either the shillelagh, or the thumps. There was more flour in the spuds the year he was born.

OOSHLA [*Very disappointed*]: Well that's dull news! So your father'll leave him the farm?

THADY: He will. Evermore in our family the farm is left to the best fighter. So herself and myself must go foreign in search of a living.

OOSHLA: But did you not tell him, Honor, that ye can marry in here, and have my land.

HONOR: I told him all.

THADY: We're very thankful to you, Ooshla, but the way it is our people bore an honest name evermore, and how then could we go living with a rogue?

OOSHLA [*Rising in dignified reproach*]: Is it me to be a rogue? Thady Durkin, blow that from your mind. [*He crosses to dresser, and takes up the poteen jar.*] My course of life was that I passed a year one time spending her money, and lost the habit of work, so I had to have the other tenant farmers do the work for me the same as they do for the gentlemen, their landlords. But I couldn't take their crops openly the same as the landlords do. All I could do was take enough to keep me living of spuds and oatmeal in the midnight, when the world is in bed. [*He comes from the dresser* with the jar, and two eggshells. He fills one eggshell, and gives it to Thady. Honor takes the turf creel, and goes out the front door.]

THADY: But, Ooshla, 'tis God's law that all should work, but the gentlemen.

OOSHLA [*Quickly and solemnly*]: That's it, work for all but the gentlemen, so no work for Ooshla, because God appointed Ooshla to be a gentleman too. [*He sits down, and pours out an eggshellful for himself.*]

THADY [*Chuckling*]: How could God appoint you for a gentleman when he gave you no riches?

OOSHLA: He overlooked the riches some way or other; still He appointed Ooshla to be a gentleman.

THADY: He did! Give me the ins and outs of that, Ooshla.

OOSHLA: When men that aren't gentlemen get riches, they go ahead with the work, more or less of it; they wouldn't be content unless they were doing something. But from the first minute I had money to spend, I took to idleness as ready and easy as a woman takes to scolding. I didn't care if I never left hand, foot, or toe on a piece of work again.

THADY: At that gait of going every idler in the country was appointed to be a gentleman; every idler and lazy old scratch that does no work only lying across the hearth like a pig that'd be full up. [*Honor enters with a creel of turf.*]

OOSHLA [*Rising indignantly*]: Thady Durkin, is every drone in the country the same as me? Can they set their words out on their edges one after another the same as me? [*Taking up an impressive stance.*] Can they stand like gentlemen with their toes out and as straight as whipping posts the same as me? Can they step out like gentlemen the same as me? Steady your sight now. [*He walks up and down the kitchen a couple of times in imposing style.*]

THADY [*Admiringly*]: No lie, you can show your boot soles as good as any gentleman.

OOSHLA: Wait a minute. You didn't see the half of me yet. [*He goes into the bedroom peeling off his jacket as he goes.*]

THADY: The divil a such a man ever I clapped an eye on! Honor, 'tis time you went outside to see is the sky inclined to fall. In a minute he'll be back with nothing covering him only his spine.

HONOR [*Smiling, for she knows Ooshla of old*]: When you see him next, he'll surprise you.

[*Ooshla comes out dressed as before except for the important*

185

additions of a top-hat and dress coat, both more or less damaged cast-offs. He swings an ashplant peeled so as to resemble a cane. He crosses the stage, comes back, and confronts Thady triumphantly.]

OOSHLA: Is it any wonder all call me Ooshla, meaning "the Gentleman"! Haven't I the cut of a gentleman every way you take me?

THADY: I give in you have. But still you're not entitled to go taking your needs from the poor people, and give them no return. The landlord gentlemen take a share of their crops, but they give them the use of their land.

OOSHLA [*Vigorously*]: But amn't I giving my cleverness free to the poor of this country? Here they are lowing with the hunger, and rackrented and robbed and threatened by rogue landlords, and rogue Bailiffs and rogue Attorneys. Whenever a poor man can see no way out, he'll come to me, and say: "Ooshla, I'm an honest man, and no match for these rogues; but you're the cleverest rogue since the Gobawn, and maybe you could save me." So Ooshla makes a little thought, and in a minute has a trick made that'll bring that man safe. Isn't that so, Honor?

HONOR: No lie at all: the poor people are swarming like bees to Ooshla for help. Ooshla has as many tricks as the cat, and one more than him.

THADY: Still and all, Ooshla, if we went living with you, the rogue's brand'd be on all ever we'd have, or spend, or buy. The backbiting lot'd say all, and our daughters' fortunes as well, were saved up out of your rogueries.

HONOR: That's the hobble we're in, Ooshla, so we must go foreign, unless you'll give up the roguery, and earn your living with the spade any more.

OOSHLA: But the digging'd dull my brain again, and I'd not be clever enough to help the poor against the rogue Bailiffs and the rogue landlords. 'Twould be the greatest sin in the world for me to go digging again.

HONOR [*Sympathetically*]: Never mind so, Ooshla, we'll go foreign to America; and in no time we'll be at the top of Fortune's wheel in it. [*She rises to go.*]

OOSHLA [*Genuinely concerned*]: But I hear tell there's a bad time out there lately, with a power of banks failing, the foreign men begging for want of work, and the foreign girls having to earn their daily bread by night.

THADY: Still they reckon the American country is so wide and the people so few, that the dog never barks at a stranger in it. So there'll be land in plenty smiling at us to take it. [*He goes to the door.*]

HONOR: We'll be all right, Ooshla. Thady is coming up now to meet my mother and my brother. [*She goes to the door.*]

OOSHLA: I'll be up to ye the minute I have my supper down; and maybe I'll save ye yet from going foreign.

HONOR: Let you not be troubling your mind about that at all, Ooshla. [*She goes. Thady turns in the doorway, and addresses Ooshla cheerfully.*]

THADY: Ooshla, you have yourself believing you're entitled to be a rogue; but you're as soft as a penny book to believe the like of that. You're not entitled to make a living by roguery; 'tis oul' Nick himself is making a fool of you. But we're greatly obliged to you, whatever. [*He goes. Ooshla looks downcast and doubtful for a moment or two; then as if to restore his confidence he rises, and does another superbly gentlemanlike walk around the kitchen. He takes off the tall hat, brushes a speck of dust from it, and goes into the room. He is back in a moment wearing his old jacket and minus the tall hat. He settles down to his breakfast. Sibby comes in, and makes her way up to him. She is haggard and listless with hunger and worry.*]

SIBBY: Sir, aren't you Ooshla Clancy, the rogue of Killeenreevagh?

OOSHLA [*With dignity*]: I'm Ooshla Clancy, the friend of the poor!

SIBBY [*Sitting down and looking into the fire listlessly*]: Last year the spuds failed on us greatly. Seven children we have, and you wouldn't know which of them is the biggest or the smallest with the hunger. Five of them maybe'll be able to stop in our house, but the other two'll be gone to their graves before the new spuds are grown.

OOSHLA: Who is your landlord?

SIBBY: Captain Blake of Lowberry, sir.

OOSHLA: The Captain is a thorough-bred gentleman, and from the real old stock; still he'll give ye no help.

SIBBY [*Unemotionally*]: He won't, sir. He has two dogs as big as asses for tearing down poor people that's come annoying him for help.

OOSHLA: To be sure he has. If a gentleman gave food to one poor person, he'd be swarmed out with people asking. A poor person'll get no help from them unless he'll trick them some way.

SIBBY: All tell me so, and all tell me you're the best hand at tricks on account you're a rogue.

OOSHLA [*Impressively in his best professional style*]: Sit over there out of my view, while I'm reckoning up a remedy for your hobble.

SIBBY: God spare you the health, sir. God spare you the health. [*She takes up the stool, crosses to the back wall, and sits there watching Ooshla anxiously, blessing herself and praying hard.*]

OOSHLA [*After eating away for a few moments*]: Likely the Captain steps out viewing his estate middling often?

SIBBY: Every morning after his breakfast he walks out, but he'll give no hearing to any poor person that'll come looking for help.

OOSHLA: If you ask him for help, your case is lost. Instead, when he's coming the way, let you pass him out, and you driving the ass and baskets with a child in each basket. Let you be looking very wild, and be crying like the Banshee; then he'll halt you and ask you where you're off to. Tell him you're bringing the children to the lake to drown them; that you couldn't be looking at them starving. For that he'll blacken your body with his walking stick; but you'll see he'll put you under keen commands to send the children down to his kitchen door every day till the new spuds are grown.

SIBBY [*Jumping to her feet, and wild with relief and excitement*]: Ooshla Clancy, you have my lot saved! And, if you're a rogue itself, you're the best friend the poor ever had!

OOSHLA [*Confidentially*]: Maybe now you could tell me of some well-doing farmer in yere country that has more than his needs of spuds and oatmeal, and that wouldn't suffer if Ooshla fetched away a few hatfuls in the midnight.

SIBBY: Ooshla, I'll give you tidings of where a clever rogue such as you can win riches and valuables.

OOSHLA: You can! Where?

SIBBY: There's a Paddy Pedlar on the roadside below, and several have offered him a night's shelter, but he's refusing them all. So some reckon he must have stolen valuables in his bag, and he's afeared any man'd go looking in the bag, while he'd be sleeping.

OOSHLA: No Paddy Pedlar ever refused a night's shelter before, so he must have more in his bag than the feathers and horsehair and spuds the Paddy Pedlars do be gathering. And, if 'tis stolen valuables he has, they aren't his by right, and isn't Ooshla as much entitled to a share of them?

SIBBY: I have no learning about the right and wrongs of roguery. 'Tis yourself can set the water running clear about that point. [*She moves to the door.*]

OOSHLA: Tell him there's a lone blind man in this house. Then he'll not be afeared that I'd look in the bag. I'll only take what'll buy a strip of land for a young couple that must go foreign without it.

SIBBY: I'll tell him you're blind no matter if it withers my blood. My seven can stop in my house thanks to you ... [*She goes. Ooshla takes a couple of sheaves of straw from the corner, and makes a bed near the hearth. From the room on the right he brings out a blanket, which he spreads over the straw. He brings his stick from the corner. He sits on the blanket with his back to the door, takes off his jacket, then his shoes. He is thus engaged when Matthias Duggan appears. He is a huge powerful fierce-looking man of forty-five or so; and he carries a murderous looking shillelagh. He looks at Ooshla for a moment, advances upon him silently, takes him by the back of the collar, and throws him full length on the floor.*]

MATTHIAS [*Roaring ferociously*]: You limb of the divil up from Hell! You robber and thief and murderer!

OOSHLA [*Gasping*]: Matthias Duggan!

MATTHIAS: Say your last prayers quick before Matthias puts you into eternity. [*He draws back shillelagh for a finishing blow.*]

OOSHLA: Matthias, what did I do on you?

MATTHIAS: Last night you fetched away my spade, and sold it to Toby Kelly for a jar of his poteen.

OOSHLA [*Desperately*]: Matthias, I'm as innocent of that as of burning myself in the fire. I never steal anything only enough spuds and oatmeal to keep me living.

MATTHIAS: Didn't my own neighbour see the spade in Kelly's kitchen with my mark upon it, and wasn't it he told for true you sold it last night for poteen? My spade that was my only way of living, and now the hunger'll bring my ghost up in no time. You murderer and rogue; you'll rogue and murder no more. Say your last prayers directly; then I'll clout your two temples together, and kill you.

OOSHLA: But, Matthias, if I die without paying you back for your spade, my prayers'll be worth no more than the braying of an ass, and I'll be scorching in Purgatory for maybe ten years. Give me a small while to gather up the costs for a new spade. Then you can thrash my soul out to your heart's content.

MATTHIAS [*Suspiciously*]: And where would you get the costs for a new spade?

OOSHLA [*Quickly*]: There's a Paddy Pedlar on the road below, and he's coming lodging here for the night. In his bag he has stolen

189

valuables, and in the midnight when he's asleep, I'll steal enough that'll buy you the finest spade in the Barony.

MATTHIAS: D'ye want to make me as black a rogue as yourself?

OOSHLA: What roguery is in it? They're stolen valuables, so they aren't the pedlar's by right, and we're as much entitled to them.

MATTHIAS: But what about the gentleman that owned them?

OOSHLA: Sure he's unknown, and the pedlar'll never tell who he is. And anyway, how do the gentlemen get the costs for their valuables? By rackrenting their poor tenants till they're lowing with the hunger.

MATTHIAS [*In a fury*]: They took the last crop I had left in the year of the floods, and the wife and children sickened and died on me. But she didn't die till she cursed the gentlemen with a curse that'll wear them from the earth at last. And now they have the rent raised on me again, so I can afford no pinch of salt with my spuds, nor a sup of milk ever! For every meal of the year I have nothing only potatoes and spits!

OOSHLA: You'll want to go, or he'll be afeared to come in. I sent him word there was a lone blind man in this house, and the like couldn't look in his bag.

MATTHIAS: I'll lie ahiding in the furze until the Paddy Pedlar is sleeping. [*He goes to door.*]

OOSHLA: Tap at the window here after about an hour of the night.

MATTHIAS: Here he's coming with his basket and his bag!

OOSHLA: Creep away in the shadow of the wall.

[*Matthias goes. Ooshla slips back to the straw bed, and is kneeling down smoothing out the straw and the blanket when the Pedlar comes into the doorway. On his left arm the Pedlar carries the long rectangular shallow basket containing pins and needles, combs, brooches, laces, etc., each in its separate department, and separated from its neighbours by a wicker-work partition. In his right hand he carries a home-made walking-stick. On his back he carries the large bag in which the pedlars usually carried the feathers and horsehair and rags with which many country people paid for their purchases. The bag is hung upon his back in the traditional manner. Two potatoes are stuck in the two bottom corners of the bag, and, around the base of the bulges which these potatoes make, two straw ropes are tied, the ropes coming up around the chest and shoulders, where they are tied to the top corners of the bag. A third straw rope tied around the middle of the bag and around his chest keeps the other ropes from slipping off his shoulders. The Pedlar is middle-aged,*] insignificant looking, and stupefied by extreme physical exhaustion. *Dogged devoted will-power keeps him going; but every time he relaxes he seems to crumble up both mentally and physically. He is a sad and lonely-looking figure, and remarkably timid. He peeps in first, and takes stock of Ooshla, and of everything. He works his way stealthily until he is close to Ooshla. Ooshla is kneeling down facing him, and talking to himself, rubbing his back painfully as he does so.*]

OOSHLA: You had the pains as bad before, still God Almighty picked you up again, and you know well He can do as much for you this time, too. Evermore you're complaining about the pains in your back, and the darkness in your eyes; but wouldn't you be a score of times worse off, if you were an unbeliever, or a murderer, or a rogue? And when you see Heaven at last, won't it be twice more wonderful, because you seen nothing at all when you were living in this world? [*After peering into Ooshla's eyes at close range, the Pedlar seems to be satisfied, so he withdraws a little, and then speaks.*]

PEDLAR [*Timidly*]: God save you, sir.

OOSHLA [*His gaze falling well wide of the Pedlar*]: God and Mary save you, whoever you are. Your voice is strange to me.

PEDLAR: I'm a pedlar, sir.

OOSHLA: A paddy pedlar is it? Draw down to the fire, Paddy, and take your ease.

PEDLAR: I'm thankful to you, sir. [*He sits on the stool to the left of Ooshla.*]

OOSHLA: And very apt, Paddy, you'd like a night's shelter. Between rain and hailstones 'tis nicer weather for looking out than for looking in.

PEDLAR [*Anxiously*]: But will there be any in the house besides ourselves two, sir?

OOSHLA [*Gravely*]: No living person, Paddy; but on account I haven't the sight, I couldn't say whether my people that are dead and gone, come back ever in the midnight. They say no word, Paddy, whatever.

PEDLAR: I'll stop so, sir, till morning at the first light, sir; and I'm thankful to you, sir. [*He loosens the straw rope tied around his chest.*]

OOSHLA: And, Paddy, have you any wife, or Christian that'd like shelter too?

PEDLAR: I had no wife ever, sir; and I'm thinned out of the last of my friends. All dead and gone, sir.

OOSHLA [*Rising with his stick, and tapping his way to the door, which he bolts*]: Still you're luckier than myself that is without sight or friends, and as bad as Ossian that was blinded and withered by the first sting of Ireland's ground when he ventured back after three hundred years in the Land of Youth. [*From the dresser he takes the poteen jar and two eggshells.*] The poor fellow—was it any wonder he soaked three towels every day with tears for his lost sight, and for the Land of Youth, and for his Queen Niamh of the Golden Hair?

[*All this talk is to keep the Pedlar from suspecting the fact that Ooshla is watching his movements out of the corner of his eye. For the moment Ooshla moved to the door, the Pedlar pulls himself together, slips off his shoes, and carries the bag stealthily into the room on left, handling it with extraordinary care, as if it contained something very valuable and fragile. He slips back to the stool, and puts on his shoes again.*]

OOSHLA: Fine floury spuds are roasted in the ashes there, Paddy, and let you be making free with them. [*He comes back to his stool with the jar and the eggshells.*]

PEDLAR: 'Tisn't long since I had a good bite, sir; and I don't be inclined for eating in a house, sir, on account I'm eating in the wind evermore.

OOSHLA: Well, you'll down a jorum of poteen. Long travelling'll have you burning for a drink. [*He pours out an eggshellful.*]

PEDLAR [*Taking the eggshell*]: I'm very thankful to you, sir. [*He drinks it.*]

OOSHLA: Are you a well-doing man at the peddling, Paddy?

PEDLAR: Middling only, sir. I never was able enough, or severe enough at the bargaining; and the times are going worse, too, sir. [*Again and again his gaze returns uneasily to the main subject of his thoughts—the bag in the room.*]

OOSHLA: That's true, Paddy; but did you hear Dan O'Connell is to get a better Act of Parliament passed that'll make everyone well-to-do?

PEDLAR [*Sadly*]: Every year, sir, that is foretold, and every year Dan has great actions done for Ireland, and great speeches made; but still and all every year the poor are poorer.

OOSHLA: The gentlemen are rackrenting their poor tenants, Paddy.

PEDLAR: The gentlemen are taking more than they're entitled to, sir. [*Again he looks around uneasily in the direction of the bag.*]

OOSHLA: In the olden times Spain and Ireland had the same king;

and 'tis foretold that the same will come again. Maybe there will be fair play and plenty for all when that time comes.

PEDLAR: Maybe in God, sir.

OOSHLA [*Transferring to straw bed*]: Myself must go sleeping now, Paddy, on account the pains kept tickling me every hour of last night. The turf for raking the fire you'll find in the room beyond ... Do you see where I'm pointing, Paddy?

PEDLAR [*Rousing himself*]: I do, sir; I'll rake the fire directly, sir. [*He goes into the room on left. He comes out carrying an armful of turf.*]

OOSHLA: Myself must sleep anear the heat of the fire for fear the pains'd come back. You can sleep in my bed in the room there, Paddy. [*Indicating the room on right.*]

PEDLAR [*Stopping in his tracks*]: Is it sleep in the room beyond, sir? [*He looks towards it, and then back to the room where the bag is, with obvious dismay.*]

OOSHLA: A fine bed you'll have, Paddy. A goose-feather mattress and bolster and all. 'Twould delight you to look at it, not to mind sleeping in it.

PEDLAR [*Sorely tempted*]: A feather bed, sir! Never in my lifetime did I get sleeping in the like.

OOSHLA: One night's rest in it, Paddy, and you'll be five years a younger man.

PEDLAR: No lie, sir, 'twould do me great good, for too long carrying and trouble, sir, have me made dizzy, like a goose that'd be struck on the back of the head, sir. [*He is still hesitating.*]

OOSHLA: Good night, Paddy. [*He rolls over, and settles down to sleep.*]

PEDLAR: Good night, sir. [*The Pedlar 'rakes' the fire by covering some live coals and fresh sods with ashes. Then he comes around, and peers into Ooshla's face, whispering, "Sir, sir" softly. But there is no reply, and, the Pedlar, satisfied at last that Ooshla is asleep, crosses to the room on left where the bag is, looks in a moment, hesitates again, then comes over to the hearth, and places his pedlar's basket on a stool right beside Ooshla, so that he is bound to feel it the moment he stirs. Then he takes the candle, and goes into the bedroom on the right. A few moments after he has gone, closing the door behind him, a tapping is heard at the kitchen window. Ooshla jumps up and runs to the window.*]

OOSHLA: Go easy, you divil, he's hardly in his bed at all yet. [*He hurries to the door, and admits Matthias.*]

193

MATTHIAS: The bag. Where is it?

OOSHLA: Wait till I light a candle. [*He lights a rush candle at the fire.*]

MATTHIAS: D'ye think he has valuables in the bag?

OOSHLA: From his carry-on I'd take my book oath he has valuables in it. 'Tis in the room beyond. Carry it easy now for fear you'd hurt any of the valuables. [*Matthias goes into the room ahead of him, while Ooshla stands in the doorway holding aloft the candle.*]

OOSHLA: There it is above in the far corner. Go easy with it, man; go easy. [*Matthias comes out, and places the bag on the floor.*]

MATTHIAS: 'Tis as heavy as the Hill of the Heads. He must have half the gentlemen of Ireland robbed, and the Divil mend them. [*He is opening the bag.*]

OOSHLA: Go easy, or you'll rouse him.

[*Matthias opens the bag, and pokes his head into it in his eagerness. Instantly a smothered cry is heard from him, and he pulls out his head as if it had been bitten.*]

MATTHIAS [*In horror putting his hands to his eyes*]: Thunder and fire! My sight is scattered! God's Curse has struck me for my league with a rogue!

OOSHLA: Go easy will you! What's in the bag?

MATTHIAS: A fearful thing, or my eyes are false and my friends no more! [*He is screwing his eyes, and blinking, as if testing them.*]

OOSHLA [*Incredulous*]: 'Tis the truth what they say that you don't be yourself half the time. [*He looks into the sack, and gasps.*] By the kingdom of O'Neill! ... A woman's body and she killed and cold!

MATTHIAS [*Bounding to his feet in a fury*]: The blackhearted son of the Earl of Hell! He smothered her life out for her gold!

OOSHLA: She hasn't the looks of money. 'Tis poor clothes that's on her body.

MATTHIAS: Sure isn't it the likes of her that'd have the money. A miser that never let a penny go for clothes, or anything.

OOSHLA [*Closing the bag thoughtfully*]: Maybe that was it; or maybe 'twas for her body he killed her.

MATTHIAS: For her body, Clancy?

OOSHLA: Yes, to sell it to the doctors. Up the country the high doctors are paying a wonderful great price for bodies for the apprentice doctors to be practising how to cut the insides out of people.

MATTHIAS: One thing is sure, he banished her life someway; and, if we let him go ahead, he'll do the same to many a poor person more. Come in, and we'll take him by the legs, and keep pelting him into the lake until he dies. [*He sets out for the bedroom brandishing his shillelagh.*]

OOSHLA [*Urgently*]: Matthias, wait a minute.

MATTHIAS [*Impatiently*]: What's it?

OOSHLA: We'll make a prisoner of him first. Then we'll call in the neighbours to hear his case and judge him. No man should be put to death without a hearing.

MATTHIAS: Very well so. Bring the ropes, you.

[*They creep into the bedroom, Matthias going first and Ooshla following with the candle, and the two straw ropes. In a moment the smothered cries of the Pedlar are heard, and over all the bullthroated roars of Matthias: "Stop quiet, or we'll kill you." "Hold him down." "Tie him to the bedpost." "That's it." "Be saying your last prayers now." "Short till you'll be on trial before your God." They come out, Ooshla carrying the candle.*]

OOSHLA: Let you ring the word out around the village, and bring down a big flock of men to judge him.

MATTHIAS: I will that; and let you stand here in garrison over him; and if he ventures on more villainy, dash his brains against the gable.

[*Matthias goes, and Ooshla closes the door. He hauls the bag containing the dead woman back into the room again. He comes out, and considers for a few moments, then he takes a large knife from the dresser, feels the edge and the point of it, takes the candle in his left hand, and goes into the room. He comes out leading the Pedlar by the cut end of the straw rope which had bound him to the bed-post. His hands are still bound with the straw-rope. He does not seem to be frightened or trembling, perhaps he is too tired for that; but he does seem to be downcast and worried.*]

OOSHLA [*Motioning him to a stool near the hearth*]: Take your ease there till my comrade comes back. [*He swings out the fire-crane, and ties the loose end of the rope to it.*]

PEDLAR [*With humble matter-of-factness*]: It is to cut my neck ye mean, sir?

OOSHLA [*Gravely*]: My comrade turned very wild and savage ever since the wife and children were starved on him. Wait till I see now ... Tell him he'll be fattening Hell, if he kills you this minute, without first giving you time and chance to get the Holy Sacraments from the priest.

195

M. J. Molloy

PEDLAR: 'Tis little money I have, sir, but ye're welcome to the lot, sir, if ye'll free me out, and not cut my neck, sir.

OOSHLA [*Pouring the last of the poteen into an eggshell*]: You'll be wanting extra courage soon, Paddy, so here's what the cobbler gave his wife—the last.

PEDLAR [*Taking the eggshell resignedly*]: I'm thankful to you, sir.

OOSHLA [*Gravely*]: Myself is a rogue, too, Paddy. I was stealing enough spuds and oatmeal to keep me living until at last the roguery made its home the same as if it was a maggot in my brain. Then last night I was troubled over the girl going foreign, and the next thing the maggot twisted, and I stole a poor man's spade, and sold it for poteen to banish my trouble. The dirtiest turn ever I done; and was it the same way the roguery kept ever growing till it made a ruffian of you?

PEDLAR: I was no rogue, ever, sir, nor anybody belonging to me.

OOSHLA [*Jumping up*]: You were no rogue ever! Your impudence is enough to make a dog beat his father. [*He strides into the room, and drags out the bag.*] Didn't you rob this poor old woman of her life? [*On the instance the Pedlar springs to his feet in a state of intense agitatiom.*]

PEDLAR: Mamma! Mamma! [*He pronounces it M'ma in the western fashion.*] What are you doing to Mamma? [*He runs towards her blindly, but is stopped by the rope tying him to the crane.*] God and Mary and Patrick help me!—help me! [*Struggling like a madman he breaks the rope, and running forward drops on his knees beside the body.*] Mamma! Mamma! did he bruise you? He threw you down, and bruised you; and 'twas my fault, Mamma: for a feather bed I left you. Mamma, Mamma, down on your back he flung you, and injured you sore.

OOSHLA [*Mildly*]: Paddy, how could we injure her? She was dead when we opened the bag?

PEDLAR: Two days she's dead, sir. My heart could never bear to see her harmed any way at all, sir. [*With feverish haste, and as skilfully as his bound hands will allow he is laying her out in the bag. Then he turns to Ooshla in passionate pleading, pointing to his own throat.*] Let ye cut my neck if ye like, sir, but in the honour of God, sir, let ye not harm Mamma, sir.

OOSHLA: We'll not harm either of ye, but tell me, Paddy, why have you her in the bag?

PEDLAR: When she was dying in Clanrickard's country, sir, she asked me to bury her with my father in the north in Lord Leitrim's country, sir.

OOSHLA: And we judged 'twas some old woman you robbed and killed. I'll get the knife and free your hands out.

PEDLAR: Then I'll be able to lay her out nice and decent. God bless you, sir.

OOSHLA [*Taking the knife from the dresser*]: She must have a great wish for your father, Paddy, when she asked you to carry her that length.

PEDLAR: He cared for whiskey, only, sir. He'd make her go begging money for whiskey, and, if she wouldn't bring back enough, he'd give her blood to drink, sir.

OOSHLA [*Feeling edge of the knife*]: Blood! What blood, Paddy?

PEDLAR: Blood from her lips and teeth, sir, from fisting her down on the mouth, sir. I had to be ever watching and ever fighting him, sir; and that's what has myself left without marriage or a son that'd lift me out of the dust, or the mud, when the age sets me tumbling at last, sir. [*Holding up his bound wrists pleadingly.*] In the honour of God, sir.

OOSHLA [*Approaching*]: But, Paddy, if he was that cruel to her, why would she ask to be buried with him?

PEDLAR: She well knew, sir, there wouldn't be one in the world wide only herself to say a good word for him on the Judgment Day; so she'd like to rise near him that day. He was good to her in his younger days before the drink made him ravenous.

OOSHLA: I understand all now, Paddy, and I'll free your hands out.

PEDLAR [*Holding up his wrists, his eyes shining with eager joy*]: God be good to you, sir. I'll be every day asking God to be good to you, sir. [*The moment the rope joining his wrists is cut, he whips a long bladed knife from some kind of hidden sheath in his belt, and leaps to his feet brandishing it fiercely, while Ooshla backs away in the utmost dismay.*]

PEDLAR: Hullabaloo! Hullabaloo! [*Twice he leaps into the air with that hiss of savage joy; drawing back the knife each time as if about to charge at Ooshla. But instead he leaps again, and cries aloud in triumph.*] Now, Mamma! Timmy has his knife! Timmy has his knife! No one'll dare harm you no more!

OOSHLA: Why should I want to harm her, Paddy? [*But the Pedlar does not hear him. He is standing still, and looking down at his mother, and the life has gone out of him.*]

PEDLAR [*Numbly*]: She never looked! She heard no word! She'll hear no more till we meet on God's floor. [*He sinks on his knees beside her, and puts the knife back into his belt.*]

OOSHLA: Was she very old, Paddy?

197

PEDLAR: She wasn't too old, sir. She was young enough and she dying to have sense and reason to talk to God and His Son and the Blessed Virgin.

OOSHLA: You'll be very lonesome after her, Paddy?

PEDLAR: She had the priest in time, sir, and a happy death, so I'm happy since, but lonesome.

OOSHLA: And you're mortal tired too, Paddy?

PEDLAR [*His eyes never leave her face*]: Two days I'm walking, sir, every hour that the clock struck. I must have her in her grave soon, before the death alters her, sir.

OOSHLA: Well, if you're only fit to carry her half a mile itself, you should do that, Paddy, for my comrade was never safe since the wife and children were starved on him. He mightn't believe she was your mother, and he might go against your knife, and in the fighting she might take harm.

PEDLAR [*Rising quickly*]: I'll fetch her away directly, but two of my ropes are spoiled, sir. Have you two idle, sir, that you'd swap for your needs from the basket beyond?

OOSHLA: I have two fine ropes idle in the barn, and you're heartily welcome to them. [*He hurries out. The Pedlar droops a little, and sinks on his knees beside the body again. He murmurs to himself drowsily, and half dazedly.*]

PEDLAR: He's proving a decent man at last, Mamma, still we'll trust no other house till you're safe for ever from the badness of the world. [*Exhaustion seems to overwhelm him for a few moments, but, with a great effort, he pulls himself together, and speaks to her mildly, as if in reply to a comment by her.*] Sure I'm not denying it, Mamma, I am tired. [*Then pressing his hands to his head dazedly.*] My mind is very near off its firmness I'm that tired. I'm not safe carrying you I'm that tired ... [*His eyes wander about a little desperately, and suddenly light up as they see the crude wooden cross on the dresser. He whispers to her excitedly.*] Wait, Mamma. [*He rises, and crosses slowly towards the Cross on the right hand wall. He does not come too near. He speaks with quiet, tired, matter-of-factness.*] They do say Yourself was mortal tired, too, that day, and stumbled greatly while You were carrying it. Just the same way myself is now, my two shoulders cut and scalded with the ropes, and my two feet gripping the ground they're that tired. 'Tis an old saying we have that God is strong, and His Mother is kind, and let the two of Ye help me out this night, so as I won't injure Mamma with stumbles ... I'll be thankful to Ye evermore; and I'll send no

198

complaint over no more against the hunger or the cramp, or the rain every day rotting my clothes, or the snow and hailstones blinding my eyes; or against the want of a son or a daughter that'd keep the rats from my head when I'll be getting death at last. Let ye brace me up till I have Mamma safe in her grave, and after that please Yereselves about me. [*He is on his way back when he turns suddenly.*] And let Ye mind the darkness too. Yereselves will well remember of how awkward the darkness is when the paths are crooked, and rough. [*He comes back to the body, drops on his knees beside it, glances in the direction of the Cross as if to make sure he is not being overheard, and whispers.*] You'll see, Mamma; They'll be with us at every turn and twist.

OOSHLA [*Hurrying in with two stout straw ropes*]: Here are two good hardy lads that'll carry her till ye come to the mountains whatever.

PEDLAR: Take your needs from the basket here, sir. [*He rolls up the two straw ropes, puts them into the basket.*]

OOSHLA: I'm in want of nothing, Paddy. [*He wanders off to the fireplace thinking hard, makes up his mind, and exclaims aloud.*] Well here! Hit or miss! [*He takes a stool, and sits down at the centre of the kitchen, facing the Pedlar.*] I'm after making a little thought, Paddy; and I'd reckon I'd be a good man to carry a bag, and a good help at bargaining, too, for I had a quick tongue ever, and it got great practice while I was a gentleman. Maybe 'twould suit you if I went peddling with you through Ireland for evermore.

PEDLAR: Is it to go leaving your home and land, sir?

OOSHLA: I was believing I was entitled to take my needs from the tenants the same as the gentlemen; but it appears now that that was the Divil's notion; for last night the roguery betrayed me all out, and I sold a poor man's spade for poteen, and today he found out, so I'm disgraced for life and for ever in this Barony; and my life'll be in danger from him too. So 'tis God's Will for me to leave this country, and the roguery.

PEDLAR: But who'll have your house and land, sir?

OOSHLA: That was pledged to a young girl nearby, and 'tis God's Will, too, she to get it, and be saved from going foreign.

PEDLAR [*Earnestly looking at corpse*]: In three days I'll have no comrade no more, and I'm falling into age, moreover; so 'twould suit me greatly you to come with me. But she was evermore happy when she'd hear good praise of me, and she'd be shamed now when she'd hear I had a rogue for comrade.

OOSHLA [*Rising vigorously*]: Sure to shake off the roguery is what I want, Paddy; for 'twas commencing to make a mean man of me altogether. With you I'll be in honest company, and you'll help me against the roguery. [*He is getting together the dress coat, top-hat, and cane and some food from the dresser for the journey.*]

PEDLAR [*Eagerly*]: Maybe I could cure you, sir, the way I cured my father out of hurting Mamma, sir?

OOSHLA [*With enthusiasm*]: What way did you cure him, Paddy?

PEDLAR [*Taking out knife gravely*]: Every time he'd set into lashing her I'd give him a dart of this, sir. I could give you a dart, too, sir, every time you'd commit a roguery.

OOSHLA: Oh, murther! And would it be a deep prod, Paddy?

PEDLAR [*Earnestly*]: Sure if it wasn't, sir, 'twould do you no good, sir.

OOSHLA [*With a shudder*]: But if it was too deep, 'twould do me no good either.

PEDLAR: I'd make sure not to give you a dart in the killing places, sir.

OOSHLA: Oh, murther! Oh, murther! ... Still you'll cure me. The divil a bit of roguery'll stop long more in me. [*They are busy readying. Thady and Honor enter.*]

THADY [*Excitedly*]: Matthias Duggan is up and down telling that you went robbing another rogue for the price of a farm for us.

OOSHLA: Ye're just in time! I'm going peddling for a living with Paddy here, so ye can have this place all to yerselves.

THADY: You're going living in the wind so as you can leave us your place!

HONOR: Ooshla, we'd give ourselves up to the Divil before we'd send you living in the wind—at your age and all.

OOSHLA: But I must leave this country whether or no. Last night I stole a poor man's spade!

HONOR: You did!

THADY: Thunder and turf!

OOSHLA: I did, and by tomorrow all the country'll know. [*He gets his stick from a corner.*]

THADY: 'Tis as well for you to go so before the roguery gets the better of you altogether.

HONOR: Yes, Ooshla, 'tis time for you to go. [*She goes to the hearth, and seems shocked and depressed.*]

OOSHLA [*Vigorously*]: Never fret, girl. Paddy here has a wonderful great cure for the roguery. Soon he'll have me as honest as a

Bishop. [*He turns to Thady.*] Out of your sailing money that you won't need now, give two shillings to Silke the Smith, and he'll sledge out a new spade for Matthias. [*He puts on his dress coat.*]

THADY: I'll not fail you in that, Ooshla.

OOSHLA [*Turning to Pedlar who is on his way to the door with bag on his back*]: Timmy! Timmy! They do call me Ooshla. I'm fresh. Let me carry the bag for to-night.

PEDLAR [*Quickly, the wild look coming back into his eyes*]: You will not! You might shake or jolt Mamma! Let you carry the basket. [*He opens the door, and looks out anxiously. He draws his knife, holds it at the ready. He speaks with his humble matter-of-factness, never taking his eyes off the dangerous darkness outside.*] If he crosses me, 'twill be me or him, and if 'tis me, let ye put me down along with Mamma in whatever graveyard is nearby, and we'll be very thankful to ye. [*He goes.*]

HONOR: Did you see the knife! Is he safe at all?

OOSHLA: 'Tis only how he's afeard anything might happen the mother. It appears he was very good to her while she was living, and her dying wish was he to bury her with his father in Lord Leitrim's country.

THADY: Well, when he was that good to the mother, there's no badness in him.

HONOR [*As Ooshla goes to the door*]: Ooshla, as soon as you're middling honest at all, draw back to us before the hardship breaks you down.

OOSHLA [*In the best of spirits*]: What hardship? Carrying a basket or a bag? What is that only walking? And buying and selling? What is that only talking? Walking and talking isn't that how the gentlemen pass the time? So isn't God good that's after rummaging out a way I can live like a gentleman, and be no rogue? [*At the door he claps the tall hat on his head.*] Ooshla'll be the gentleman-pedlar, keeping only the best, he'll say, and entitled to charge twice more than the rest. When Ooshla comes the way again, he'll be a well-doing man, with a white waistcoat fastened, and a watch chain slinging, and gold guineas sounding and all. Till that day God be good to ye. [*He goes.*]

THADY: Good luck, Ooshla.

HONOR [*At the door waving after him*]: God be with you, Ooshla.

THADY [*Returning to the fire*]: Ooshla'll be all right. He's in lucky company whatever. The Pedlar was very good to his mother while she lived, and the like do be lucky, they reckon. [*He takes out the clay pipe.*]

201

HONOR [*Turning excitedly*]: Right enough, Thady: the like do be lucky, all reckon.

THADY [*Filling his pipe*]: And they say the mother doesn't be slow about sending the luck either.

HONOR [*Coming back to fire*]: As sure as the day Ooshla himself is the first good luck she sent the Pedlar, for Ooshla should make an able Pedlar, and a hearty comrade for the road! [*She sits beside him.*]

THADY [*Taking her hand in his, and smiling wisely*]: She sent her son a comrade, and she sent Ooshla an honest way of living, and she sent you and me our own fireside. She has good fortune won for everyone, so she must be well thought of where she is.

CURTAIN.

14. EXTRACTS FROM NOVEL: "GIRL WITH GREEN EYES"

EDNA O'BRIEN

Religion and sex continue to pervade Irish fiction, but there is a marked evolution noticeable from the background Jansenism of Sean O'Faolain's early tales, through the light-hearted bawdiness of Benedict Kiely, to the inroads of the permissive society reflected in the novels of Edna O'Brien.

Edna O'Brien was born and reared in the countryside of County Clare. The observant candour of her account of Caithleen Brady's progress from this background into the wider world of polite bourgeois society secured the banning of each of her first novels in Ireland, as they appeared in the 1960's, and their easy success elsewhere. (In recent years, most of her books have been 'unbanned' in Ireland.)

The Lonely Girl (1962), which, after the success of the film, reappeared as *Girl With Green Eyes*, is the middle volume of a trilogy dealing with the adventures of Caithleen and her friend Baba, the first being *The Country Girls* (1960) and the last being *Girls in Their Married Bliss* (1964). The opening extract here given introduces us to the raw country girls, now working in Dublin, and their first meeting with the sophisticated writer, Eugene Gaillard, whose not very efficient mistress Caithleen subsequently becomes. The second extract shows the irate parents up from the country discomforted in their attempt to recapture their erring daughter.

Edna O'Brien

From
GIRL WITH GREEN EYES

Chapter One

It was a wet afternoon in October, as I copied out the September accounts from the big grey ledger. I worked in a grocery shop in the north of Dublin and had been there for two years.

My employer and his wife were country people; like myself. They were kind but they liked me to work hard and promised me a rise in the new year. Little did I know that I would be gone by then, to a different life.

Because of the rain, not many customers came in and out, so I wrote the bills quickly and then got on with my reading. I had a book hidden in the ledger, so that I could read without fear of being caught.

It was a beautiful book, but sad. It was called *Tender is the Night*. I skipped half of the words in my anxiety to read it quickly, because I wanted to know if the man would leave the woman or not. All the nicest men were in books—the strange, complex, romantic men; the ones I admired most.

I knew no one like that except Mr Gentleman; and I had not seen him for two years. He was only a shadow now and I remembered him the way one remembers a nice dress that one has grown out of.

At half four I put on the lights. The shop looked shabbier in artificial light too, the shelves were dusty and the ceiling hadn't been painted since I went there. It was full of cracks. I looked in the mirror to see how my hair was. We were going somewhere that night, my friend Baba and me. My face in the mirror looked round and smooth. I sucked my cheeks in, to make them thinner. I longed to be thin, like Baba.

'You look like you were going to have a child,' Baba said to me the night before, when I was in my nightgown.

'You're raving,' I said to her. Even the thought of such a thing

204

worried me. Baba was always teasing me, although she knew I'd never done more than kiss Mr Gentleman.

'It happens to country mopes like you, soon as you dance with a fellow,' Baba said, as she held an imaginary man in her arms and waltzed between the two iron beds. Then she burst into one of her mad laughs and poured gin into the transparent plastic tooth-mugs on the bedside table.

Lately Baba had taken to carrying a baby gin in her handbag. We didn't like the taste of gin and tonic so much, but we loved the look of it, we loved its cool blue complexion as we sprawled on our hard beds, drinking and pretending to be fast.

Baba had come back to Joanna's boarding-house from the sanatorium and it was like the old days except that neither of us had men. We had dates of course—no steady men—but dates are risky.

Only the Sunday before Baba had a date with a man who sold cosmetics. He came to collect her in a car painted all over with slogans: 'Give her pink satin', 'Lovely pink satin for that schoolgirl bloom'. It was a blue, flashy car and the slogans were in silver. Baba heard him honk and she looked out to see what kind of car he had.

'Oh Holy God! I'm not going out in *that* circus wagon. Go down and tell him I'm having a haemmoridge.'

I hated the word haemmoridge, it was one of her new words to sound tough. I went down and told him that she had a headache.

'Would you like to come instead?'

I said no.

On the back seat there were advertisement cards and little sample bottles of 'pink satin face lotion', packed in boxes. I thought he might offer me a sample but he didn't.

'Sure you wouldn't like to see a show?'

I said that I couldn't.

Without another word he started up the car, and backed out of the cul-de-sac.

'He was very disappointed,' I said when I got back upstairs.

'That'll shake him. Feck any samples? I could do with a bit of sun-tan stuff for my legs.'

'How could I take samples with him sitting there in the car?'

'Distract him. Get him interested in your bust or the sunset or something.'

Baba is unreasonable. She thinks people are more stupid than they are. Those flashy fellows who sell things and own shops, they can probably count and add up.

'He hardly spoke two words,' I said.

'Oh the silent type!' Baba said, making a long face. 'You can imagine what an evening with him would be like! Get your mink on, we're going to a hop,' and I put on a light dress and we went down town to a Sunday-night dance.

'Don't take cigarettes from those Indian fellows with turbans; they might be doped,' Baba said.

There was a rumour that two girls were doped and brought up the Dublin mountains the week before.

Doped cigarettes! We didn't even get asked up for one dance; there wasn't enough men. We could have danced with each other but Baba said that was the end. So we just sat there, rubbing the goose-flesh off our arms and passing remarks about the men who stood at one end of the hall, sizing up the various girls who sat, waiting, on long stools. They never asked a girl to dance, until the music started up, and then they seemed to pick girls who were near. We moved down to that end of the hall, but had no luck there either.

Baba said that we ought never go to a hop again; she said that we'd have to meet new people, diplomats and people like that.

It was my constant wish. Some mornings I used to get up, convinced that I would meet a new, wonderful man. I used to make my face up specially and take short breaths to prepare myself for the excitement of it. But I never met anyone except customers, or students that Baba knew.

I thought of all this in the shop as I gummed red stickers on any bills which were due for over three months and addressed them hurriedly. We never posted bills, because Mrs Burns said it was cheaper to have Willie, the messenger boy, deliver them. Just then he came in, shaking rain from his sou'wester.

'Where were you?'

'Nowhere.'

As usual at that time of evening, he and I had a snack, before the shop got busy. We ate broken biscuits, raisins, dried prunes, and some cherries. His hands were blue and red with cold.

'Do you like them, Will?' I said, as he made a face at my new white shoes. The toes were so long that I had to walk sideways going upstairs. I put them on because Baba and I were going to a wine-tasting reception that night. We read about it in the papers and Baba said that we'd crash it. We had crashed two other functions—a fashion show and a private showing of a travel film of Ireland. (All lies, about dark-haired girls roaming around Connemara in red petticoats. No wonder they had to show it in private.)

At half five, customers began to flock in on their way from work, and around six Mrs Burns came out, to let me go off.

'Very stuffy here,' she said to Willie. A hint to mean that we shouldn't have the oil heater on. Stuffy! There were draughts everywhere and a great division between the floor and the wainscoting.

I made my face up in the hall and put on rouge, eye-shadow, and lashings of ashes-of-roses perfume. The very name of ashes-of-roses made me feel alluring. Willie sneaked me in a good sugar bag, so that I could bring my shoes in the bag, and wear my wellingtons. The gutters were overflowing outside, and rain beat against the skylight in the upstairs hall.

'Don't do anything I wouldn't do,' he said, as he let me out by the hall door and whistled as I ran to the bus shelter a few yards down the road. It was raining madly.

The bus was empty, as there were very few people going down to the centre of the city at that hour of evening. It was too early for the pictures. There were toffee papers and cigarette packets on the floor and the bus had a sweaty smell. It was a poor neighbourhood.

I read a paper which I found on the seat beside me. There was a long article by a priest, telling how he'd been tortured in China. I knew a lot about that sort of thing, because in the convent where I went to school the nun used to read those stories to us on Saturday nights. As a treat she used to read a paper called *The Standard*. It was full of stories about priests' toe-nails being pulled off and nuns shut up in dark rooms with rats.

I almost missed my stop, because I had been engrossed in this long article by the Irish priest.

Baba was waiting for me outside the hotel. She looked like something off a Christmas tree. She had a new fur muff and her hair-set was held in place with lacquer.

'Mother o'God where are you off to in your wellingtons?' she asked.

I looked down at my feet and realized with desolation that I'd left my shoes on the bus.

There was nothing for it but to cross the road and wait for the bus on its return journey. It was an unsheltered bus-stop and Baba's hair-style got flattened. Then, to make everything worse, my shoes were not on the bus and there was a different conductor. He said that the other conductor must have handed them in to the lost property office on the way to his tea.

'Call there any time after ten in the morning,' he said, and when Baba heard that, she said, 'Turalu,' and ran across the road back to the hotel. I followed, dispiritedly.

We had trouble getting in to the banquet room, even though Baba told the girl at the entrance door that we were journalists. She rooted in her bag for the invitation cards and said that she must have forgotten them. She said they were pink cards edged with gold. She knew because the girl at the door held a pile of them in her hand and flicked their gold edges impatiently. Baba's hands trembled as she searched, and her cheeks looked flushed. The two spots of rouge on her cheekbones had been washed unevenly by the rain.

'What paper do you represent?' the girl asked. A small queue had gathered behind us.

'*Woman's Night,*' Baba said. It was what she planned to say. There is no such magazine.

'Go ahead,' the girl said grudgingly, and we went in.

As we walked across the polished floor, my rubber-boots squeaked loudly and I imagined that everyone was staring at me. It was a very rich room—chandeliers alight, dusky-blue, velvet curtains drawn across, and dance music playing softly.

Baba saw our friend Tod Mead and went towards him. He was a public relations officer who worked for a big wool company and we had met him at a fashion show a few weeks before. He took us for coffee then and tried to get off with Baba. He affected a casual world-weary manner, but it was only put on, because he ate loads of bread and jam. We knew he was married but we hadn't met his wife.

'Tod!' Baba hobbled over to him on her high heels. He kissed her hand and introduced us to the two people with him. One was a lady journalist in a big black hat and the other a strange man with a sallow face. His name was Eugene Gaillard. He said 'Pleased to meet you', but he didn't look very pleased. He had a sad face and Tod told us that he was a film director. Baba began to smirk and show her dimples and the gold tooth, all at once.

'He made so and so,' Tod said, mentioning a picture I'd never heard of.

'A classic documentary, a classic,' the lady journalist said.

Mr Gaillard looked at her earnestly, and said, 'Yes, really

208

splendid; shatteringly realistic poverty.' His long face had an odd
expression of contempt as he spoke.

'What are you doing now?' she asked.

'I've become a farmer,' he told her.

'A squire,' Tod corrected.

The lady journalist suggested that she go out there some day and
do an article on him. She was nicely dressed and reeked of perfume
but she was over fifty.

'We might as well get some red ink,' Baba told me. She was
disappointed when neither of the men had offered to get it for her. I
followed her across towards the long row of tables which were
placed end to end along the length of the room. There were white
cloths on each table and waiters stood behind, pouring half glasses
of red and white wine.

'They weren't very pally,' Baba said.

Their voices reached me and I heard Tod say, 'That's the literary
fat girl I was telling you about.'

'Which one?' Eugene Gaillard asked, idly.

'Long hair and rubber boots,' Tod said, and I heard him
laughing.

I ran and got myself a drink. There were plates of water biscuits
but I couldn't reach them and I felt hungry, having had no tea.

'Literary fat girl!' It really stabbed me.

'Your fashions are original—rubber boots and a feather hat,'
Eugene said behind my back, and I knew his soft voice without even
turning round to look at him.

'You brave coward,' he said. He was tall, about the same height
as my father.

'It's nothing to laugh at—I lost my shoes,' I said.

'But it is so original, to come in your rubber boots. You could
start a whole trend with that kind of thing. Have you heard of the
men who can only make love to girls in their plastic macs?'

'I haven't heard,' I said sadly, ashamed at knowing so little.

'Tell me about you,' he said, and I felt suddenly at home with
him, I don't know why. He wasn't like anyone I knew, his face was
long and had a grey colour. It reminded me of a saint's face carved
out of grey stone which I saw in the church every Sunday.

'Who are you, what do you do?' he asked, but when he saw that I
was shy, he began to talk himself. He said that he had come
because he met Tod Mead in Grafton Street and Tod dragged him
along.

'I came for the scenery—not the wine,' he said, looking round at the gilt wall-brackets, the plush curtains, and at a tall, intense woman with black earrings, who stood alone near the window. If only I could say something interesting to him.

'What's the difference between white wine and red wine?' I asked. He wasn't drinking.

'One is red and one is white,' he laughed.

But Baba came along, with the white muff and a bunch of potato crisps.

'Has Mary of the Sorrows been telling you a lot of drip about her awful childhood?' She meant me.

'Everything. From the very beginning,' he said.

Baba started to frown, then quickly gave one of her big false laughs and moved her hands up and down in front of her eyes. 'What's that?' she asked. She did it three times but he could not guess it.

'Past your eyes—milk—pasteurized milk. Ha, ha, ha.' She told Eugene Gaillard that she worked on the lonely-hearts' column of *Woman's Night* and had a great time reading hilarious letters.

'Only yesterday,' she ran on, 'I had a letter from a poor woman in Ballinasloe, who said, "Dear Madam, my husband makes love to me on Sunday nights and I find this very inconvenient as I have a big wash on Mondays and am dog tired. What can I do without hurting my husband's feelings?"

'I told Mrs Ballinasloe,' Baba said, ' "Wash on Tuesdays." ' She threw her little hands out to emphasize the simple way she dealt with life's problems, and he laughed obligingly.

'Baba is a funny girl,' he said to me, still smiling. As if I ought to rejoice! It was my joke. I read it in a magazine one day when I had to wait two hours in the dental hospital to have a tooth filled. I read it and came home and told Baba; and after that she told it to everyone. Baba had got so smart in the last year—she knew about different wines, and had taken up fencing. She said that the fencing class was full of women in trousers asking her home for cocoa.

Just then Tod Mead came up waving an empty glass.

'The drink is running out, why don't we all go somewhere?' he said to Eugene.

'Those are two nice girls you found,' Eugene said, and Baba began to hum, 'Nice people with nice manners that have got no money at all ...'

'All right,' Eugene said. 'We'll have dinner.'

On the way out, Baba ordered twelve bottles of hock to be sent C.O.D. to Joanna—our landlady. The idea was that, having tasted the wine, people would order some. I knew that Joanna would have a fit over it.

'Who is Joanna?' Eugene asked, as we moved towards the door. We waved to the lady journalist and one or two other people.

'I'll tell you about her at dinner,' Baba said.

My elbows touched his; and I had that paralysing sensation in my legs which I hadn't felt since I'd parted from Mr Gentleman.

Chapter Thirteen

At tea-time a wind began to rise, and rattled the shutters. Anna rushed out to bring in napkins which she had spread on one of the thorny bushes. A galvanized bucket rolled along the cobbled yard.

I had felt afraid all day, knowing that they were bound to come—but if a mountain storm blew up, it might keep them away. By the morrow I'd be gone.

*

After tea we sat in the study with a map of London spread on both our knees while he marked various streets and sights for me. I was to go early next morning and he had sent a telegram to Ginger, so that she could meet me.

'We ought to lock the doors,' I said, unnerved by the rattling of shutters.

'All right,' he said, 'we'll lock everything.' And I carried the big flashlamp around while he locked the potting-shed door, the back door, and another side door. The keys had rusted in their locks and he had to tap the bolts with a block of wood to loosen them. Anna and Denis had gone backstairs to their own apartments, and we could hear dance music from their radio.

'Tell them if there's a knock, not to answer it,' I suggested.

'Nonsense,' he said, 'they never come down once they've gone up at night. They go to bed after the nine-o'clock news.' He was very proud and did not wish to share his troubles with anyone.

'Now the hall door,' I said. We opened it for a minute and looked out at the windy night and listened to the trees groaning.

'Go away from the window, bogy man,' he said as we came in and sat on the couch in front of the study fire. The oak box was stocked with logs and he said that we were perfectly safe and that no one could harm us.

There was a shot-gun in the corner of the hall, and I thought that maybe he should get it to be on the safe side.

'Nonsense,' he said. 'You just want some melodrama. ...'

I could hear the wind and I imagined that I heard a car driving up to the house; I heard it all the time, but it was only in my imagination. I rubbed his hair and massaged the muscles at the back of his neck, and he said that it was very nice and very comforting.

'We get on well together, you and I,' he said.

'Yes,' I said, and thought how easy it would be, if he said then, I love you, or I could love, or I'm falling in love with you, but he didn't; he just said that we got on well together.

'We only know each other a couple of months,' he said to the fire, as if he had sensed my disappointment. I knew that he believed in the slow, invisible processes of growth, the thing which had to take root first in the lonely, dark part of one, away from the light. He liked to plant trees and watch them grow; he liked our friendship to take its course; he was not ready for me.

'Do you believe in God?' I said abruptly. I don't know why I said it.

'Not when I'm sitting at my own fire. I may do when I'm driving eighty miles an hour. It varies.' I thought it a very peculiar answer, altogether.

'What things are you afraid of?' I wished that somehow he would make some deep confession to me and engross me in his fears so that I could forget my own, or that we could play I-spy-with-my-little-eye, or something.

'Just bombs,' he said, and I thought that a peculiar answer too.

'But not hell?' I said, naming my second greatest fear.

'They'll give me a job making fires in hell, I'm good at fires.' I wondered how his voice could be so calm, his face so still. Sometimes I rubbed his neck, and then again I rested my arm and sat very close to him, wondering how I could live without him in London for the while—until things blew over, he said.

'The best thing you can do about hell ...' he began, but I never heard the end of the sentence, because just then the dog barked in

212

the yard outside. She barked steadily for a few seconds and then let out a low, warning howl that was almost human-sounding. I jumped up.

'Sssh, ssh,' he said, as I stumbled over a tray of tea-things that was on the floor. He ran across and lowered the Tilley lamp; then we waited. Nothing happened, no footsteps, no car, nothing but the wind and the beating rain. Yet, I knew they were coming and that in a moment they would knock on the door.

'Must have been a badger or a fox.' He poured me a drink from the whisky bottle on the gun bureau.

'You look as white as a sheet,' he said, sipping the whisky. Then the dog barked again, loudly and continuously, and I knew by her hysterical sounds that she was trying to leap the double doors in the back yard. We had not locked them. My whole body began to shake and tremble.

'It's them,' I said, going cold all over. We heard boots on the gravel and men talking, and suddenly great banging and tapping on the hall door. The dog continued to bark hysterically, and above the noise of banging fists and wind blowing I heard the beating of my own heart. Knuckles rapped on the window, the shutters rattled, and at the same time the stiff knocker boomed. I clutched Eugene's sleeve and prayed.

'Oh God,' I said to him.

'Open up,' a man's voice shouted.

'They'll break down the door,' I said. Five or six of them seemed to be pounding on it, all at once. I thought that my heart would burst.

'How dare they abuse my door like that,' he said as he moved towards the hall.

'Don't, don't!' I stood in his way and told him not to be mad. 'We won't answer,' I said, but I had spoken too late. One of my people had gone around to the back of the house, and we heard the metallic click of the back-door latch being raised impatiently. Then the bolt was drawn and I heard Anna say:

'What'n the name of God do you want at this hour of night?'

I suppose that she must have been half asleep and had tumbled down thinking that we had been locked out or that the police had come for me.

I heard the Ferret's voice speak my name. 'We've come to take that girl out of here.'

'I don't know anything about it. Wait outside.' Anna said insolently, and then he must have walked straight past her because she shouted: 'How dare you!' and the sheepdog ran up the passage from the kitchen, yelping. The others were still knocking at the front of the house.

'This is beyond endurance,' Eugene said, and as he went to open the hall door, I ran back into the study, and looked around for somewhere to hide. I crawled under the spare bed hoping that he would bring them to the sitting-room, because he did not like people in the study where he worked. I heard him say:

'I can't answer you that, I'm afraid.'

'Deliver her out,' a voice demanded.

I had to think, to recall who it was.

'Come on now.' It was Andy, my father's cousin, a cattle-dealer. I recalled strange cattle—making the noises which cows make in unfamiliar places—being driven into our front field on the evenings preceding a fair day. Then cousin Andy would come up to the house for tea, and sitting in the kitchen in his double-breasted brown suit he'd discuss the price of heifers with my father. Once he gave me a three-penny bit which was so old and worn that the King had been rubbed off.

'Where is my only child?' my father cried.

She's under the bed, she's suffocating, I said to myself, praying that I would be there only for a second, while Eugene picked up the lamp and brought them across to the sitting-room. Could I then hide in the barn—and take the torch to ward off rats!

'My only child,' my father cried again.

For two pins I'd come out and tell him a thing or two about his only child!

'Who are you looking for?' Eugene said. 'We'll confer in the other room.'

But my father had noticed the fire, and with a sinking feeling I heard them all troop into the study. Someone sat on the bed; the spring touched my back, and smelling cow-dung from his boots, I guessed that it was cousin Andy. I recognized two other voices—Jack Holland's and the Ferret's.

'Don't you think it is a little late in the day for social calls?' Eugene said.

'We want that poor, innocent girl,' cousin Andy said—he, the famed bachelor, who had spoken only to cows and bullocks all his life, bullying them along the road to country fairs. 'Hand the girl over, and by God if there's a hair astray on her, you'll pay dear for it,' he shouted, and I imagined how he looked with his miser's face and a mean little mouth framed by a red moustache. He always had

214

to carry stomach mixture with him everywhere, and had once raised his hand to my mother because she hinted about all the free grazing he took from Dada. On that occasion my father in his one known act of chivalry said, 'If you lay a finger on my missus, I'll lay you out.'

'This is outrageous,' Eugene said.

Various matches were struck—they were settling in.

'Allow me,' Jack Holland said, proceeding to make introductions, but he was shouted down by my father.

'A divorced man. Old enough to be her father. Carrying off my little daughter.'

'To set the record straight I did not bring her here, she came,' Eugene said.

I thought, he's going to let me down, he's going to send me away with them; my mother was right, 'Weep and you weep alone.'

'You got her with dope. Everyone knows that,' my father said.

Eugene laughed. I thought how odd, and immoral, he must look to them, in his corduroy trousers and his old check shirt. I hoped that all his buttons were done up. My nose began to itch with the dust.

'You're her father?' Eugene said.

'Allow me,' Jack Holland said again, and this time he performed the introductions. I wondered if it was *he* who had betrayed me.

'Yes, I'm her father,' Dada said, in a doleful voice.

'Go on now and get the girl,' Andy shouted.

I began to tremble anew. I couldn't breathe. I would suffocate under those rusty springs. I would die while they sat there deciding my life. I would die—with Andy's dungy boots under my nose. It was ironic. My mother used to scrub the rungs of the chair after his visits to our house. I said short prayers and multiplication-tables and the irregular plural of Latin nouns—anything that I knew by heart—to distract myself. I thought of a line from *Julius Caesar* which I had once recited, wearing a red nightdress, at a school concert—'I see thee still and on thy blade and dudgeon gouts of blood. ...'

'Are you a Catholic?' the Ferret asked, in a policeman's voice.

'I'm not a Catholic,' Eugene answered.

'D'you go to Mass?' my father asked.

'But, my dear man—' Eugene began.

'There's no "my dear man". Cut it out. Do you go to Mass or don't you? D'you eat meat on Fridays?'

215

'God help Ireland,' Eugene said, and I imagined him throwing his hands up in his customary gesture of impatience.

'None of that blasphemy,' cousin Andy shouted, making a noise as he struck his fist into his palm.

'What about a drink to calm us down?' Eugene suggested, and then, sniffing, he added, 'Perhaps better not—you seem to have brought enough alcohol with you.'

I could smell their drink from under the bed now, and I guessed that they had stopped at every pub along the way to brace themselves for the occasion. Probably my father had paid for most of it.

'Well ... a sip of port wine all round might be conducive to negotiation,' Jack Holland suggested in his soft, mannerly way.

'Could I have a drink of water—to take an aspirin?' my father said.

'Good idea. I'll join you in an aspirin,' Eugene said, and I thought for a second that things were going to be all right. Water was poured. I closed my eyes to pray, dropped my forehead on to the back of my hand, and gasped. My face was damp with cold sweat.

'I would like you to realize that your daughter is escaping from *you*. I'm not abducting her. *I'm* not forcing her—she is running away from you and your way of living ...' Eugene began.

'What the hell is he talking about?' Andy said.

'The tragic history of our fair land,' Jack Holland exclaimed. 'Alien power sapped our will to resist.'

'They get girls with dope,' the Ferret said. 'Many an Irish girl ends up in the white-slave traffic in Piccadilly. Foreigners run it. All foreigners.'

'Where's your wife, Mister? Would you answer that?' Andy said.

'And what are you doing with my daughter?' my father asked fiercely, as if recollecting what they had come for.

'I'm not *doing* anything with her,' Eugene said, and I thought, he has shed all responsibility for me, he does not love me.

'You're a foreigner,' Andy said contemptuously.

'Not at all,' Eugene said pleasantly. 'Not at all as foreign as *your* tiny, blue, Germanic eyes, my friend.'

'What are your intentions?' my father asked abruptly. And then he must have drawn the anonymous letter from his pocket, because he said, 'There's a few things here would make your hair stand on end.'

'He hasn't much hair, he's near bald,' the Ferret said.

216

'I haven't any *intentions*; I suppose in time I would like to marry her and have children. ... Who knows?'

'Ah, the patter of little feet,' said Jack Holland idiotically, and Dada told him to shut up and stop making a fool of himself.

He doesn't really want me, I thought as I took short, quick breaths and said an Act of Contrition, thinking that I was near my end. I don't know why I stayed under there, it was stifling.

'Would you turn?' my father said, and of course Eugene did not know what he meant by that.

'Turn?' he asked, in a puzzled voice.

'Be a Catholic,' the Ferret said. And then Eugene sighed and said, 'Why don't we all have a cup of tea?' And Dada said, 'Yes, yes.'

It will go on all night and I'll be found dead under this bed, I thought as I wished more and more that I could scratch a place between my shoulder-blades which itched terribly.

*

When he opened the door to fetch some tea he must have found Anna listening at the keyhole, because I heard him say to her, 'Oh Anna, you're here, can you bring us a tray of tea, please?' And then he seemed to go out of the room, because suddenly they were all talking at once.

'She could have got out the back way,' my father said.

'Get tough, boy, get tough,' Andy said. 'Follow him out, you fool, before he makes a run for it.'

'Poor Brady,' the Ferret said when Dada had apparently gone out, 'that's the thanks he gets for sending that little snotty-nose to a convent and giving her a fine education.'

'She was never right, that one,' cousin Andy said, 'reading books and talking to trees. Her mother spoilt her. ...'

'Ah, her dear mother,' said Jack Holland, and while he raved on about Mama being a lady, the other two passed remarks about the portrait of Eugene over the fire.

'Look at the nose of him—you know what he is? They'll be running this bloody country soon,' Andy said.

'God 'tis a bloody shame, ruining a girl like that,' Andy said, and I thought how baffled they'd be if they had known that I was not seduced yet, even though I had slept in his bed for two whole nights.

I heard the rattle of cups as Eugene and my father came back.

'How much money do you earn in a year?' my father asked, and

217

I knew how they would sneer if they heard that he made poky little films about rats, and sewerage.

'I earn lots of money,' Eugene lied.

'You're old enough to be her father,' Dada said. 'You're nearly as old as myself.'

'Look,' Eugene said after a minute, 'where is all this ill-temper going to get us? Why don't you go down to the village and stay in the hotel for the night, then come up in the morning and discuss it with Caithleen. She won't be so frightened in the morning and I will try and get her to agree to seeing you.'

'Not on your bloody life,' cousin Andy said.

'We'll not go without her,' my father added threateningly, and I lost heart then and knew that there was no escape. They would find me and pull me forth. We would go out in the wind and sit in the Ferret's car and drive all night, while they abused me. If only Baba was there, she'd find a way. ...

'She's over twenty-one, you can't force her,' Eugene said, 'not even in Ireland.'

'Can't we? We won our fight for freedom. It's our country now,' Andy said.

'We can have her put away. She's not all there,' my father said.

'Mental,' the Ferret added.

'What about that, Mister?' cousin Andy shouted. 'A very serious offence having to do with a mentally affected girl. You could get twenty years for that.'

I gritted my teeth, my head boiled—why was I such a coward as to stay under there? They'd make a goat ashamed. Tears of rage and shame ran over the back of my hand and I wanted to scream, I disown them, they're nothing to do with me, don't connect me with them, but I said nothing—just waited.

'Go and get her,' my father said. *'Now!'* And I imagined the spits that shot out of his mouth in anger.

'You heard what Mr Brady said,' cousin Andy shouted, and he must have risen from the bed because the springs lifted. I knew how ratty he must look with his small blue eyes, his red moustache, his stomach ulcer.

'Very well then,' Eugene said, 'she's in my legal care. A guest in my house. When she leaves she will do so of her own free will. Leave my house or I'll telephone for the police.' I wondered if they'd notice that there *was* no phone.

'You heard me,' Eugene said, and I thought, oh God he'll get hit.

Didn't he know how things ended—'Man in hospital with fifty-seven penknife wounds'. I started to struggle out, to give myself up.

I heard the first smack of their fists and then they must have knocked him over because the Tilley lamp crashed and the globe broke into smithereens.

I screamed as I got out and staggered up. Flames from the wood fire gave enough light for me to see by. Eugene was on the floor, trying to struggle up and Andy and the Ferret were hitting and kicking him. Jack Holland tried to hold them back, and my father, hardly knowing what he was doing, held the back of Jack Holland's coat, saying, 'Now Jack, now Jack, God save us, now Jack—oh Jack—'

My father saw me suddenly and must have thought that I had risen up from the ground—my hair was all tossed and there was fluff and dust on me. He opened his mouth so wide that his loose dental-plate dropped on to his tongue. They were cheap teeth that he had made by a dental mechanic.

'I didn't do it, I didn't do it, Maura,' he whispered, and backed away from me clutching his teeth. Long after, I realized that he thought I was Mama risen from her grave in the Shannon lake. I must have looked like a ghost; my face daubed with tears and grey dust, my hair hanging in my eyes.

I shouted at the Ferret to stop, when the door burst open and the room lit up with a great red and yellow flash, as Anna had fired the shot-gun at the ceiling. The thunder-clap made me stagger back against the bed with my head numb and singing. I tried to stay still, waiting to die. I thought I'd been shot, but it was only the shock of the explosion in my ears. The black smoke of gunpowder entered our throats and made me cough. Jack Holland was on his knees, praying and coughing, while Andy and the Ferret were turned to the door with their hands to their ears. My father leaned over a chair gasping, and Eugene moaned on the floor and put his hand to his bleeding nose. Shattered plaster fell down all over the carpet and the white dust mixed with gun smoke. The smell was awful.

'There's another one in it. I'll blow your brains out,' Anna said. She stood at the study door, in her nightdress, holding Eugene's shot-gun. Denis stood beside her with a lighted Christmas candle.

'Out you get,' she said to them, holding the gun steadily up.

'By God, I'm getting out of this,' the Ferret said. 'These people would kill you!' I went to Eugene, who was still sitting on the floor with blood coming from his nose. I put my handkerchief to it.

'Dangerous savages,' my father said, his face white, holding his teeth in one hand. 'She might have killed us.'

'I'll blow your feet off if you don't clear out of here,' Anna said in a quivering voice.

'Get out,' Eugene said to them as he stood up. His shirt was torn. 'Get out. Go. Leave. Never come inside my gates again.'

'Have you a drop of whisky?' my father said, shakily, putting his hand to his heart.

'No,' Eugene said. 'Leave my house, immediately.'

'A pretty night's work, a pretty night's work,' Jack Holland said sadly, as they left. Anna stood to one side to let them pass and Denis opened the hall door. The last thing I saw was the Ferret's hooked iron hand being shaken back at us.

Eugene slammed the door and Denis bolted it. I collapsed on to the bed, trembling.

'That's the way to handle them,' Anna said, as she put the gun on the table.

'You saved my life,' Eugene said, and he sat on the couch and drew up the leg of his trousers. There was blood on his shin, where he had been kicked. His nose also was bleeding.

'I'm sorry, I'm sorry,' I said between sobs.

'Oh tough men, tough men,' Denis said solemnly as we heard them outside arguing, and the dog barking from the back yard.

'Get some iodine,' Eugene said. I went upstairs but couldn't find it, so Anna had to go and get it, along with a clean towel and a basin of water. He lay back on the armchair, and I opened his shoe-laces and took off his shoes.

'Wh'ist,' Denis said. We heard the car drive away.

Anna washed the cuts on Eugene's face and legs. He squirmed with pain as she swabbed on iodine.

'I shouldn't have hidden,' I said, handing him a clean handkerchief from the top drawer of his desk, where he kept them. 'Oh, I shouldn't have come here.'

Through the handkerchief he said, 'Go get yourself a drink. It will help you to stop shaking. Get me one too.'

After a while the nose-bleed stopped and he raised his head and looked at me. His upper lip had swollen.

'It was terrible,' I said.

'It was' he said, 'ridiculous. Like this country.'

'Only for me where would we be?' Anna said.

'What about a cup of tea?' He said in a sad voice, and I knew

220

that he would never forget what had happened and that some of their conduct had rubbed off on to me.

*

15. STORY: "KOREA"

JOHN MCGAHERN

The novels of John McGahern (b. 1935) are contemporary with Edna O'Brien's and his background has some similarities with hers, though his mood is vastly different. His father was a police sergeant in a small midland town, where rural Ireland crowds claustrophobically up against mean streets. His first novel, *The Barracks* (1963), is a study of internecine rivalry and marital frustration in this provincial setting. His second book, *The Dark* (1965), is concerned with adolescence, religion and tightly felt family relationships. The story has some of the intensity of Joyce's *Portrait of the Artist as a Young Man*. All McGahern's writings, including *The Leavetaking* (1974), suggest an autobiographical flavour. His vision is sombre in the extreme, reflecting a yearning despair and disillusionment, a not uncommon mood in latter-day Ireland.

The story given here is from *Nightlines* (1970), a collection which has already appeared in German, French and Scandinavian translations.

John McGahern

KOREA

'You saw an execution then too, didn't you?' I asked my father, and
he started to tell as he rowed. He'd been captured in an ambush in
late 1919, and they were shooting prisoners in Mountjoy as
reprisals at that time. He thought it was he who'd be next, for after
a few days they moved him to the cell next to the prison yard. He
could see out through the bars. But no rap to prepare himself came
to the door that night, and at daybreak he saw the two prisoners
they'd decided to shoot being marched out: a man in his early
thirties, and what was little more than a boy, sixteen or seventeen,
and he was weeping. They blindfolded the boy, but the man refused
the blindfold. When the officer shouted, the boy clicked to
attention, but the man stayed as he was, chewing very slowly. He
had his hands in his pockets.

'Take your hands out of your pockets,' the officer shouted again,
there was irritation in the voice.

The man slowly shook his head.

'It's a bit too late now in the day for that,' he said.

The officer then ordered them to fire, and as the volley rang, the
boy tore at his tunic over the heart, as if to pluck out the bullets,
and the buttons of the tunic began to fly into the air before he
pitched forward on his face.

The other heeled quietly over on his back; it must have been
because of the hands in the pockets.

The officer dispatched the boy with one shot from the revolver as
he lay face downward, but he pumped five bullets in rapid
succession into the man, as if to pay him back for not coming to
attention.

'When I was on my honeymoon years after, it was May, and we
took the tram up the hill of Howth from Sutton Cross. We sat on
top in the open on the wooden seats with the rail around that made
it like a small ship. The sea was below, and the smell of the sea and
furze bloom all about, and then I looked down and saw the furze

224

pods bursting, and the way they burst in all directions seemed shocking like the buttons when he started to tear at his tunic; I couldn't get it out of my mind all day; it destroyed the day,' he said.

'It's a wonder their hands weren't tied?' I asked him as he rowed between the black navigation pan and the red where the river flowed into Oakport.

'I suppose it was because they were considered soldiers.'

'Do you think the boy stood to attention because he felt that he might still get off if he obeyed the rules?'

'Sounds a bit highfalutin to me. Comes from going to school too long,' he said aggressively, and I was silent. It was new to me to hear him talk about his own life at all. Before, if I asked him about the war, he'd draw fingers across his eyes as if to tear a spider web away, but it was my last summer with him on the river, and it seemed to make him want to talk, to give of himself before it ended.

Hand over hand I drew in the line that throbbed with fish; there were two miles of line, a hook on a lead line every three yards. The licence allowed us a thousand hooks, but we used more. We were the last to fish this freshwater for a living.

As the eels came in over the side I cut them loose with a knife into a wire cage, where they slid over each other in their own oil, the twisted eel hook in their mouths. The other fish—pike choked on hooked perch they'd tried to swallow, bream, roach—I slid up the floorboards towards the bow of the boat. We'd sell them in the village or give them away. The hooks that hadn't been taken I cleaned and stuck in rows round the side of the wooden box. I let the line fall in its centre. After a mile he took my place in the stern and I rowed. People hadn't woken yet, and the early morning cold and mist were on the river. Outside of the slow ripple of the oars and the threshing of the fish on the line beaded with running drops of water as it came in, the river was dead silent, except for the occasional lowing of cattle on the banks.

'Have you any idea what you'll do after this summer?' he asked.

'No. I'll wait and see what comes up,' I answered.

'How do you mean *what comes up*?'

'Whatever result I get in the exam. If the result is good, I'll have choices. If it's not, there won't be choices. I'll have to take what I can get.'

'How good do you think they'll be?'

'I think they'll be all right, but there's no use counting chickens, is there?'

'No,' he said, but there was something calculating in the face; it

225

made me watchful of him as I rowed the last stretch of the line. The day had come, the distant noises of the farms and the first flies on the river, by the time we'd lifted the large wire cage out of the bulrushes, emptied in the morning's catch of eels, and sunk it again.

'We'll have enough for a consignment tomorrow,' he said.

Each week we sent the eels live to Billingsgate in London.

'But say, say even if you do well, you wouldn't think of throwing this country up altogether and going to America?' he said, the words fumbled for as I pushed the boat, using the oar as a pole, out of the bulrushes after sinking the cage of eels, the mud rising a dirty yellow between the stems.

'Why America?'

'Well, it's the land of opportunity, isn't it, a big, expanding country; there's no room for ambition in this poky place. All there's room for is to make holes in pints of porter.'

I was wary of the big words, they were not in his voice or any person's voice.

'Who'd pay the fare?' I asked.

'We'd manage that. We'd scrape it together somehow.'

'Why should you scrape for me to go to America if I can get a job here?'

'I feel I'd be giving you a chance I never got. I fought for this country. And now they want to take away even the licence to fish. Will you think about it anyhow?'

'I'll think about it,' I answered.

Through the day he trimmed the brows of ridges in the potato field while I replaced the hooks on the line and dug worms, pain of doing things for the last time as well as the boredom the knowledge brings that soon there'll be no need to do them, that they could be discarded almost now. The guilt of leaving came: I was discarding his life to assume my own, a man to row the boat would eat into the decreasing profits of the fishing, and it was even not certain he'd get renewal of his licence. The tourist board had opposed the last application. They said we impoverished the coarse fishing for tourists—the tourists who came every summer from Liverpool and Birmingham in increasing numbers to sit in aluminium deck chairs on the riverbank and fish with rods. The fields we had would be a bare living without the fishing, and it'd be vinegar for him to turn what he called boarding-house zookeeper.

I saw him stretch across the wall in conversation with the cattle-dealer Farrell as I came round to put the worms where we stored them in clay in the darkness of the lavatory. Farrell leaned

on the bar of his bicycle on the road. I passed into the lavatory
thinking they talked about the price of cattle, but as I emptied the
worms into the box, the word *Moran* came, and I carefully opened
the door to listen. It was my father's voice; it was excited.

'I know. I heard the exact sum. They got ten thousand dollars
when Luke was killed. Every American soldier's life is insured to
the tune of ten thousand dollars.'

'I heard they get two hundred and fifty dollars a month each for
Michael and Sam while they're serving,' he went on.

'They're buying cattle leftandright,' Farrell's voice came as I
closed the door and stood in the darkness, in the smell of shit and
piss and the warm fleshy smell of worms crawling in too little clay.

The shock I felt was the shock I was to feel later when I made
some social blunder, the splintering of a self-esteem, and the need
to crawl into some lavatory and think.

Luke Moran's body had come from Korea in a leaden casket,
had crossed the stone bridge to the slow funeral bell with the big
cars from the embassy behind, the coffin draped in the Stars and
Stripes. Shots had been fired above the grave before they threw in
the clay. There were photos of his decorations being presented to
his family by a military attaché.

He'd scrape the fare, I'd be conscripted there, each month he'd
get so many dollars while I served, and he'd get ten thousand if I
was killed.

In the darkness of the lavatory between the boxes of crawling
worms before we set the night line for the eels I knew my youth had
ended.

I rowed as he let out the night line, his fingers baiting each
twisted hook so beautifully that it seemed a single movement. The
dark was closing from the shadow of Oakport to Nutley's
boathouse, bats made ugly whirls overhead, the wings of ducks
shirred as they curved down into the bay.

'Have you thought about what I said about going to America?'
he asked, without lifting his eyes from the hooks and the box of
worms.

'I have.'

The oars dipped in the water without splash, the hole whorling
wider in the calm as it slipped past him on the stern seat.

'Have you decided to take the chance then?'

'No. I'm not going.'

'You won't be able to say I didn't give you the chance when you
come to nothing in this fool of a country. It'll be your own funeral.'

'It'll be my own funeral,' I answered, and asked after a long silence, 'As you grow older, do you find your own days in the war and jails coming much back to you?'

'I do. And I don't want to talk about them. Talking about the execution disturbed me no end, those cursed buttons bursting into the air. And the most I think is that if I'd conducted my own wars, and let the fool of a country fend for itself, I'd be much better off today. And I don't want to talk about it.'

I knew this silence was fixed forever as I rowed in silence till he asked, 'Do you think, will it be much good tonight?'

'It's too calm,' I answered.

'Unless the night wind gets up,' he said anxiously.

'Unless a night wind,' I repeated.

As the boat moved through the calm water and the line slipped through his fingers over the side I'd never felt so close to him before, not even when he'd carried me on his shoulders above the laughing crowd to the Final. Each move he made I watched as closely as if I too had to prepare myself to murder.

16. POEM

PADRAIC FIACC

Inevitably the question arises: what has been the impact on literature of the recent years of violence in the North—with the constant threat, sometimes appearing imminent, sometimes receding, of an overspill of fighting into the South?

No new O'Casey has appeared to set the Northern tragedy on the stage. But Brian Friel's *The Freedom of the City* (1973) should be mentioned. Set in the Derry of 1970, it portrays the tragedy of three individuals caught in the crossfire of rioting and crazy rumour that followed the early Civil Rights marches. Patrick Galvin's *We do it for Love* (1975) is a play in the tragi-comic Brecht tradition, advocating reconciliation. In fiction, one may find the full gamut from the sensational IRA thriller to the introspection of Kevin Casey's *Dreams of Revenge* (1977) or to Benedict Kiely's sombre variant on the hostage theme, *Proxopera* (1977).

But it is on poetry that the main impact has shown. Indeed it seems hardly coincidence that over half the younger Irish poets publishing today are Northerners, and scarcely any poet, north or south, has failed to reflect in at least some work the pervading sense of doom or foreboding and the agonized reappraisal of the whole national condition engendered by the political events.

In a thoughtful essay, published in 1975, the Belfast poet Padraic Fiacc (b. 1924) describes how for a while he struggled to keep his poetic vision clear of politics, but finally succumbed. For a poet, he found: "There is a time to keep silence and a time to speak."

Perusal of the contemporary press, unfortunately, will show that the raw, brutal poem which follows is no exaggerated witness.

Padraic Fiacc

POEM

CHRIST GOODBYE

Or how we turn Christ into an "inhuman martyr" in Belfast

I

Dandering home from work at mid
-night, they tripped Him up on a ramp
asked Him if He were a "Catholic" ...

A wee bit soft in the head He was,
the last person in the world you'd want
to hurt:
    His arms and legs, broken,
His genitals roasted with a ship
-yard worker's blow lamp.

II

In all the stories that the Christian Brothers
tell you of Christ He never screamed
like this. Surely this is not the way
to show a "manly bearing"
screaming for them to PLEASE STOP!
and then, later, screaming for death!

When they made Him wash the stab
wounds at the sink, they kept on
hammering Him with the pick
-axe handle; then they pulled
Christ's trousers down, threatening to
"cut off His balls"!
                Poor boy Christ, for when
they finally got round to finishing Him off
by shooting Him in the back of the head
"The poor Fenian fucker was already dead!"

230

17. TWO POEMS

JOHN HEWITT

If the poet is the intuitive recorder of the deeper life behind history, John Hewitt (b. 1907) is a forerunner. Long before the smouldering volcano erupted, a poignant short poem, "The Glens", caught the Northern mood, the tragedy of a people of divided allegiance, passionately attached to the countryside of their birth, yet conscious of the centrifugal pull of two bitterly opposing national traditions. This early poem has, with justification, appeared in so many anthologies that Hewitt has asked for it not to be included here. Instead, "The Dilemma (1969)" frames the same unhappy question.

Hewitt is of Protestant stock. Born in Belfast, he spent his later life in England where for fifteen years he was curator of an art gallery in Coventry. He has now, strangely, some would say, returned to the troubled province of his boyhood for his retirement.

The last couplet of "An Irishman in Coventry" refers to the Irish legend of the children of Lir who were turned into swans until the tolling of the first Christian bell should free them from their captivity, a symbol, it would seem, for the bondage of the divided province.

John Hewitt

TWO POEMS

THE DILEMMA (1969)

Born in this island, maimed by history
and creed-infected, by my father taught
the stubborn habit of unfettered thought
I dreamed, like him, all people should be free.
So, while my logic steered me well outside
that ailing church which claims dominion
over the questing spirit, I denied
all credence to the state by rebels won
from a torn nation, rigged to guard their gain,
though they assert their love of liberty,
which craft has narrowed to a fear of Rome.
So, since this ruptured country is my home,
it long has been my bitter luck to be
caught in the cross-fire of their false campaign.

AN IRISHMAN IN COVENTRY

A full year since, I took this eager city,
the tolerance that laced its blatant roar,
its famous steeples and its web of girders,
as image of the state hope argued for,
and scarcely flung a bitter thought behind me
on all that flaws the glory and the grace
which ribbons through the sick, guilt-clotted legend
of my creed-haunted, Godforsaken race.
My rhetoric swung round from steel's high promise
to the precision of the well-gauged tool,
tracing the logic in the vast glass headlands,
the clockwork horse, the comprehensive school.

Then, sudden, by occasion's chance concerted,
in enclave of my nation, but apart,
the jigging dances and the lilting fiddle
stirred the old rage and pity in my heart.
The faces and the voices blurring round me,
the strong hands long familiar with the spade,
the whiskey-tinctured breath, the pious buttons,
called up a people endlessly betrayed
by our own weakness, by the wrongs we suffered
in that long twilight over bog and glen,
by force, by famine and by glittering fables
which gave us martyrs when we needed men,
by faith which had no charity to offer,
by poisoned memory and by ready wit,
with poverty corroded into malice
to hit and run and howl when it is hit.

This is our fate: eight hundred years' disaster
crazily tangled as the Book of Kells,
the dream's distortion and the land's division,
the midnight raiders and the prison cells.
Yet like Lir's children banished to the waters
our hearts still listen for the landward bells.

18. SEVEN POEMS

JOHN MONTAGUE

"Premonition" is the title of the opening poem of John Montague's third collection, *Tides* (1970). It is far from being a political poem and was written before street-fighting brought Northern Ireland into the world news. Yet this vignette of nightmare and love seems to have caught from the air the impending terror. The same note is petrified into passivity in the poetic-prose item "Coming Events".

John Montague was born in 1929 in New York, where his father, a Catholic, had fled to exile and bitterness after the Republican side he espoused was defeated in the first Irish civil war. The son returned to spend his childhood at the family home near the village of Garvaghey, which means the rough field, in County Tyrone. This is another of those border regions where Catholic and Protestant are almost equally matched in numbers, the Catholics being the poorer, the under-privileged sector. "The Wild Dog Rose" depicts a character incident from this rural childhood.

Montague's most ambitious work to date is a sequence of poems, *The Rough Field*, published in 1972 in an edition skilfully incorporating old woodcuts from John Derricke's *The Image of Ireland, 1581.* (This is a new genre of Irish publishing initiated by Liam Miller of the Dolmen Press.) News-clippings, Old Rhymes, politicians' speeches from past and present, and Orange Lodge resolutions are woven into the text. The book forms a unity, integrating thoughts and memories, personal, familial, communal, into a vision of the poet's home area and the unhappiness of its historical destiny. "One explores an inheritance to free oneself and others," he has written in an introductory note. It is difficult to give the quality of such a poem through extracts, because the effect is cumulative, but hopefully one passage, "The Sound of a Wound", will convey a flavour. Another section of the poem, "A New Siege", earlier published separately, parallels the events in Londonderry of the early 1970's with the famous siege of that city in 1689.

Much of Montague's work has been concerned with themes of exile and the nostalgic longing for home. "Soliloquy on a Southern Strand", from the earlier collection, *Poisoned Lands* (1961 and 1977), and "Windharp", from *A Slow Dance* (1975), reflect this preoccupation.

In 1978 he published a more confessional sequence, *The Great Cloak*, chronicling the breakdown of a marriage and the fulfilment of a new union, from which "She Dreams" is taken.

SEVEN POEMS

PREMONITION

I

The darkness comes slowly alight.
That flow of red hair I recognise
Over the knob of the shoulder
Down your pale, freckled skin,
The breasts I have never seen;
But slowly the line of the tresses
Begins to stir, with a movement

That is not hair, but blood
Flowing. Someone is cutting
Your naked body up:
Strapped in dream helplessness
I hear each thrust of the knife
Till that rising, descending blade
Seems the final meaning of life.

Mutely, you writhe and turn
In tremors of ghostly pain,
But I am lost to intervene,
Blood, like a scarlet curtain,
Swinging across the brain
Till the light switches off—
And silence is darkness again.

II

On the butcher's block
Of the operating theatre
You open your eyes.
Far away, I fall back
Towards sleep, the Liffey
Begins to rise, and knock
Against the quay walls

The gulls curve and scream
Over the Four Courts, over
This ancient creaking house
Where, released from dream,
I lie in a narrow room;
Low-ceilinged as a coffin
The dawn prises open

COMING EVENTS

In the Stadsmuzeum at Bruges, there is a picture by Geerard David of a man being flayed. Four craftsmen are concerned with the figure on the table: one is opening the left arm, another lifting away the right nipple, a third incising the right arm while the last (his knife caught between his teeth) is unwinding the results of his labour so as to display the rich network of veins under the skin of the left leg. The only expression in the faces of those looking on is a mild admiration: the Burgmeister has caught up the white folds of his ermine gown and is gazing into the middle distance. It is difficult even to say that there is any expression on the face of the victim, although his teeth are gritted and the cords attaching his writs to the legs of the table are stretched tight. The whole scene may be intended as an allegory of human suffering but what the line of perspective leads us to admire is the brown calfskin of the principal executioner's boots.

THE WILD DOG ROSE

I go to say goodbye to the *Cailleach*[1]
that terrible figure who haunted my childhood
but no longer harsh, a human being
merely, hurt by event.
           The cottage,
circled by trees, weathered to admonitory

---

[1] *Cailleach*: Irish and Scots Gaelic for an old woman, a hag.

238

shapes of desolation by the mountain winds,
struggles into view. The rank thistles
and leathery bracken of untilled fields
stretch behind with—a final outcrop—
the hooped figure by the roadside,
its retinue of dogs
                which give tongue
as I approach, with savage, whinging cries
so that she slowly turns, a moving nest
of shawls and rags, to view, to stare
the stranger down.
              And I feel again
that ancient awe, the terror of a child
before the great hooked nose, the cheeks
dewlapped with dirt, the staring blue
of the sunken eyes, the mottled claws
clutching a stick
              but now hold
and return her gaze, to greet her,
as she greets me, in friendliness.
Memories have wrought reconciliation
between us, we talk in ease at last,
like old friends, lovers almost,
sharing secrets.
            Of neighbours
she quarrelled with, who now lie
in Garvaghey graveyard, beyond all hatred;
of my family and hers, how she never married,
though a man came asking in her youth.
"You would be loath to leave your own"
she sighs, "and go among strangers"—
his parish ten miles off.
            For sixty years
since she has lived alone, in one place.
Obscurely honoured by such confidences,
I idle by the summer roadside, listening,
while the monologue falters, continues,
rehearsing the small events of her life.
The only true madness is loneliness,
the monotonous voice in the skull
that never stops
            because never heard.

239

John Montague

II

And there
Where the dog rose shines in the hedge
she tells me a story so terrible
that I try to push it away,
my bones melting.

Late at night
a drunk came, beating at her door
to break it in, the bolt snapping
from the soft wood, the thin mongrels
rushing to cut, but yelping as
he whirls with his farm boots
to crush their skulls.

In the darkness
they wrestle, two creatures crazed
with loneliness, the smell of the
decaying cottage in his nostrils
like a drug, his body heavy on hers,
the tasteless trunk of a seventy year
old virgin, which he rummages while
she battles for life

bony fingers
reaching desperately to push
against his bull neck. "I prayed
to the Blessed Virgin herself
for help and after a time
I broke his grip."

He rolls
to the floor, snores asleep,
while she cowers until dawn
and the dogs' whimpering starts
him awake, to lurch back across
the wet bog.

III

And still
the dog rose shines in the hedge.
Petals beaten wide by rain, it
sways slightly, at the tip of a
slender, tangled, arching branch
which, with her stick, she gathers
into us.

240

       "The wild rose
is the only rose without thorns"
she says, holding a wet blossom
for a second, in a hand knotted
as the knob of her stick.
"Whenever I see it, I remember
the Holy Mother of God and
all she suffered."
       Briefly
the air is strong with the smell
of that weak flower, offering
its crumbling yellow cup
and pale bleeding lips
fading to white
         at the rim
of each bruised and heart-
shaped petal.

John Montague

THE SOUND OF A WOUND

      Who knows
the sound a wound makes?
      Scar tissue
can rend, the old hurt
      tear open as
the torso of the fiddle
      groans to
carry the tune, to carry
      the pain of
a lost (slow herds of cattle
      roving over
soft meadow, dark bogland)
      pastoral rhythm.

      I assert
a civilisation died here;
      it trembles
underfoot where I walk these
      small, sad hills:
it rears in my blood stream
      when I hear
a bleat of Saxon condescension,
      Westminster
to hell, it is less than these
      strangely carved
five thousand year resisting stones,
      that lonely cross.

      This bitterness
I inherit from my father, the
      swarm of blood
to the brain, the vomit surge
      of race hatred,
the victim seeing the oppressor,
      bold Jacobean
planter, or gadget laden marine,
      who has scatter-
ed his household gods, used
      his people
as servants, flushed his women
      like game.

242

SOLILOQUY ON A SOUTHERN STRAND

A priest, holidaying on the coast outside Sydney,
thinks nostalgically of his boyhood in Ireland

When I was young, it was much simpler;
I saw God standing on a local hill,
His eyes were gentle and soft birds
Sang in chorus to his voice until
My body trembled, ardent in submission.
The friar came to preach the yearly sermon
For Retreat, and cried among the flaring candles:
"O children, children if you but knew,
"Each hair is counted, everything you do
"Offends or sweetens His five wounds!"
A priest with a harsh and tuneless voice,
Raising his brown-robed arms to cry:
"Like this candle-end, the body gutters out to die!"
Calling us all to do penance and rejoice.

Hearing the preacher speak, I knew my mind
And wished to serve, leaving the friendly farm
For years of college. At first I found it strange
And feared the boys with smoother hands and voices:
I lay awake at night, longed for home.
I heard the town boys laughing in the dark
At things that made me burn with shame,
And where the votive candles whispered into wax
Hesitantly I spoke my treasured doubts,
Conquering all my passions in your Name.
I weathered years of sameness
Until I stood before the Cathedral altar,
A burly country boy but new-made priest;
My mother watched in happiness and peace.

John Montague

WINDHARP (*for Patrick Collins*)

The sounds of Ireland,
that restless whispering
you never get away
from, seeping out of
low bushes and grass,
heatherbells and fern,
wrinkling bog pools,
scraping tree branches,
light hunting cloud,
sound hounding sight,
a hand ceaselessly
combing and stroking
the landscape, till
the valley gleams
like the pile upon
a mountain pony's coat.

SHE DREAMS

Habituée of darkness I have become,
Familiar of the secret feeding grounds
Where terror and dismay ceaselessly hatch,
Black forms curling and uncoiling;
The demons of the night feel like friends.

Something furry brushes along my arm,
A bat or screech owl hurtling by.
I clamber over stained rocks and find
The long gathered contents of our house
Swarming with decay, a filthied nest.

I came to where the eggs lay in the grass.
I watched them for a long time, warming them
With my swollen eyes. One after another
They chipped, and scraggy heads appeared;
The embryos of our unborn children.

They turn towards me, croaking "Mother!"
I gather them up into my apron
But the shape of the house has fallen
And you are asleep by the water's edge:
A wind and wave picked skeleton.

19. FOUR POEMS

RICHARD MURPHY

A Southern contemporary of Montague's, Richard Murphy (b. 1927), a Protestant, has also been concerned with meditations on historic themes and their echoes in popular memory today. A long poem, *The Battle of Aughrim* (1968), recalls nostalgically the last great battle when the Catholic Irish followers of England's James II were defeated by the Protestant forces of William of Orange. The extract given here, "The Wolfhound", has now been published as an isolated lyric, but within the longer poem the lost hound serves as a symbol of the defeated nation. It is also a good illustration of the extreme classicism of Murphy's style, where unadorned, staccato sentences serve to focus undivided attention on the image evoked.

Murphy's home is on the picturesque west coast of Connemara and many of his poems are about the lives of the fishermen there and on the neighbouring islands. He himself bought a local trawler in which he would take friends and visitors sailing. Such expeditions are the background to two of his collections, *Sailing to an Island* (1955) and *The Last Galway Hooker* (1961). His home has often been a meeting-place for fellow-poets, and the uncollected "For Sylvia Plath" refers to this.

"The Reading Lesson" describes the struggle to teach a tinker, or Irish gypsy boy, to read. "Enigma" is the discovery of a new love.

Richard Murphy

FOUR POEMS

THE WOLFHOUND

1

A wolfhound sits under a wild ash
Licking the wound in a dead ensign's neck.

When guns cool at night with bugles in fog
She points over the young face.

All her life a boy's pet.
Prisoners are sabred and the dead are stripped.

Her ear pricks like a crimson leaf on snow,
The horse-carts creak away.

Vermin by moonlight pick
The tongues and sockets of six thousand skulls.

She pines for his horn to blow
To bay in triumph down the track of wolves.

Her forelegs stand like pillars through a seige,
His Toledo sword corrodes.

Nights she lopes to the scrub
And trails back at dawn to guard a skeleton.

Wind shears the berries from the rowan tree,
The wild geese have flown.

She lifts her head to cry
As a woman keens in a famine for her son.

A redcoat, stalking, cocks
His flintlock when he hears the wolfhound growl.

Her fur bristles with fear at the new smell,
Snow has betrayed her lair.

"I'll sell you for a packhorse
You antiquated bigoted papistical bitch!"

She springs: in self-defence he fires his gun.
People remember this.

By turf embers she gives tongue
When the choirs are silenced in wood and stone.

THE READING LESSON

Fourteen years old, learning the alphabet,
He finds letters harder to catch than hares
Without a greyhound. Can't I give him a dog
To track them down, or put them in a cage?
He's caught in a trap, until I let him go,
Pinioned by "Don't you want to learn to read?"
"I'll be the same man whatever I do."

He looks at a page as a mule balks at a gap
From which a goat may hobble out and bleat.
His eyes jink from a sentence like flushed snipe
Escaping shot. A sharp word, and he'll mooch
Back to his piebald mare and bantam cock.
Our purpose is as tricky to retrieve
As mercury from a smashed thermometer.

"I'll not read any more." Should I give up?
His hands, long-fingered as a Celtic scribe's,
Will grow callous, gathering sticks or scrap;
Exploring pockets of the horny drunk
Loiterers at the fairs, giving them lice.
A neighbour chuckles. "You can never tame
The wild-duck: when his wings grow, he'll fly off."

If books resembled roads, he'd quickly read:
But they're small farms to him, fenced by the page,
Ploughed into lines, with letters drilled like oats:
A field of tasks he'll always be outside.
If words were bank-notes, he would filch a wad;
If they were pheasants, they'd be in his pot
For breakfast, or if wrens he'd make them king.

ENIGMA

Her hair has a sweet smell of girlhood under his face
    Darkening the moon on her pillow.

Tenderly her fingertips probe the furrows of his temple
    And find the questionmark of an ear.

How can she play in the rubble of his pleasure ground
    Paths overgrown with laurel and briar?

How can he pick the fruit she will bear in time to come
    On her lips' not yet flowering bud?

Her future is an apple tree, his past a dark old yew
    Growing together in this orchard now.

FOR SYLVIA PLATH
1932–1963

Let's violate the tower
And carve your initials on the Coole tree,
Child of the Cape Cod shore:

Then steal apples from Yeats,
While over our heads in beaked out masonry
Jackdaws perch, like fates.

We breathe Atlantic air.
A squeaking bat you startle sticks to me,
Toothed like a vampire.

The blackthorn has a sloe
Bitter to bite. I know you love the yew
Whose leaves at my birth-place sough.

On my boat like a figurehead
You kneel to smell the deaths that oil the sea,
Cowled in the moon's hood.

I dread your crystal power
Tranced over a wine-glass like a gipsy
To brew the black shower.

Gone, you write from a graveyard,
And truths like headstone whitecaps furled away
Out in a great swell flood.

O Shade, at the moon's edge,
You took the tower lamp for a guide at sea.
We sound for anchorage.

20. EIGHT POEMS

THOMAS KINSELLA

In his own great epitaph, *Under Ben Bulben*, W. B. Yeats gave the following advice to his successors:

> *Irish poets, learn your trade,*
> *Sing whatever is well made,*
> *Scorn the sort now growing up*
> *All out of shape from toe to top.*

Of all poets since, Thomas Kinsella (b. 1929) is the one who appears to have taken that advice most to heart. There are even curious parallels in the work of the two men. We find the same dedicated craftsmanship manifesting itself in frequent revision even of the published work. Like Yeats, Kinsella's early poems are lyrical and romantic and change slowly to a personal classic tone. In both, a steady theme is suffering associated with human love—in Kinsella's case arising from the illness of the beloved—spurring the poet to an introspective awareness that a happier love might not have evoked. There is the same preoccupation with the passage of time and its effects on human lives, and human history. Most striking of all, in each case in middle age, when there were hints that poetic inspiration might be reaching a dead end in the exploration of purely private emotion, a sudden violent turn in Ireland's history offered a fresh, dynamic theme for work.

The first two poems here are from the 1958 collection, *Another September*. "A Lady of Quality" introduces us to the first of many hospital scenes. The rather Gothic imagery of "In the Ringwood" may need a little explanation for non-Irish readers. Vinegar Hill, overlooking the river Slaney in County Wexford, was the scene of one of the more savage episodes in Ireland's past when the insurrectionaries of 1798 were butchered (after doing a share of butchering themselves) by the British soldiery. The sense of blood in the air becomes associated in the poet's mind with the passion of Christ and the mortality of human love.

The ironic self-portrait "Prologue", which forms the introduction to the 1962 *Downstream* collection, shows us the poet approaching his quiet desperation of middle age. He was then a civil servant in the Irish

251

Thomas Kinsella

Department of Finance, an occupation he was shortly to leave for that of free-lance teacher and lecturer in the United States and at home.

Nightwalker and Other Poems followed six years later. The long title poem opens with the magnificently cryptic line:

I only know things seem and are not good.

This is a poem in which Kinsella integrates personal experience, religious faith, and mid-century political Ireland, seen as a microcosm of the world's ill, into a single synthesis. "First Light", "A Moment's Peace" and the prose-verse of "Wormwood" are from this volume.

On Sunday, 30 January 1972, thirteen unarmed Catholic demonstrators against British rule in Northern Ireland were shot down in the city of Derry. Kinsella visited the scene soon after, and was deeply moved. He did not need on this occasion to seek the impression of blood in the air. It was still visible on the streets. A few weeks later to the surprise of all, and the consternation of certain of his admirers, he produced a violently political satire, *Butcher's Dozen*. This is completely different from any of his other work, and indeed from that of any modern Irish poet. The antecedents are Swift and Dante. The poet imagines himself walking the streets of Derry as Dante walked Heaven, Purgatory and Hell. Shades of the recent past appear and describe the events of what has gone down in Irish history as 'Bloody Sunday'. The metre and savage indignation are Swift's.

Good poetry is what good poets feel deeply and express vigorously, and I have no hesitation in including this poem here, though I know some critics will disagree. The opening passage sets the scene, and we then meet first one, then a group of three of the victims. The third episode refers to another of the youthful victims who was alleged by the soldiery to have had a nail bomb sticking from his jeans pocket when they gathered up the body. A doctor who examined the body where it fell, and other witnesses, testified that he was unarmed. And so on.

Kinsella wrote another long poem around a public theme: *The Good Fight* (1973), a penetration in depth of the assassination of President Kennedy.

In his more recent work the poet seems to have returned to his early introspective manner, striving ever more deeply into the mysterious crux of human existence: *Notes from the Land of the Dead* (1972), *One* (1974) and *A Technical Supplement* (1976). "Finistère" comes from *One*.

EIGHT POEMS

A LADY OF QUALITY

IN hospital where windows meet
With sunlight in a pleasing feat
   Of airy architecture
My love has sweets and grapes to eat,
The air is like a laundered sheet,
   The world's a varnished picture.

Books and flowers at her head
Make living-quarters of her bed
   And give a certain style
To our pillow-chat, the nonsense said
To bless the room from present dread
   Just for a brittle while.

For obvious reasons we ignore
The leaping season out-of-door,
   Light lively as a ferret,
Woodland walks, a crocused shore,
The transcendental birds that soar
   And tumble in high spirit

While under this hygienic ceiling
Where my love lies down for healing
   Tiny terrors grow,
Reflected in a look, revealing
That her care is spent concealing
   What, perhaps, I know:

The ever-present crack in time
Forever sundering the lime-
   Paths and the fragrant fountains,
Photographed last summer, from
The unknown memory we climb
   To find in this year's mountains.

"Ended and done with" never ceases,
Constantly the heart releases
   Wild geese to the past.
Look, how they circle poignant places,
Falling to sorrow's fowling-pieces
   With soft plumage aghast.

We may regret, and must abide.
Grief, the hunter's, fatal stride
   Among the darkening hearts
Has gone too long on either side.
Our trophied love must now divide
   Into its separate parts

And you go down with womankind
Who in her beauty has combined
   And focused human hungers,
With country ladies who could wind
A nation's love-affair with mind
   Around their little fingers,

And I communicate again
Recovered order to my pen
   To find a further answer
As, having looked all night in vain,
A weary prince will sigh and then
   Take a familiar dancer.

Now the window's turning dark
And ragged rooks across the Park
   Mix with the branches; all
The clocks about the building mark
The hour. The random is at work
   On us: two petals fall,

A train lifts up a lonely cry ...
Our fingertips together lie
   Upon the counterpane.
It will be hard, it seems, and I
Would wish my heart to justify
   What qualities remain.

IN THE RINGWOOD

As I roved out impatiently
Good Friday with my bride
To drink in the rivered Ringwood
The Draughty season's pride
A fell dismay held suddenly
Our feet on the green hill-side.

The yellow Spring on Vinegar Hill,
The smile of Slaney water,
The wind that swept the Ringwood,
Grew dark with ancient slaughter.
My love cried out and I beheld her
Change to Sorrow's daughter.

"Ravenhair, what rending
Set those red lips a-shriek,
And dealt those locks in black lament
Like blows on your white cheek,
That in your looks outlandishly
Both woe and fury speak?"

As sharp a lance as the fatal heron
There on the sunken tree
Will strike in the stones of the river
Was the gaze she bent on me.
O her robe into her right hand
She gathered grievously.

"Many times the civil lover
Climbed that pleasant place,
Many times despairing
Died in his love's face,
His spittle turned to vinegar,
Blood in his embrace.

Love that is every miracle
Is torn apart and rent.
The human turns awry
The poles of the firmament.
The fish's bright side is pierced
And good again is spent.

255

Thomas Kinsella

Though every stem on Vinegar Hill
And stone on the Slaney's bed
And every leaf in the living Ringwood
Builds till it is dead
Yet heart and hand, accomplished,
Destroy until they dread.

Dread, a grey devourer,
Stalks in the shade of love.
The dark that dogs our feet
Eats what is sickened of.
The End that stalks Beginning
Hurries home its drove."

I kissed three times her shivering lips.
I drank their naked chill.
I watched the river shining
Where the heron wiped his bill.
I took my love in my icy arms
In the Spring on Ringwood Hill.

PROLOGUE

I wonder whether one expects
Flowing tie or expert sex
Or even absent-mindedness
Of poets any longer. Less
Candour than the average,
Less confidence, a ready rage,
Alertness when it comes to beer,
An affectation that their ear
For music is a little weak,
These are the attributes we seek;
But surely not the morning train,
The office lunch, the look of pain
Down the blotched suburban grass,
Not the weekly trance at Mass ...
Drawing on my sober dress
These, alas, I must confess.

I pat my wallet pocket, thinking
I can spare an evening drinking;
Humming as I catch the bus
Something by Sibelius,
Suddenly—or as I lend
A hand about the house, or bend
Low above an onion bed—
Memory stumbles in the head;
The sunlight flickers once upon
The massive shafts of Babylon
And ragged phrases in a flock
Settle softly, shock by shock.

And so my bored menagerie
Once more emerges: Energy,
Blinking, only half awake,
Gives its tiny frame a shake;
Fouling itself, a giantess,
The bloodshot bulk of Laziness
Obscures the vision; Discipline
Limps after them with jutting chin,
Bleeding badly from the calf;
Old Jaws-of-Death gives laugh for laugh
With Error as they amble past,
And there as usual, lying last,
Helped along by blind Routine,
Futility flogs a tambourine ...

From WORMWOOD

Beloved,
A little of what we have found ...
It is certain that maturity and peace are to be sought through
ordeal after ordeal, and it seems that the search continues until we
fail. We reach out after each new beginning, penetrating our
context to know ourselves, and our knowledge increases until we
recognise again (more profoundly each time) our pain, indignity
and triviality. This bitter cup is offered, heaped with curses, and we
must drink or die. And even though we drink we may also die, if

257

*every drop of bitterness—that rots the flesh—is not transmuted.
(Certainly the individual plight is hideous, each torturing each, but
we are guilty, seeing this, to believe that our common plight is only
hideous. Believing so, we make it so: pigs in a slaughteryard that
turn and savage each other in a common desperation and disorder.)
Death, either way, is guilt and failure. But if we drink the bitterness
and can transmute it and continue, we resume in candour and doubt
the only individual joy—the restored necessity to learn. Sensing a
wider scope, a more penetrating harmony, we begin again in a
higher innocence to grow toward the next ordeal:*

*Love also, it seems, will continue until we fail: in the sensing of
the wider scope, in the growth toward it, in the swallowing and
absorption of bitterness, in the resumed innocence ...*

FIRST LIGHT

A prone couple still sleeps.
Light ascends like a pale gas
Out of the sea: dawn–
Light, reaching across the hill
To the dark garden. The grass
Emerges, soaking with grey dew.

Inside, in silence, an empty
Kitchen takes form, tidied and swept,
Blank with marriage—where shrill
Lover and beloved have kept
Another vigil far
Into the night, and raved and wept.

Upstairs a whimper or sigh
Comes from an open bedroom door
And lengthens to an ugly wail
—A child enduring a dream
That grows, at the first touch of day,
Unendurable.

A MOMENT'S PEACE

Summer evening: reclining
Lovers, a pike near the bank,
Stone-still—carnivores,
Ephemerides, touched with gold.
The river surface flows
On in blank passion.

BUTCHER'S DOZEN: A LESSON
FOR THE OCTAVE OF WIDGERY

I went with Anger at my heel
Through Bogside of the bitter zeal
—Jesus pity!—on a day
Of cold and drizzle and decay.
A month had passed. Yet there remained
A murder smell that stung and stained.
On flats and alleys—over all—
It hung; on battered roof and wall,
On wreck and rubbish scattered thick,
On sullen steps and pitted brick.
And when I came where thirteen died
It shrivelled up my heart. I sighed
And looked about that brutal place
Of rage and terror and disgrace.
Then my moistened lips grew dry.
I had heard an answering sigh!
There in a ghostly pool of blood
A crumpled phantom hugged the mud:
"Once there lived a hooligan.
A pig came up, and away he ran.
Here lies one in blood and bones,
Who lost his life for throwing stones."
More voices rose. I turned and saw
Three corpses forming, red and raw,
From dirt and stone. Each upturned face

259

Stared unseeing from its place:
"Behind this barrier, blighters three,
We scrambled back and made to flee.
The guns cried *Stop*, and here lie we."
Then from left and right they came,
More mangled corpses, bleeding, lame,
Holding their wounds. They chose their ground,
Ghost by ghost, without a sound,
And one stepped forward, soiled and white:
"A bomber I. I travelled light
—Four pounds of nails and gelignite
About my person, hid so well
They seemed to vanish where I fell.
When the bullet stopped my breath
A doctor sought the cause of death.
He upped my shirt, undid my fly,
Twice he moved my limbs awry,
And noticed nothing. By and by
A soldier, with his sharper eye,
Beheld the four elusive rockets
Stuffed in my coat and trouser pockets.
Yes, they must be strict with us,
Even in death so treacherous!"
He faded, and another said:
"We three met close when we were dead.
Into an armoured car they piled us
Where our mingled blood defiled us,
Certain, if not dead before,
To suffocate upon the floor.
Careful bullets in the back
Stopped our terrorist attack,
And so three dangerous lives are done
—Judged, condemned and shamed in one."
That spectre faded in his turn.
A harsher stirred, and spoke in scorn:
"The shame is theirs, in word and deed,
Who prate of Justice, practise greed,
And act in ignorant fury—then,
Officers and gentlemen,
Send to their Courts for the Most High
To tell us did we really die!
Does it need recourse to law

260

To tell ten thousand what they saw?
Law that lets them, caught red-handed,
Halt the game and leave it stranded,
Summon up a sworn inquiry
And dump their conscience in the diary.
During which hiatus, should
Their legal basis vanish, good,
The thing is rapidly arranged:
Where's the law that can't be changed?
The news is out. The troops were kind.
Impartial justice has to find
We'd be alive and well today
If we had let them have their way.
Yet England, even as you lie,
You give the facts that you deny.
Spread the lie with all your power
—All that's left; it's turning sour.
Friend and stranger, bride and brother,
Son and sister, father, mother,
All not blinded by your smoke,
Photographers who caught your stroke,
The priests that blessed our bodies, spoke
And wagged our blood in the world's face.
The truth will out, to your disgrace."
He flushed and faded. Pale and grim,
A joking spectre followed him:
"Take a bunch of stunted shoots,
A tangle of transplanted roots,
Ropes and rifles, feathered nests,
Some dried colonial interests,
A hard unnatural union grown
In a bed of blood and bone,
Tongue of serpent, gut of hog
Spiced with spleen of underdog.
Stir in, with oaths of loyalty,
Sectarian supremacy,
And heat, to make a proper botch,
In a bouillon of bitter Scotch.
Last, the choice ingredient: you.
Now, to crown your Irish stew,
Boil it over, make a mess.
A most imperial success!"

Thomas Kinsella

He capered weakly, racked with pain,
His dead hair plastered in the rain;
The group was silent once again.
It seemed the moment to explain
That sympathetic politicians
Say our violent traditions,
Backward looks and bitterness
Keep us in this dire distress.
We must forget, and look ahead,
Nurse the living, not the dead.
My words died out. A phantom said:
"Here lies one who breathed his last
Firmly reminded of the past.
A trooper did it, on one knee,
In tones of brute authority."
That harsher spirit, who before
Had flushed with anger, spoke once more:
"Simple lessons cut most deep.
This lesson in our hearts we keep:
Persuasion, protest, arguments,
The milder forms of violence,
Earn nothing but polite neglect.
England, the way to your respect
Is via murderous force, it seems;
You push us to your own extremes.
You condescend to hear us speak
Only when we slap your cheek.
And yet we lack the last technique:
We rap for order with a gun,
The issues simplify to one
—Then your Democracy insists
You mustn't talk with terrorists!
White and yellow, black and blue,
Have learnt their history from you:
Divide and ruin, muddle through,
Not principled, but politic.
—In strength, perfidious; weak, a trick
To make good men a trifle sick.
We speak in wounds. Behold this mess.
My curse upon your politesse."
Another ghost stood forth, and wet
Dead lips that had not spoken yet:

"My curse on the cunning and the bland,
On gentlemen who loot a land
They do not care to understand;
Who keep the natives on their paws
With ready lash and rotten laws;
Then if the beasts erupt in rage
Give them a slightly larger cage
And, in scorn and fear combined
Turn them against their own kind.
The game runs out of room at last,
A people rises from its past,
The going gets unduly tough
And you have (surely ... ?) had enough.
The time has come to yield your place
With condescending show of grace
—An Empire-builder handing on.
We reap the ruin when you've gone,
All your errors heaped behind you:
Promises that do not bind you,
Hopes in conflict, cramped commissions,
Faiths exploited, and traditions."
Bloody sputum filled his throat.
He stopped and coughed to clear it out,
And finished, with his eyes a-glow:
"You came, you saw, you conquered ... So.
You gorged—and it was time to go.
Good riddance. We'd forget—released—
But for the rubbish of your feast,
The slops and scraps that fell to earth
And sprang to arms in dragon birth.
Sashed and bowler-hatted, glum
Apprentices of fife and drum,
High and dry, abandoned guards
Of dismal streets and empty yards,
Drilled at the codeword 'True Religion'
To strut and mutter like a pigeon
'Not An Inch—Up The Queen';
Who use their walls like a latrine
For scribbled magic—at their call,
Straight from the nearest music-hall,
Pope and Devil intertwine,
Two cardboard kings appear, and join

263

Thomas Kinsella

In one more battle by the Boyne!
Who could love them? God above ..."
"Yet pity is akin to love,"
The thirteenth corpse beside him said,
Smiling in its bloody head,
"And though there's reason for alarm
In dourness and a lack of charm
Their cursed plight calls out for patience.
They, even they, with other nations
Have a place, if we can find it.
Love our changeling! Guard and mind it.
Doomed from birth, a cursed heir,
Theirs is the hardest lot to bear,
Yet not impossible, I swear,
If England would but clear the air
And brood at home on her disgrace
—Everything to its own place.
Face their walls of dole and fear
And be of reasonable cheer.
Good men every day inherit
Father's foulness with the spirit,
Purge the filth and do not stir it.
Let them out! At least let in
A breath or two of oxygen,
So they may settle down for good
And mix themselves in the common blood.
We all are what we are, and that
Is mongrel pure. What nation's not
Where any stranger hung his hat
And seized a lover where she sat?"
He ceased and faded. Zephyr blew
And all the others faded too.
I stood like a ghost. My fingers strayed
Along the fatal barricade.
The gentle rainfall drifting down
Over Colmcille's town
Could not refresh, only distil
In silent grief from hill to hill.

FINISTÈRE

I ...
One ...

I smelt the weird Atlantic.
Finistère ...
                    Finisterre ...

The sea surface darkened. The land behind me,
and all its cells and cysts, grew dark.
From a bald boulder on the cairn top
I spied out the horizon to the northwest
and sensed that minute imperfection again.
Where the last sunken ray withdrew ...
A point of light?

A maggot of the possible
wriggled out of the spine
into the brain.

We hesitated before that wider sea
but our heads sang with purpose
and predatory peace.
And whose excited blood was that
fumbling our movements? Whose ghostly hunger
tunneling our thoughts full of passages
smelling of death ash and clay and faint metals
and great stones in the darkness?

At no great distance out in the bay
the swell took us into its mercy,
grey upheaving slopes of water
sliding under us, collapsing,
crawling onward, mountainous.

265

Thomas Kinsella

Driven outward a day and a night
we held fast, numbed by the steady
might of the oceanic wind.
We drew close together, as one,
and turned inward, salt chaos
rolling in silence all around us,
and listened to our own mouths
mumbling in the sting of spray:
—Ill wind end well
   mild mother
   on wild water pour peace

   who gave us our unrest
   whom we meet and unmeet
   in whose yearning shadow
   we erect our great uprights
   and settle fulfilled
   and build and are still
   unsettled, whose goggle gaze
   and holy howl we have scraped
   speechless on slabs of stone
   poolspirals opening on
   closing spiralpools
   and dances drilled in the rock
   in coil zigzag angle and curl
   river ripple earth ramp
   suncircle moonloop ...
   in whose outflung service
   we nourished our hunger
   uprooted and came

   in whale hell

         gale gullet

   salt hole

         dark nowhere

  calm queen

         pour peace

The bad dream ended at last.
In the morning, in a sunny breeze,
bare headlands rose fresh out of the waves.
We entered a deep bay, lying open
to all the currents of the ocean.
We were further than anyone had ever been
and light-headed with exhaustion and relief
—three times we misjudged and were nearly driven
on the same rock.
                    (I had felt all this before ...)
We steered in along a wall of mountain
and entered a quiet hall of rock echoing
to the wave-wash and our low voices.
I stood at the prow. We edged to a slope of stone.
I steadied myself. 'Our Father ...', someone said
and there was a little laughter. I stood
searching a moment for the right words.
They fell silent. I chose the old words once more
and stepped out. At the solid shock
a dreamy power loosened at the base of my spine
and uncoiled and slid up through the marrow.
A flow of seawater over the rock fell back
with a she-hiss, plucking at my heel.
My tongue stumbled

Who
        is a breath
that makes the wind
that makes the wave
that makes   this   voice?

Who
        is the bull with seven scars
the hawk on the cliff
the salmon sunk in his pool
the pool sunk in her soil
the animal's fury
the flower's fibre
a teardrop in the sun?

Thomas Kinsella

Who
    is the word that spoken
the spear springs
    and pours out terror
the spark springs
    and burns in the brain?

When men meet on the hill
dumb as stones in the dark
    (the craft knocked behind me)
who is the jack of all light?
Who goes in full into
the moon's interesting conditions?
Who fingers the sun's sink hole?
    (I went forward, reaching out)

21. EXTRACT FROM NOVEL: "THE CONFESSIONS OF PRIONSIAS O'TOOLE"

JOHN MORROW

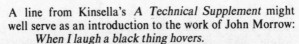

A line from Kinsella's *A Technical Supplement* might well serve as an introduction to the work of John Morrow: *When I laugh a black thing hovers.*

Black humour has always been one safety valve out of intolerable situations. It is better to laugh than to cry. The First World War produced *The Good Soldier Schweik.* and the miseries of Stalinism produced, among other things in Russia, the satirical novels of Ilf and Petrov. Violence in Ulster has given rise to a new folk-lore running from scurrilous ditties on the life of Bernadette Devlin to strip cartoons of "Bill and Ben, the IRA Men". *The Confessions of Prionsias O'Toole*, from which the following is taken, transcends such ephemera.

John Morrow was born in Belfast in 1930 of working-class Protestant background. He left school at fourteen and entered the Belfast shipyards, from which, he tells us, he exited as quickly as possible. He next followed a variety of trades, including navvying in England and selling insurance. He then started to write short stories and humorous essays, blackish in nature, working extensively in radio. He received an Arts Council bursary in 1975. *Prionsias* is his first novel.

Some introduction to dramatis personae may be necessary. The narrator is an adroit double-crosser on the make. Toby and Burton are British secret service men, one of whom has original tastes. The Duncher resembles a well-known Protestant clergyman who has been much in the news, while O'Lig is a commandant on the opposing side. Punchy, so-called because on a previous occasion he didn't punch first, has been detailed to frighten a well-known politician by phoning his house night and day, threatening if the man answers, keeping silent and breathing deeply, if the supposedly well brought-up wife does—but this has unexpected results.

John Morrow

From
THE CONFESSIONS OF PRIONSIAS O'TOOLE

At three-thirty precisely we re-crossed the bridge into home territory. I'm certain of the time now because, as though in salute, a distant blast went off just as we passed through the military checkpoint. If I could have foreseen then my involvement in the gruesome aftermath of that bang, I think I'd have forced Burton at penpoint to do an about-turn and sought sanctuary with the Duncher rather than face it.

At least it stopped Burton slabbering. Since our breathless departure from the Big House he had painted—and repeatedly re-touched—an idyllic picture of Kate and the kids in their beach bungalow on the estate, well away from the Simbas, tended hand and foot by a cook and two houseboys, the only blacks within two miles. The kids, he assured me, were having a grand time on the beach and were brown as berries; Kate was scoffing all put in front of her and steadily reading her way through the condensed *Jalna* series, supplied by Meg.

My heart went out to them ... the cook and the houseboys, I mean.

Of course I didn't tell Burton that last bit. From the moment I had rushed into the lounge and dashed the glass from his hand—likewise Steffers's—he had taken the attitude that he was dealing with someone 'Spurred by Grief', hence the lengthy and guilt-stricken reassurance. Far from it: my one thought had been to put as many furlongs between me and the townland containing Kate in the shortest time possible.

'And now, Francie,' Toby had ended this briefing, clipping my pen in my breast pocket, 'as a small bonus perhaps I could arrange an interview with your lady wife?' My reply—something like, 'You'll do no such fucking thing if you want my help'—had left him speechless; pondering, perhaps, on the value of his hostages.

He need not have worried: I now had no intention of welshing—but not because of Kate and the kids. Of course I'd never stand by and let them be harmed—if only because of a firm belief that the grave would prove no barrier to her venom—but in those last seconds in the Warden's Den with Toby something that had been niggling me since entering suddenly jelled. In Good Old Galwally there had been another door in that room, a door which led to a small storeroom containing such deterrents as truncheons, birches, straitjackets, boxing-gloves (for chronic nocturnal wankers), and the position of that door, unless I'd got my topography all wrong, had matched the position of Toby's apparently hard-set little strong-box. It made things begin to look a bit more ... portable, somehow (if not blowable).

Burton stopped the car in front of the University halls of residence and I gave Steffers a dunt. She had fallen into her usual backseat coma almost before we'd cleared the Big House driveway (only then had I permitted Burton to mention Kate and the kids, for various reasons) and, as usual, she awoke in a huff. I would have preferred it otherwise, now having a vested interest in keeping her sweet not unconnected with future plans concerning the Big House and Toby's honey-pot therein; but there is only one way of making a waking Steffers happy and that I was not prepared to do in broad daylight.

Completely out of character, I dismounted and held open the back door, grasping her elbow and guiding her away from the car, all the while making furtive faces and whispering: 'It'll be easier to give this chancer the slip if you get out here. There's big things afoot and I've a helluva lot to do. But I'll need to see you as soon as possible to night. Can you make it to the chalet later?'

She nodded and I completed the de-huffing process—and forestalled an incipient question—by muttering: 'For God's sake make sure you're not tailed!'

So, leaving her in what Burton would term 'a state of conspiratorial euphoria' I rejoined him in the car. I hadn't a notion what I was going to do a helluva lot of—though he seemed to think he did ... 'It might be best to work on the Duncher first,' he rambled as we sped westward through a fringe area of homely-looking dereliction: 'less volatile than O'Lig. The one thing we must avoid at all costs is a tendency to jump the gun. As soon as I get the fake memos I'll let you have them; that'll be the time to put the boot down.'

I didn't have to give him the slip after all. All the way he kept skellying at his watch, and as we approached the 'Peace' line which bounds the ghetto he asked if I'd mind being dropped there,

confirming me in Chloe's opinion that he was homing on some piece
of hair-pie with Matron's drawers tucked up his jersey.

Unhorsed once more, I strode out joyously on my native
peat—literally peat, all the pavements having been torn up and
flung at the British army long since—in the general direction of the
chalet.

The place seemed strangely deserted for the time of day. The
first living thing I came across was roped to a lamp-post and coated
with hardened tar and lumps of old mattress ticking. A placard
around its neck bore the traditional inscription 'Informer'; so where
better, I thought, to learn the score.

He appeared to be asleep. When I hacked at his ankle and he
raised a clobbered head to say, 'Fugg aff!' I recognised the
malevolent eyes as belonging to one of O'Lig's twenty-year-old
Lieutenant-Generals.

I gave him a drag at my fag and inquired: 'What have you been
up to? Singing off-key?'

'You'll laugh on the other side of yer bake some of these days,
Francie Fallis,' he girned ungratefully, 'you an' that fat fugger
O'Lig. Ma hair'll niver grow again an' all because that pig's arse
wanted a patsy for a shortage in last week's collection. Wait'll—'

'—Any more of yer oul' buck and I'll start picking the tar off you
now,' I threatened; 'or better still, I'll tell the first Para patrol I
meet and they'll be round with a blowlamp to clean you up
sharpish. So just tell me where everybody is and I'll leave you in
peace.'

'Didn't you hear that big blow awhile back? Deef if you didn't.
Well that's where they all are ... helpin' the morgue men scrape
five fellas off a wall—it went up in the car ... Here ... Hi ...
look ... Francie,' he cried out as I turned to go; 'do us a favour—'

'Before you start, mate, it's more than my neck's worth to cut
them ropes—'

'—No, nothin' like that,' he assured me. 'Look, d'you see thon
bastard of a dog slinkin' up this way—?' I did; a patchy looking,
corgi-type survivor, sniffing its way towards us along the gutter ...
'I've been here since four this mornin' an' that ghett's been roun'
ivery half-hour on the dot to piss up agin me! Would y'ever wait till
he gits this length an' hit him a good dunder up the balls, Francie?'

Request granted—evoking barely distinguishable howls of agony
and delight from pisser and pissed-on—I moved off.

Passing the chapel I noted with approval that, splattered patriots
or no, O'Driscoll's verger was still at his work, shepherding a

Protestant-looking gent into the school yard to select his car from the dozen or so parked discreetly in the white-lined bays reserved for the teaching staff (all of whom had been languishing in Long Kesh since the day the lavatory ceiling had collapsed on Sergeant McNinch's head under the weight of secreted ammo). O'Driscoll himself had started the service in a spurt of ecumenical fervour when the flogged car ramp had been at its height in the first days of barricades and no-go—though he now denied all knowledge of it. In that era of jubilant anarchy the lads would whip a car from across the river and drive it back to the ghetto, there to joyride with impunity until the petrol ran out, all without thought of profit. The car would then either be set alight or added to a barricade; and this O'Driscoll considered a sinful waste. So, unofficially, he had organized the whippers. After they'd 'made their protest', which is the 'in' term for joy-riding, they would drive, or push, the car to the school yard and receive a small payment from the verger, who would then circulate the car's number across the river via the underground and await the arrival of the grateful owner to claim his property—grateful to the tune of as much as twenty-five quid, depending on make and year of registration, so I've heard. Certainly it had gone some way to compensate the parish for the fall-off in attendance at Bingo because of the troubles. It also had the blessing of Sergeant McNinch and his merry men who, although not daring to lay a hand on car or culprit within the ghetto for fear of having Lord Brockway and the Gay Liberation Front on the next plane from London, still had to balance a crime sheet bloated by the joyriders. This they did by means of a side arrangement with the verger whereby he removed the tax disc from each repossession and informed McNinch of registration number and e.t.a. before the owner set off to re-cross the bridge, thus giving time for the laying of an ambush on the other side and the preparation of a summons for not displaying a Road Fund Licence. And thus each theft was balanced by a conviction.

I dwell on it because it is one of the very few profitable capers I never managed to get a finger in—a state of affairs that hitherto had rankled badly. Now, with Toby and Burton and the big game still fresh in my mind, it all seemed like diving for so much ha'pence in a swill bucket.

I found the Cavan man shuttered, barred and bolted, an extraordinary situation for a Sunday (the Calvinist licensing laws had been the first thing to go and to appear to be keeping them was an invitation to an illuminated address). I hurled lumps of pavers at the mauve-coloured upper shuttering until the bald and blotchy head of the man himself appeared ... 'Fer frigsake Francie! Ye putt the heart crosswise in me! We've had a turrible time, a turrible time ... Wait'll I open up ...'

Sporting the regalia of his particular Masonic, a wide-sleeved blue silk kimono with embroidered dragons, he flung open the door and pawed me inside frantically, for all the world like the central figure in a points Peeler's nightmare. After a thorough bit of slamming and barring he followed me into the snug and shoved Jeremy the renegade medic and Dominic the barman upstairs, both giggling wildly. Trembling, he splashed me a mammoth Powers. 'God, Francie, tongue can't tell what I've gone through these past two days! I've met some bold boys in my time but never the likes ...'

He'd been raided, looted and cuckolded by an assault platoon of Lifeguards. He'd been bursting to tell somebody, poor lonely bugger (whoops! as Chloe would say) and was well into an eye-rolling, wrist-flapping description of his trials at the hands of the kinky khaki hun before I could get my spoke in ...

'Before I forget—did Punchy ring?' I enquired at what seemed a natural break in his (unnatural!) narrative, not wishing to offend him too much.

'Yes ... he left a number. I wrote it down somewhere ... aye, here it is. Well here dear, Francie, what d'ya think, the next thing I sees—'

'—Houl' hard a minute till I give him a ring—in case it's anything urgent.'

'Oh well ... please yerself.'

He flounced off muttering and I got on the blower to Punchy, who was, if anything, in a more 'turrible' state ... 'Jeezus! Am I glad to hear your voice! This Rarity job has me near roun' the twist. I'll hafta come roun' an' see you rightaway. Can't stan' the sight of a phone these days let alone talk into one—'

I arranged to meet him in the chalet in ten minutes time and managed to sneak out with a bottle of buckshee Powers ('Never let the sun set') while the Cavan man still bickered in his harem above.

I'll not say that Punchy looked haggard—that Chicago darky long ago had fixed his expression once and for all—but he sounded it. And he was drinking whisky, always a bad sign with him.

As I progressed round the chalet, clearing pathways through debris left by week-end squatters—including a nest of heretical rubber goods on the bedroom floor—he followed me, jabbering ...

'—It's not him—he's a sucker for it—shits hesself ivery time—offers me hunners of pouns an' a steady job on his body-guard. But hur!—oh my Christ, Francie, that woman's far from right! I've niver spoke one word to her—all I do is breathe an' she goes off like a handbell! An' the things she comes off with! ... Yid niver believe it. Them WAAFs durin' the war was bad enough—but they were only jokin'. This one's dead serious. She says Rarity's no good till her—all she has to do is give him a flash an' he decorates the ceilin'. Some oul' goat of a Priest up in that posh school gave her a rub of the relic an' she says she's niver overed it ... I'm tellin' you, Francie, I'm shit scared of her doin' herself damage. You've niver heard the like of the way she gits on. She says ...'

What she said was for the most part physically impossible; yet it was imaginative, testifying to a thwarted creativity that in other circles would have merited a by-line in a posh Sunday and a place in the front rank of literary bawdy-dom. What appalled Punchy—a survivor of a time when sex had been merely one point in the Devil's triangle, the others being Drink and Gambling—amused me.

'You can laugh!' he moaned; 'but it's hard to listen to stuff like that—especially in a phone box with a queue of oul' dolls glarin' in an' you tryin' to look as if yer gittin' the hard word about yer nearest and dearest from the emergency ward. I'm tellin' ye, Francie, we'll hafta pack it or I'll not be responsible for that one's actions.'

I could see he was in no mood for levity. Also, he was brandishing our big breadknife, with which, plus a half-a-loaf, a slab of marg, and a pot of raspberry jam, he was assisting me to prepare our Olde Englishe High Tea. I thought it prudent to provoke no further.

'Rest easy, Punchy,' says I, setting down a pot of black tea and shaking the fag-ends out of two beakers; 'we no longer need to run O'Lig's errands. Rarity will be the furthest thing from his mind after I've filled his ear with a thing or two. We, Punchy, are onto the killing of a lifetime—and here's something to prove it—' So saying, I produced and flourished the hundred fivers in front of his one visible eye. Peeling off four, I tucked them behind the razor in his waistcoat pocket ... 'So sup up yer tay like a good lad and listen—'

I gave him the general outline of Operation Starkey—meaning I told him only what was needed to ensure his efficient co-operation while leaving out such spine-draining items as the Simbas, Kate, etc. In particular I briefed him on the two-way rumour-mongering campaign, suggesting that he handle the O'Lig end while I concentrated on the more subtle approach to the Duncher. Whatever it was, the relief of being rid of the Rarity account or the sight of the fivers, I've seldom seen him so enthusiastic about anything.

'Just to get shot of this madhouse for a wee while would be like winnin' the sweep,' says he, stuffing lumps of bread and jam, apparently, up his nose. 'Did you hear about that big blow the day?'

'Aye; five of them. Whose were they and who were they?'

'Mickey Close, Slack McGuigan, Silver Roche, Barney Moore, Liam Conaty; a fifty-pounder—boomf—in the back seat; spaghetti. Then to make it worse them lazy bastards of morgue men start offerin' the kids a tanner a time for gatherin' the bits!—an' you know what the kids roun' that quarter are like ... I heard tell O'Driscoll had give the rites to six-bobs worth of skinned cats before he caught on.'

Poor Mickey. I wondered if he'd been wearing his velvet slacks ... More to the point, I also wondered if my sub-contractor had managed to relieve Slack of the French TV proceeds before his fragmentation.

The fifty-pounder, it appeared, had been meant for the off-licence premises of one Bo McGookin, who had fallen badly behind in his subscriptions to the Marrowbone Liberation Front (Mickey, Slack, two wives and a total of twenty-five childer). On reaching the target Mickey had gone in to have a scout round before planting the stuff; and, lo, who should be standing at the counter but Sergeant McNinch and one of his underlings, having a free wet while Mr McGookin made out his cheque to the police Social and Athletic Club. At the sight of Mickey both drew and emptied their Walthers, blowing Mr McGookin's front door to shreds but not touching Mickey, who had taken off like a hare for the car. Slack had put the boot down, but they'd covered barely a hundred yards before it blew ... They'd been mates since boyhood, Mickey and Slack; through every vicissitude—Approved School, Burroo School, Borstal and gaol—they'd been inseparable; it was somehow appropriate that they should end up sharing the same plastic bag ...

'If it was as bad as all that, how can they be sure how many was in the car?' I wondered aloud.

'Easy,' said Punchy; 'they picked up five guns. An' anyway, the five of them were seen drinkin' in the United Club this mornin'.'

Other grisly details of the event, too boke-making to relate here, came forth as we finished our tea and lashed into the Powers. I also remember discussing the toss school, the collection for the Internees Book Club, a fresh attempt on O'Lig's life that had cost a reporter from *Izvestiya* his right ear (Tully!)—and then I must have dozed off.

I awoke because Punchy seemed bent on dislocating my shoulder. Someone was trying to leave footprints on the front door.

'It's Duncher's wee fellas,' whispered Punchy. 'I forgot to tell ye, they were roun' askin' after you yesterday. What'll we do?'

It was eight o'clock and still daylight. Might as well start earning some of the five hundred now, I thought.

'I'll go and see him. You stick around here until that bird I was with in the Prince comes over. Tell her I'll not be long—with any luck.'

'He—' they began to howl in unison when I opened the door.

'—Lead on!' I screamed.

22. FOUR POEMS

SEAMUS HEANEY

The starting point of Seamus Heaney's vision is the simple world of nature: farmyard animals, the march of the seasons, carefully harvested fields, the silence of a countryside at night, a child's enthralment at the mystery of God's creation. In the early poems, "Good Night", "The Outlaw", and "The Wife's Tale", we catch glimpses of this world seen through the eyes of a witness who knows that industrialized farming will soon banish them for good.

Seamus Heaney (b. 1939) was brought up on a Northern farm outside Derry. His first two collections, *Death of a Naturalist* (1966) and *Door into the Dark* (1969), record the opening out of a young man's sensitivity against this background. His third collection, *Wintering out* (1972), shows a wider vision, influenced by travel and a year's teaching in America. He has since lived in Dublin. The collection *North* (1975) reflects a struggle to come to terms with a northern European identity.

As on all his generation, the Ulster crisis has left its mark, in his case a sense of powerlessness and unease. Is he guilty, the poet seems to ask himself, of casting

the stones of silence?

"The Tollund Man" is based on a news item which attracted particular attention in Ireland—the discovery some years ago of a human victim of prehistoric sacrifice perfectly preserved in a Danish bog. For Heaney this evoked a parallel nearer home.

Seamus Heaney

FOUR POEMS

GOOD-NIGHT

A latch lifting, an edged den of light
Opens across the yard. Out of the low door
They stoop into the honeyed corridor,
Then walk straight through the wall of the dark.

A puddle, cobble-stones, jambs and doorstep
Are set steady in a block of brightness.
Till she strides in again beyond her shadows
And cancels everything behind her.

THE OUTLAW

Kelly's kept an unlicensed bull, well away
From the road: you risked fine but had to pay

The normal fee if cows were serviced there.
Once I dragged a nervous Friesian on a tether

Down a lane of alder, shaggy with catkin,
Down to the shed the bull was kept in.

I gave Old Kelly the clammy silver, though why
I could not guess. He grunted a curt "Go by

Get up on that gate". And from my lofty station
I watched the business-like conception.

The door, unbolted, whacked back against the wall.
The illegal sire fumbled from his stall

Unhurried as an old steam engine shunting.
He circled, snored and nosed. No hectic panting,

Just the unfussy ease of a good tradesman;
Then an awkward, unexpected jump, and

His knobbled forelegs straddling her flank,
He slammed life home, impassive as a tank,

Dropping off like a tipped-up load of sand.
"She'll do," said Kelly and tapped his ash-plant

Across her hindquarters. "If not, bring her back."
I walked ahead of her, the rope now slack

While Kelly whooped and prodded his outlaw
Who, in his own time, resumed the dark, the straw.

THE WIFE'S TALE

When I had spread it all on linen cloth
Under the hedge, I called them over.
The hum and gulp of the thresher ran down
And the big belt slewed to a standstill, straw
Hanging undelivered in the jaws.
There was such quiet that I heard their boots
Crunching the stubble twenty yards away.

He lay down and said "Give these fellows theirs.
I'm in no hurry," plucking grass in handfuls
And tossing it in the air. "That looks well."
(He nodded at my white cloth on the grass.)
"I declare a woman could lay out a field
Though boys like us have little call for cloths."
He winked, then watched me as I poured a cup
And buttered the thick slices that he likes.
"It's threshing better than I thought, and mind
It's good clean seed. Away over there and look."
Always this inspection has to be made
Even when I don't know what to look for.

But I ran my hand in the half-filled bags
Hooked to the slots. It was hard as shot,
Innumerable and cool. The bags gaped
Where the chutes ran back to the stilled drum
And forks were stuck at angles in the ground
As javelins might mark lost battlefields.
I moved between them back across the stubble.
They lay in the ring of their own crusts and dregs
Smoking and saying nothing. "There's good yield,
Isn't there?"—as proud as if he were the land itself—
"Enough for crushing and for sowing both."
And that was it. I'd come and he had shown me
So I belonged no further to the work.
I gathered cups and folded up the cloth
And went. But they still kept their ease
Spread out, unbuttoned, grateful, under the trees.

THE TOLLUND MAN

I

Some day I will go to Aarhus
To see his peat-brown head,
The mild pods of his eye-lids,
His pointed skin cap.

In the flat country nearby
Where they dug him out,
His last gruel of winter seeds
Caked in his stomach,

Naked except for
The cap, noose and girdle,
I will stand a long time.
Bridegroom to the goddess,

She tightened her torc on him
And opened her fen,
Those dark juices working
Him to a saint's kept body,

282

Trove of the turfcutters'
Honeycombed workings.
Now his stained face
Reposes at Aarhus.

II
I could risk blasphemy,
Consecrate the cauldron bog
Our holy ground and pray
Him to make germinate

The scattered, ambushed
Flesh of labourers,
Stockinged corpses
Laid out in the farmyards,

Tell-tale skin and teeth
Flecking the sleepers
Of four young brothers, trailed
For miles along the lines.

III
Something of his sad freedom
As he rode the tumbril
Should come to me, driving,
Saying the names

Tollund, Grabaulle, Nebelgard,
Watching the pointing hands
Of country people,
Not knowing their tongue.

Out there in Jutland
In the old man-killing parishes
I will feel lost,
Unhappy and at home.

23. FIVE POEMS

EAVAN BOLAND

Two young women poets must complete the poetry part of this anthology. Eavan Boland (b. 1945) has published two collections, *New Territory* (1968), from which the first of these poems comes, and *The War Horse* (1975). She is a Dubliner, and hers is a sophisticated intelligence. The delicate, mannered conceit of "The Other Woman" recalls the first Elizabethans. (One may mention that her husband is the novelist, Kevin Casey.) "The Hanging Judge" explores starkly an episode that, with an ironic twist of nuance, gave a new word to the English language.

Eavan Boland is a part-time teacher and also a professional journalist. In this latter capacity, she has covered some of the events of the recent troubles. "Child of Our Time" relates to the day in 1974 when a car bomb bomb exploded without warning in a Dublin street, killing thirty passers-by and injuring many others. Her belief that this death would awaken a southern Irish conscience out of its long sleep of complacency has hardly been justified by events. "The War Horse" develops an allied theme.

Eavan Boland

FIVE POEMS

NEW TERRITORY

Several things announced the fact to us:
The captain's Spanish tears
Falling like doubloons in the headstrong light,
And then of course the fuss—
The crew jostling and interspersing cheers
With wagers. Overnight
As we went down to our cabins, nursing the last
Of the grog, talking as usual of conquest,
Land hove into sight.

Frail compasses and trenchant constellations
Brought us as far as this,
And now air and water, fire and earth
Stand at their given stations
Out there, and are ready to replace
This single desperate width
Of ocean. Why do we hesitate? Water and air
And fire and earth and therefore life are here,
And therefore death.

Out of the dark man comes to life and into it
He goes and loves and dies,
(His element being the dark and not the light of day)
So the ambitious wit
Of poets and exploring ships have been his eyes—
Riding the dark for joy—
And so Isaiah of the sacred text is eagle-eyed because
By peering down the unlit centuries
He glimpsed the holy boy.

THE OTHER WOMAN

(for Kevin)

I know you have a world I cannot share
Where a woman waits for you, beautiful,
Young no doubt, protected in your care
From stiffening and wrinkling, not mortal

Not shy of her own mirror. How can I rival
Her when like a harem wife she waits
To come into the pages of your novel
Obediently as if to your bed on nights

She is invited, nor as in your other life
I do, reminds you daily of the defeat
Of time, nor as does your other wife,
Binds you to the married state.

She is the other woman. I must share
You with her time and time again,
Book after book, yet I am aware
Love, how I have got the better bargain

For I imagine she has grown strange
To you among the syntax and the sentences
By which you distance her and would exchange
Her speaking part for any of our silences.

THE HANGING JUDGE

Come to the country where justice is seen to be done,
Done daily. Come to the country where
Sentence is passed by word of mouth and raw
Boys split like infinitives. Look, here
We hanged our son, our only son
And hang him still and still we call it law.

287

Eavan Boland

James Lynch Fitzstephen, magistrate,
First Citizen of Galway, 1493,
Spanish merchant trader, his horror
Of deceit a by-word, a pillar of society
With one weakness, Walter, whose every trait
Reversed his like a signature in a mirror.

The torches splutter, the dancing, supple,
Spanish-taught, starts. James Lynch Fitzstephen
May disapprove but he, a man of principle
Recalls young Gomez is a guest in town,
And the girl beside, his son's choice, may restore
A new name and honour in an heir.

Dawn: Gomez dead, in a wood: the Spanish heart
Which softened to her rigid with the steel
Of Walter Lynch's blade. Wild justice there—
Now to its restraint, but not repeal,
He returns, friendless, to be met
By his father, mounted, hunting. In the stare

Which passed slowly between them, a history
Poises: repression and rebellion, the scaffold
And its songs, the principle unsung
Are clues in this judicial murder to a mystery
Unsolved still and only to be told
As a ghost story against a haunting.

As you, father, haunt me: the rope trails
From your fingers, below you the abyss.
Your arms balanced as the scales of justice,
You loop him while from your eyes fall other scales
Too late, tears of doubt, tears of remorse
Dropping on your own neck like a noose.

CHILD OF OUR TIME

(for Aengus)

Yesterday I knew no lullaby
But you have taught me overnight to order
This song, which takes from your final cry
Its tune, from your unreasoned end its reason;
Its rhythm from the discord of your murder
Its motive from the fact you cannot listen.

We who should have known how to instruct
With rhymes for your waking, rhythms for your sleep,
Names for the animals you took to bed,
Tales to distract, legends to protect,
Later an idiom for you to keep
And living, learn must, learn from you, dead,

To make our broken images rebuild
Themselves around your limbs, your broken
Image, find for your sake whose life our idle
Talk has cost, a new language. Child
Of our time, our times have robbed your cradle.
Sleep in a world your final sleep has woken.
17 May 1974

THE WAR HORSE

This dry night, nothing unusual
About the clip, clop, casual

Iron of his shoes as he stamps death
Like a mint on the innocent coinage of earth.

I lift the window, watch the ambling feather
Of hock and fetlock, loosed from its daily tether

Eavan Boland

In the tinker camp on the Enniskerry Road,
Pass, his breath hissing, his snuffling head

Down. He is gone. No great harm is done.
Only a leaf of our laurel hedge is torn

Of distant interest like a maimed limb,
Only a rose which now will never climb

The stone of our house, expendable, a mere
Line of defence against him, a volunteer

You might say, only a crocus its bulbous head
Blown from growth, one of the screamless dead.

But we, we are safe, our unformed fear
Of fierce commitment gone; why should we care

If a rose, a hedge, a crocus are uprooted
Like corpses, remote, crushed, mutilated?

He stumbles on like a rumour of war, huge,
Threatening; neighbours use the subterfuge

Of curtains; he stumbles down our short street,
Thankfully passing us. I pause, wait,

Then to breathe relief lean on the sill
And for a second only my blood is still

With atavism. That rose he smashed frays
Ribboned across our hedge, recalling days

Of burned countryside, illicit braid:
A cause ruined before, a world betrayed.

24. POEM

JUANITA CASEY

It is often suggested that Irish writers are relatively conservative as to form, being for historical reasons more preoccupied with content. By way of contrast, here is a light-hearted poem in a more modern manner by a young writer of gypsy parentage who, after travelling many roads, has settled (should one append a question-mark?) in the County Kerry. She has published one book of poems and two D. H. Lawrence-like novels, *The Horse of Selene* (1971) and *The Circus* (1974).

Juanita Casey

POEM

HOUSEMAID'S UNCONNECTED KNEE

Must
I,
taking brush
in hand,
disturb the
dust
of Here and Now
when
since in reality
(Zen)
all
is void
whereon can the dust
fall . .
All
this and Heaven too!
Cleanliness
is next to
Godliness!
they
say,
Writer . .
May
I
point out that
tomes
are traditionally dusty
and what about the
names
of spiders
Now I'm
dead,

if there's anyone up there then—
cease—
God the Great Arranger
leave mine in
peace—
just
dust.
must
you, like some
dread
House wife of All
set your
House in Order
so relentlessly.
I liked Set,
he had an ass's
head.
A New Heaven! a New
Earth!
Death!
to be
swept
under some other well
kept
carpet
or just Up
or, with a
Frown—worse,
Down . .
minus
breath, come
shout hallelujah,
thatisifyoubelieveyour
souls
may be Brassoed
to brilliance on the rainbow
weave
of the
sleeve
of God's old
vest
to

Juanita Casey

rest
on that Glassy
Floor,
or,
thrown out with the
rest
of the
rust
and holed,
old
black
kettles
in the
nettles at the
back
door;
poor
dust
having to
settle
all over
again
and again
and
again
and
my god
possibly like the
young lady of
Spain—
ad
infinitum.

25. PART OF AN AUTOBIOGRAPHY AND ONE POEM

FRANCIS STUART

One whom many would consider the most impressive figure of all in modern Irish writing has been left to last: Francis Stuart. Now in his seventies, Stuart suffered a long period of eclipse for reasons largely political, but in the last decade has become almost a cult figure among younger Irish intellectuals. His work is deeply rooted in the tradition of Irish republicanism, yet goes far beyond parochial nationalism. He is in fact the only English-speaking writer to have experienced from inside the full holocaust of the last war in Europe. Almost as if by predestination, his earlier life had prepared him well for the soul-searching that experience brought about. It is hardly coincidence that Stuart's novels found more success in their German and French translations than in England.

Stuart was born in 1902 in Australia of Ulster Protestant stock. The family returned to Ireland, and he spent his childhood in the country outside Derry. As a young man he fought for Irish independence against the British. At eighteen he met and married Iseult Gonne, natural daughter of the fabled rebel and beauty, Maud Gonne, who features in so many of Yeats's poems. The marriage was unhappy and led to eventual separation. Stuart became a Catholic around the same time and has been deeply influenced by Catholic mysticism and sanctity. After publishing one book of poems, he turned to novel-writing in the 1930's. Yeats praised his "cold, exciting strangeness", but his work ran too much counter to pre-war moods to achieve public recognition.

In 1939 Stuart went to Berlin as a university lecturer and stayed in Germany throughout the war, enduring the obliteration bombing of Berlin. His role in Germany has been questioned. He made some broadcasts in English. It was easy for an Irishman to speak out against Britain, but when asked to make pro-Nazi propaganda, he refused. He refused, equally, to climb on the anti-Fascist bandwagon after Germany's defeat. He seems to have welcomed the estrangement from the post-war establishment that

295

attitude provoked. A key passage in his long, semi-autobiographical novel, *Blacklist, Section H*, sheds light on this:

> he'd told Iseult that what the poet needed to keep him unspotted from the world was dishonour. It hadn't been a phrase he'd thought up. It had come out instinctively without premeditation. Now it was time to catch up and to come to a conscious grasp of this attitude. He believed that nothing short of the near despair of being utterly cast off from society and its principles could create the inner condition conducive to the new insights that it was the task of the poet to reveal.

In some respects Stuart is an Irish Dostoevsky.

Stuart's novels are difficult to extract from. *The White Hare* (1936), *Redemption* (1949), *The Flowering Cross* (1950) and *Blacklist, Section H* (1975) should be read in their entirety by anyone eager to understand where Ireland dovetails into the European experience.

Here are two chapters from *Things to Live For: Notes for an Autobiography*, published in 1934, but losing none of its freshness for today.

By way of epitaph to this anthology, which has been almost as much concerned with the questionmarks suggested by the Irish cultural-historical experience as with 'pure' literature, I give Stuart's more recent poem "Homecoming".

From
THINGS TO LIVE FOR: NOTES FOR AN AUTOBIOGRAPHY

CHAPTER I

PROLOGUE

There is an emptiness within the human breast, a hunger for we hardly know what, that is the deepest and wildest of all desires. It is the falling in love with life, the dark deep flow below the surface. Subtle, crude, beautiful, terrible. A few have dared to open their arms to it, to plunge into it, and always they are wounded and humiliated, but they have been touched, have been caressed by those fiery fingers that curved the universe and there remains about them a breadth, a spaciousness, a warmth of genius.

I, too, have felt that hunger. I, too, have been wounded and humiliated. Above all, I, too, have given that yea to life, and now I look back over a dozen years or so as one might look across a stormy sea at night and see white crest after white moonlit crest and hardly notice the long black depths between.

I have known all sorts of joys. Some so great that I cannot write of them, or only in passing. Others so secret that I dare not mention them. I have felt an ecstasy of happiness working in the hospital at Lourdes. I have fallen in love so that life glowed and shone and sang. Fighting for Ireland through a civil war, and through months of imprisonment, I have been fired by the strange joy of patriotism. In writing I have felt the exaltation of creation; in my novels I have at times exulted because it seemed to me I had made permanent in them some part of truth wrested from the chaos around me. I think of days and nights with friends, at home or in far places, and that, too, was happiness. Not the piercing, lyrical joy, but calm and without the dark depths on its fringes. I have stood on stands at race-courses trembling so that I could scarcely keep the glasses steady at my eyes, and seen horses of mine win or lose races when everything depended on the result. Oh all that exaltation, all that joy that I can remember with my mind but which cannot again set my heart pounding! The greater and the less. I have been so happy for hours alone with children, flying aeroplanes, seeing new cities and catching the first glimpse of the Pyrenees like a blue wall in the far distance from a train. And these are not all the things, not all, not perhaps even the greatest. There were those secret moments when, for no reason that I knew of, joy flooded through me and life was blessed. It might be because of the way the light shone on roofs above a city, or the look of a room at night, or the look of a street in the dusk from a café just before the lamps lit up. These are the moonlit wave-crests behind me and for a moment I turn and look at them. But not only at them. I look, too, at the black depths of moving water in between. I will tell of those, too. But of some again only in passing, because they are too secret, too terrible, or too near. Of the waning of religious certitude, of the feeling of being outcast, damned, soiled and filthy. Of the failure and torture of human love. Suffering, remorse and despair. And of lesser things, too, that did not seem lesser at the time. I have risked all the money I have had in the world on a horse, when there seemed little prospect of getting any more for a long time, and seen it beaten. I have been so lonely that nothing in life seemed to matter if only one had one friend. I have lain in bed, in prison, on hunger-strike, and seen the cause for which I had fought broken and defeated and believed myself defeated too. And again, for no reason, the future has seemed to hold nothing, nothing, and despair has taken hold of me and only perhaps because some particle of reason remained that told me this, too, would pass have I not killed myself. But I look back, not from the shore, but still from this little battered, tossing boat. And perhaps for that above all I am grateful. That I am not yet old, not yet crystallized, mummified, indifferent, cold, protected against life. That I can still be exalted and still wounded. Yes, yes, that too; the wounds are as precious to me as the ecstasy. For both bring me as close to that lovely, terrible, profligate, austere thing that is life.

To love, that is all that matters. To lavish love even on objects unworthy of it is infinitely better than living a cold, ordered life in a study, in an office, or even in a garden tending flowers. It is only through opening one's arms to life that one will find the ultimate peace and security. Only through suffering and loving. There is no short-cut. Protecting oneself against life is not peace but death. Of all the strange varied people I have met it has not been the sinners, the degraded, the drunkards, the gamblers, the crooks, the harlots who have made me shudder, but the dead, the respectable dead; cut off like a branch from the tree.

CHAPTER V

THE WHITE GIRL

It took twenty-two hours from Boulogne to Lourdes on the Pilgrimage train. We were seven in the carriage. I had never been in France before, never been in Paris. We weren't going to stop at Paris. We were shunted round it on to the southern line. It got dark soon after we left Boulogne. I was going to Lourdes. A few weeks before I had read a little book about Blessed Bernadette and the apparitions, and I had been so inspired by it that Lourdes seemed to me the most wonderful place in the world. A strange hidden place aflame with that secret beauty that would always stir me. Oh how hard it is to explain what spark is at the back of all those conflagrations that flare up on this dark earth and lure one and enchant one and make one throw oneself into the midst of them.

Just now I stopped to look through that little book on Bernadette written by Father Martindale. I thought that in some passages I might recapture that first joy I felt on reading them, that I might quote them here and so explain the subtle beauty that had so stirred me. But only a faint fragrance remains. It is not that I do not believe any more what I believed then, but I do not *feel* it as I did then. I saw in Bernadette a beauty that I had never before seen in anyone. A sort of radiance, sweet and tender and austere, shed on her from, it might be, heaven. I fell in love with her, I think. I started on this Pilgrimage to Lourdes. I thought that there I would find something of that so enthralling atmosphere, lyrical, romantic, joyous and yet suffering, that was evoked by her or by the Apparitions.

'I lifted my eyes,' she said, describing the first Apparition, 'and I saw a mass of branches and brambles tossed and waving this way and that under the opening in the grotto, though nothing stirred around. Behind these branches, in the opening, I saw immediately afterwards, a white girl, no bigger than I ... I saw the girl smiling at me very sweetly *(avec beaucoup de grâce)*.'

A white girl! That was how the Blessed Virgin appeared to her. A white girl who said to her: 'I am the Immaculate Conception', words that meant nothing to Bernadette. Words that puzzled theologians. To me those words shone and I was enthralled. I knew the joy of the Quest of the Knights of the Round Table for a love that is ever-bright, everlasting, ever-new; tender and sweet and yet demanding everything even to the last sacrifice.

Near Paris our train was pulled on to a siding to let the express from the coast go through. I watched it go past, an arrow of golden light. There were people having dinner in the restaurant car. For a second I caught a glimpse of a man and a woman at a table together. Suddenly, called up by that half-seen image in the night, another longing took possession of me. I did not want to be going to Lourdes any more. I wanted to go to Paris. Romance seemed to me to lie after all over there where already we could see the night stained red with the lights of the city from our carriage window. All the lyrical beauty, all the romantic love that I had dreamt of, seemed to be there just over the dark horizon. And I was not going there, I was going to be shunted round it in a train full of cripples and old farmers and their wives from Connemara. What could they know of my secret quest? What could they know? The carriage was stifling. The old fellow next me prodded me with his elbows and puffed plug tobacco from his yellow clay pipe. My throat was very sore. A nurse came in and opened the window and icy air blew in. A pale-faced boy from Kerry opposite me who had lost his overcoat on the boat wrapped himself in newspapers that crackled all night with every movement. The red glow of Paris faded behind us and I craned my neck to watch it disappear. My heart ached and the talk of the other Pilgrims became insupportable. What did they know? What did they know? I got up and went out into the corridor. At one end of it there was a group of St. John Ambulance Brigade men playing cards. I did not want to play cards. I walked on through another coach. I met a man sitting on his suit-case at the end of the corridor, drinking coffee. He offered me some. We began to talk. He had been through the Florida boom a year or so before. He told me the most fantastic tales about money. When I started to ask him about Paris he interrupted me.

'Paris, London, New York, what are they?' he said. 'So much tinsel and trash. Last year I could have had anything I wanted out of them. If I'd met you then and you'd said "Paris", I'd have given you a couple of thousand dollars, told you to go and have a look at it. Now I can do something better. I can tell you to keep away. There's nothing in all that for a fellow like you. You're like myself. You're a romantic. That's why we're going to Lourdes. That's fine. That's where we should be going. If we had lived in the Middle Ages we'd be off to Jerusalem. We'd be Crusaders, by God! But don't expect too much from Lourdes either. Don't expect too much from anything or anyone. It's from here, here, that we must keep alive the flame,' and he struck his chest with his large red hand. Because, I suppose, of being strung-up and tense that night I thought everything he said wonderful. I listened to him wide-eyed. He took from his pocket a photograph of a nun whose face looked worn and ill. She was kneeling in front of a large Calvary. Who she was or what she had to do with what he was saying I did not know.

'To Jerusalem,' he repeated, jolting against me as the train gathered speed. After a bit I went back to my compartment. The window had been shut again and the air was hot and filthy. I slept in snatches and finally woke up in the dawn at Bordeaux, stiff and tired and with my throat very sore.

O Lourdes, Lourdes, how can I write about you? The most tawdry and the most lovely, the most blatant and the most secret. You are like a woman dressed and painted as a prostitute, who in reality is full only of a passionate innocence.

Street after street of shops full of religious objects. Hotels named after all the saints in the calendar. And even about the grotto itself so much concrete, and the rock of Massabielle blackened by candle smoke and hung with the most hideous contrivances discarded by the cured. I have listened to flights of tawdry rhetoric and clap-trap oratory from an Irish bishop preaching in the pulpit in front of the grotto. I have listened till I felt ill and have gone into the baths and helped the sick pilgrims to undress, stripping tortured bodies of filthy underclothes matted with blood and worse, and breathed freely again.

But the secret Lourdes, the Lourdes of Bernadette, of 'the white girl', how can I write of that? I tried to write of it in a novel of mine called *Women and God*, but I was too near to it then. And now perhaps I am too far away.

All those things, all those things in which burns that fire or even its pale reflection, how can I catch them with their radiance and put them down on to the dead leaves of a book. In horses, in my country, in children, in love, in Lourdes, in places and people I have seen it, the reflection of the same white flame that is life at its white-hottest, its most intense and loveliest, hovering on the verge of uncreated beauty.

I have kissed the stone slab that marks the spot where Bernadette knelt at the time of the first Apparition. I have touched with my fingers the rock beneath the niche where the 'White Girl' stood. That touch and that kiss have left a memory more vivid than any others in my life. I have spent hours in front of that statute of the Apparition, so lovely and always rather dirty. I have had no hours more happy. I have gazed for a long time at the painting of the

Blessed Virgin in the Rosary Church, in ermine with outstretched arms. I have never felt such security and such peace.

'Surely you didn't like that painting of Our Lady with her mouth a yard long,' a friend asked me the other day in London. The fact is I like it so much that I cannot speak of it calmly. All the things I admire most I feel to be but a reflection of that picture which itself is a pale reflection of the reality seen by Bernadette. What inspires me when I see horses like Miracle and Gregalach, in my little boy Ian, in Marlene Dietrich, in that Antrim bogland, in poems, in people, are sparks from that furnace.

All day from six I worked in the Asile, in the baths, at the grotto, tending the sick pilgrims and wheeling them on their stretchers. There was a Spanish girl whom I used to wheel to the grotto and from the grotto to the square in front of the Rosary Church for the blessing of the sick. She only spoke a few words of English so that we did not talk to each other much. She was very ill with tuberculosis. When I had finished helping those of the men patients who were able to dress I went for a stretcher and wheeled my little girl to the grotto. If I was delayed she would not let anyone else wheel her but waited until I came. She had not come to Lourdes to be cured, she said, but to pray. She did not mind dying. Once when there was a friend with her to act as interpreter we had a long conversation. I remember some of the things she said lying on her stretcher, her head under a hood and her body covered by a waterproof sheet because it was raining. The rain poured on to the concrete in front of the grotto. But the hundreds of candles went on burning under the rock, their golden flames glistening and sparkling through the rain. Behind us the Gave, dark between poplars, hurried by with a faint monotonous sigh.

'I must tell you about the bull-fights,' she said, 'because you would love them too.' She spoke about the different fighters and their merits, their bravery or cowardice and their skill. She had been to a lot of bull-fights for two seasons before she had become too ill. I thought I would like bull-fighting. The rain streamed from my hat on to my shoulders and down my raincoat. Her friend huddled herself on the other side of the stretcher under an umbrella. I told the girl about horse-racing, each sentence being translated by our interpreter.

'Yes, yes, I can see that is good too. That is lovely. But there is no death in it,' the girl said. 'The loveliest things have death in them, like here at Lourdes,' she added.

I began to see what she had seen in a flash of intuition from the first—that we were very like each other. Only she was very holy. She would be lured by the same things that have lured me. Perhaps she would never have been lured away from that holiness even if she had lived.

'If I am alive I will come back here this time next year. Can you come here then too?'

I promised.

'Even if you don't it doesn't matter,' she said. 'We'll meet in Heaven and we'll have a lovely time. All the same, I would like to see you next year,' she added.

But I could not go the next year to Lourdes, and I do not think that she went either because she was so ill.

In the evenings I went to the Café Terrasse, built over the Gave, with some of the other pilgrims, or with Dr. Sherry of the Medical Faculty of Lourdes, an extraordinary man who inspired me by his austerity and about whom I would like to write a lot but that I know he would not wish it.

On the last morning I was in Lourdes, that first time, I got up at four and went down to the grotto. Even at that hour it was not completely deserted. It was a warm September morning before dawn. The statue of the White Girl looked pale in its dark niche above the cave of candles. I stayed there for half an hour or so taking a sort of farewell.

Our train left about seven and I looked up from the station at a deep blue early morning sky with a bright silver paring of new moon in it and I know that does not sound worth writing about. But if I was a better writer I would have it appear as it was for me at that moment.

303

HOMECOMING

By plane, bus and forced march
Across a city after midnight
With nothing to guide me but what you'd called
Your candlelit window amid the electric ones
(But the phone was cracked and the tone was poor
And perhaps I hadn't heard aright).
I reached a house and struck a light
To read what was chalked beside the bell:
"Once for the Captain, twice for Sue."
Three times I pressed;
Give me a minute to catch my breath
Before you open, whoever you are.

Francis Stuart, 1975

Suggestions for Further Reading

In the entries below, *only principal works* of fiction are listed, and for poets the *more important collections*. Date of original publication is given, but inevitably many early works will be out of print. Where there has been a recent reprint, this is indicated by "r." and the date of this. Where there is a current paperback, this is indicated by "pb." and the publisher's series. Work published to mid-1978 is included, but announced titles and publishers of forthcoming works are shown in double brackets.

Students or librarians eager to keep abreast of contemporary Irish writing should write for the catalogues of the DOLMEN PRESS, Richmond Industrial Estate, North Richmond Street, Dublin 1; the BLACKSTAFF PRESS, 255A Upper Newtownards Road, Belfast; the WOLFHOUND PRESS, 98 Ardilaun, Portmarnock, Co. Dublin; the POOLBEG PRESS, Knocksedan House, Swords, Co. Dublin; the GOLDSMITH PRESS, Curragh, Co. Kildare; and other publishers. Some Irish poets often issue their own work first in small limited editions, notably Kinsella from PEPPERCANISTER, 47 Percy Place, Dublin 4, and Montague from GOLDEN STONE, 25 Grattan Hill, Cork.

For secondary material, the twice-yearly *Irish University Review* (listed as IUR below), edited by Maurice Harmon from Room J210 Arts Building, University College, Dublin 4, is a principal source for articles on contemporary Irish writers and has often issued special issues on individual writers. Likewise, *Eire-Ireland* (EI), the quarterly journal of the Irish American Cultural Institute, 683 Osceola Avenue, St. Paul, Minnesota 55101, and the *Journal of Irish Literature* (JIL), edited by Robert Hogan from the Proscenium Press, PO Box 361, Newark, Delaware 19711. The Bucknell University Press (BUP), Lewisburg, Pennsylvania, has published some forty short monographs in their "Irish Writers" series.

The literary pages of all the Irish newspapers, of the weekly *Hibernia*, and the quarterly *Studies* are, of course, further important sources for both primary and secondary material. Also *Books Ireland: a Monthly Review*, an organ of the book trade.

305

Suggestions for Further Reading

(1) The anthology *Rogha an Fhile* (Goldsmith Press), from which O Cearbhail's poem is taken, gives the Irish originals with literal English translations of some thirty modern poems written in Irish.

To savour the quality of modern Irish prose the non-Gaelic reader may enjoy Flann O'Brien's *An Béal Bocht*, posthumously translated as *The Poor Mouth* (1973; pb. Picador). Unfortunately the classic modern novel in Irish, Màirtín O Cadhain's *Cré na Cille* (Conversation in a Graveyard), is widely considered untranslateable.

Secondary: David Greene, *Writing in Irish Today* (Cultural Relations Committee, 1972).

(2) **Liam O'Flaherty.** NOVELS: *Thy Neighbour's Wife* (1923); *The Black Soul* (1924); *The Informer* (1925); *Mr Gilhooley* (1925); *Skerrett* (1932; r. 1977); *Famine* (1937). STORIES: *Spring Sowing* (1924); *The Mountain Tavern* (1929); *The Pedlar's Revenge and other Stories* (1976). AUTOBIOGRAPHY: *Two Years* (1930); *I Went to Russia* (1931); *Shame the Devil* (1934).

Secondary: James H. O'Brien, *Liam O'Flaherty* (BUP 1973); Patrick Sheeran, *The Novels of Liam O'Flaherty: Background Profile Analysis* (1976); ((Angeline A. Kelly, *The Short Stories of Liam O'Flaherty—* WOLFHOUND)).

(3) **Peadar O'Donnell.** NOVELS: *Islanders* (1928; r. 1975; pb. E. & T. O'BRIEN); *Adrigoole* (1929); *The Knife* (1930); *The Big Windows* (1955). AUTOBIOGRAPHY: *The Gates Flew Open* (1932); *There Will be Another Day* (1963).

Secondary: Grattan Freyer, *Peadar O'Donnell* (BUP 1973); Michael McInerney, *Peadar O'Donnell: Irish Social Rebel* (1974).

(4) **Frank O'Connor.** STORIES: *Guests of the Nation* (1931). There have been various collections and selections since, but the last revisions are all in PAN paperbacks: *The Mad Lomasneys; Fish for Friday; Masculine Protest; Day Dreams; The Holy Door.* AUTO-BIOGRAPHY: *An Only Child* (1961; pb. PAN); *My Father's Son* (1968; pb. PAN). CRITICAL: *The Backward Look* (1967).

Secondary: Michael/Frank: Studies on Frank O'Connor, edited by Maurice Sheehy (1969); James Matthews, *Frank O'Connor* (BUP 1976).

(5) **Sean O'Faolain.** STORIES: *Midsummer Night Madness* (1932); *Teresa and other Stories* (1947); *I Remember! I Remember!* (1961); *The Heat of the Sun* (1966); *Foreign Affairs* (1975); *Selected Stories* (1978). NOVEL: *Bird Alone* (1936: pb. MILLINGTON). AUTO-BIOGRAPHY: *Vive Moi!* (1964).

Secondary: Maurice Harmon, *Sean O'Faolain* (University of Notre Dame, 1967); IUR Special Issue, Spring 1976.

(6) **Donagh McDonagh.** POETRY: *The Hungry Grass* (1947); *A Warning to Conquerors* (1968). DRAMA: *Happy as Larry* (1946); *God's Gentry.*

(7) **Patrick Kavanagh.** POETRY: *Collected Poems* (1964); *Complete Poems* (Peter Kavanagh Handpress, 250 East 30th Street, New York, 1972). NOVELS: *Tarry Flynn* (1948; pb. PENGUIN); *By Night Unstarred* (1978). CRITICAL: *Collected Pruse* (1967). AUTO-BIOGRAPHY: *The Green Fool* (1938; pb. PENGUIN). POST-HUMOUS MISCELLANY: *Lapped Furrows* (1969); *November Haggard* (1971).

Secondary: Alan Warner, *Clay is the Word* (1974); Darcy O'Brien, *Patrick Kavanagh* (BUP 1975); *JIL: Special Patrick Kavanagh Number,* January 1977.

(8) **Austin Clarke.** POETRY: *Collected Poems* (1974). DRAMA: *Collected Plays* (1963). AUTIOBIOGRAPHY: *Twice Round the Black Church* (1962).

Secondary: IUR, Spring 1974: Austin Clarke Special Issue; ((Maurice Harmon, *Austin Clarke: Tilting with Faith*—WOLFHOUND)).

(9) **Brendan Behan.** DRAMA: *The Quare Fellow* (1956: pb. METHUEN); *The Hostage* (1958; pb. METHUEN). AUTO-BIOGRAPHY: *Borstal Boy* (1958: pb. CORGI); *Confessions of an Irish Rebel* (1964).

Secondary: Ulick O'Connor, *Brendan Behan* (1970: pb. CORONET); Colbert Kearney, *Brendan Behan, Writer* (1978).

(10) **Tom Murphy.** DRAMA: *A Whistle in the Dark* (1962); *The Morning after Optimism* (1972); ((*The Sanctuary Lamp*)).

(11) **Flann O'Brien.** NOVELS: *At Swim-Two-Birds* (1939: pb. PENGUIN); *The Third Policeman* (1967); pb. PICADOR). MISC-ELLANY: *The Best of Myles* (1968; pb. PAN).

Secondary: Myles: *Portraits of Brian O'Nolan,* edited by Timothy O'Keefe (1973); Anne Clissmann, *Flann O'Brien: A Critical Introduction* (1975).

(12) **Benedict Kiely.** NOVEL: *The Cards of the Gambler* (1953; pb. MILLINGTON). STORIES: *A Journey to the Seven Streams* (1963; *A Ball of Malt and Madame Butterfly* (1973; pb. PENGUIN); *A Cow in the House and other Stories* (1978).

Secondary: Daniel J. Casey, *Benedict Kiely* (BUP 1974).

Suggestions for Further Reading

(13) **M. J. Molloy.** DRAMA: *Three Plays* (Proscenium Press, Delaware, 1975). ((A collected edition of the plays is under consideration.))

Secondary: chapter in Robert Hogan, *After the Irish Renaissance* (1968).

(14) **Edna O'Brien.** NOVELS: *The Country Girls* (1960; pb. PENGUIN); *The Lonely Girl* (1962; pb. as *Girl with Green Eyes*, PENGUIN); *Girls in their Married Bliss* (1964; pb. PENGUIN); *A Pagan Place* (1970; pb. PENGUIN). STORIES: *The Love Object* (1968; pb. PENGUIN).

Secondary: Grace Eckley, *Edna O'Brien* (BUP 1974).

(15) **John McGahern.** NOVELS: *The Barracks* (1963; pb. QUARTET); *The Dark* (1965; pb. QUARTET); *The Leavetaking* (1974; pb. QUARTET). STORIES: *Nightlines* (1970; pb. QUARTET); *Getting Through* (1978; ((pb. QUARTET))).

(16) **Padraic Fiacc.** POETRY: *By the Black Stream* (1969); *Odour of Blood* (1973); *Nights in the Bad Place* (1977); ((*Selected Poems, 1948–78*—BLACKSTAFF)).

Secondary: chapter in Terence Brown, *Northern Voices* (1975).

(17) **John Hewitt.** POETRY: *Collected Poems* (1968); *Out of My Time* (1974); *Time Enough* (1976).

Secondary; chapter in Brown, *op. cit.*

(18) **John Montague.** POETRY: *Poisoned Lands* (1961; r. 1977); *A Chosen Light* (1967); *Tides* (1970); *The Rough Field* (1972); *A Slow Dance* (1975); *The Great Cloak* (1978). STORIES: *Death of a Chieftain and other Stories* (1964; r. 1978).

Secondary: chapter in Brown, *op. cit.*; Frank Kersnowski, *John Montague* (BUP 1975).

(19) **Richard Murphy.** POETRY: *The Archaeology of Love* (1955); *Sailing to an Island* (1963); *New and Selected Poems* (1974) includes *The Battle of Aughrim* and *High Island*: ((*Selected Poems*—FABER)).

Secondary: Richard Murphy: Poet of Two Traditions, edited by Maurice Harmon (1978).

(20) **Thomas Kinsella.** POETRY: *Another September* (1958); *Downstream* (1962); *Nightwalker and other Poems* (1968); *New Poems 1973* (1973); *The Good Fight* (1973); *One* (1974); *A Technical Supplement* (1976); *Song of the Night* (1978); *The Messenger* (1978). TRANSLATION: *The Tain* (1969). ((*Fifteen Dead* and *One and other Poems*—DOLMEN & OUP.))

Secondary: Maurice Harmon, *The Poetry of Thomas Kinsella* (1976).

(21) **John Morrow.** NOVEL: *The Confessions of Prionsias O'Toole* (1977). ((STORIES: *Northern Myths*—Blackstaff.))

(22) **Seamus Heaney.** POETRY: *Death of a Naturalist* (1966); *Door into the Dark* (1969); *Wintering Out* (1972); *North* (1975); ((*Easter Water*—Faber)).
Secondary: chapter in Brown, *op. cit.*; Robert Buttel, *Seamus Heaney* (BUP 1975).

(23) **Eavan Boland.** POETRY: *New Territory* (1967); *The War Horse* (1975).

(24) **Juanita Casey.** POETRY: *Horse by the River* (1968). NOVELLAS: *The Horse of Selene* (1971); *The Circus* (1974).

(25) **Francis Stuart.** NOVELS: *Pigeon Irish* (1932); *Try the Sky* (1933); *The Angel of Pity* (1935); *The White Hare* (1936); *The Pillar of Cloud* (1948; r. 1974); *Redemption* (1949; r. 1974); *The Flowering Cross* (1950); *Black List, Section H* (1971); *Memorial* (1973); *A Hole in the Head* (1977); ((*The Black Rainbow*—Martin Brian & O'Keefe)).
Secondary: A Festschrift for Francis Stuart, edited by W. J. McCormack (1972); J. H. Natterstad, *Francis Stuart* (BUP 1974).

For further titles from authors not represented in this anthology, consult Maurice Harmon, *Select Bibliography for Anglo-Irish Literature and its Backgrounds: An Irish Studies Handbook* (1977).